BIOCHEMICAL
ENGINEERING

BIOCHEMICAL ENGINEERING

Shuichi Aiba
University of Tokyo

Arthur E. Humphrey
University of Pennsylvania

Nancy F. Millis
University of Melbourne

1965   ACADEMIC PRESS   New York

CHEMISTRY

Published in Japan by University of Tokyo Press and in the Americas, England, and Europe by Academic Press, New York and London. Published jointly by University of Tokyo Press and Academic Press in all other countries.

LIBRARY OF CONGRESS CATALOG CARD NUMBER: 65-27085

PRINTED IN JAPAN

PREFACE

Biochemical processes have been carried out by man since ancient times, but it was not until a little more than a hundred years ago that Louis Pasteur pointed out the role that living organisms play in these processes. In the years that followed, an increasing number of commercially important chemicals were produced by the utilization of the activities of various microorganisms.

With the discovery of the usefulness of penicillin, man began to appreciate more fully the potential of microorganisms for useful purposes. Urgent demands for penicillin throughout World War II thrust microbiologists, biochemists, and chemical engineers into a "crash" program of developing and designing processes in areas which were in many ways unfamiliar to them. As a result, most early process know-how was acquired through empirical procedures.

Following the war, industrial fermentation was rapidly developed to an advanced state. Microorganisms are now used to produce a host of complex chemicals—antibiotics, enzymes, and vitamins—and to perform highly specific changes in complicated chemical molecules. The techniques of submerged fermentation are not limited to microorganisms. They are now also being used for propagation of mammalian tissue. With these developments there has been produced a wealth of new knowledge, much of which is scattered throughout the scientific literature.

A major objective in writing this book has been to gather together the information dealing with the industrial utilization of microorganisms. This has been done not for the purpose of a literature review, but rather to develop in a single presentation an engineering approach to the subject; hence the title "Biochemical Engineering."

To achieve this objective, the authors have borrowed heavily from chemical engineering science. The microbial process is treated as a complex chemical reaction involving biological catalysts, enzymes, provided by living matter. In this way, it is possible to view microbial process in much the same way as the chemical engineer views chemical process and to treat the associated physical operations as "unit operations." This approach affords a rational basis on which it is possible to analyze and integrate the scattered knowledge into unit processes. The authors believe that this approach will provide the industrial worker with a useful source book that will aid his interpretation of the knowledge he has at hand, and at the same time provide the biochemical engineering student with a logical scheme of approach to the subject.

This book was written with the assumption that the background of its readers would be quite varied. It begins with an introduction to biochemical engineering. Next, the characteristics and biochemical activities of microorganisms are reviewed

i

for the engineering reader who may be seeking a greater appreciation of the biological catalysts that he will be dealing with later on in the book. The biochemist and microbiologist may want to begin with the next chapters dealing with kinetics and continuous fermentations. The chapters dealing with aeration, agitation, and scale-up are the heart of the subject. It is in problems of scale-up where the talents of the biochemical engineer are brought to a focus. Further, scale-up is the area of greatest controversy. Much of the practice in this area is still more of an art than a science. The final chapters deal with the auxiliary operations of microbial processes and product recovery. Material in this book has been developed from first principles of physics, chemistry, and engineering. Mathematical developments require no more than an understanding of calculus.

The information presented in this book was largely gathered together as a result of a course in biochemical engineering taught jointly by all three of the authors at the University of Tokyo in the spring of 1963. It has been derived from the authors' experience in the pharmaceutical, chemical, and food industries; from courses taught by the authors in biology and engineering at the University of Tokyo, University of Melbourne, and University of Pennsylvania; from various researches in this field; and from numerous articles in the scientific literature. Where it has seemed judicious to do so, studies of other investigators have been reinterpreted in the light of more extensive data. Where experimental data was lacking or where phenomena were little understood, the authors have indulged in some speculation.

The application of engineering principles to microbial processes is relatively new. Recognition of biochemical engineering dates back only to July, 1947, when the Merck Chemical Company received the McGraw-Hill Award for Chemical Engineering Achievement for its process development described in the article entitled "A Case Study in Biochemical Engineering." One of the first symposia on the subject was held at the American Chemical Society meeting in Atlantic City in September, 1949. Considerable knowledge has accumulated in the last fifteen years. However, much is yet to be learned. The authors hope that this book will serve to stimulate further research of a fundamental nature in the subject. The authors believe that microbial processes will have a tremendous impact, both economical and social, on the world in the next thirty-five years. Biochemical engineering will play a key role in developing these microbial processes to the benefit of mankind. It has been this belief which has been the primary stimulus in the writing of this book.

Finally, we should like to acknowledge with gratitude the encouragement and cooperation we have received from our friends and colleagues during the preparation of this book.

DECEMBER, 1964

SHUICHI AIBA
ARTHUR E. HUMPHREY
NANCY F. MILLIS

CONTENTS

BIOCHEMICAL ENGINEERING

CHAPTER 1

INTRODUCTION

1.1. DEFINITION OF BIOCHEMICAL ENGINEERING

Over the years various definitions of biochemical engineering have appeared in the literature. Several follow:

"The biochemical engineer is an engineer with broader scientific training than just chemistry, physics and mathematics. Included in his knowledge is an understanding of and application for biological processes."—Anonymous, 1947[1]

"The term biochemical engineering covers that field of chemical engineering related to our newer biochemical industries, in particular to those fermentation processes where very large plants are employed to produce micro-quantities of finished products. Such processes include the manufacture of antibiotics and vitamins and have introduced a range of problems which did not exist in older fermentation processes such as brewing, yeast manufacture and industrial alcohol production." —J. J. H. Hastings, 1954[4]

"Biochemical engineering is the practical application of our knowledge of micro-organisms. The industrial application of a biochemical process is a combined operation in which the biochemist, the microbiologist, the geneticist, and the chemical engineer are all intimately concerned. Just as chemical engineering is not applied chemistry, so is biochemical engineering not applied biochemistry. The biochemical engineer is concerned with those processes involving fermentations, food processing, manufacture of sera and vaccines, extraction of natural products such as insulin, physical processing of natural materials, and forest and crop products." —H. Hartley, 1958[3]

"Engineering is a practical art. It is a discipline firmly based on the general pool of scientific knowledge and, in fact, frequently contributes to this pool. Nevertheless, the basic engineering function is to provide solutions to the practical needs of technology. In the case of the biochemical engineer, the technology of concern is that dealing with biochemical and microbiological processes. Biochemical engineering is not simply mathematics and mechanical gadgetry, a view unfortunately held by many microbiologists. The biochemical engineer's role is to translate the microbiologist's and the biochemist's understanding of the biochemical process—by empirical means in many cases—into increased productivities." —E. L. Gaden, Jr., 1960[2]

In lectures on biochemical engineering at the University of Tokyo in 1963, the authors offered this definition: "Biochemical engineering is that activity concerned with economic processing of materials of biological character or origin to serve

3

useful purposes. The function of the biochemical engineer is that of translating the knowledge of the microbiologist and the biochemist into a practical operation. To do this the biochemical engineer must not only be well grounded in the basic engineering principles, but he also must have an appreciation of the biological sciences."

While it is obvious from the foregoing definitions that the biochemical engineer is concerned with varied biological processes, at the present time his efforts are focused on fermentations. For this reason the center of attention in this book will be the fermentation process.

1.2.   EVOLUTION OF MODERN FERMENTATION PROCESSES

Man was well aware of fermentations, even though he had little knowledge of what caused them, long before he was able to record such an awareness. The cave man discovered that meat allowed to stand a few days was more pleasing to the taste than meat eaten soon after the kill. He also was aware that intoxicating drinks could be made from grains and fruits. The aging of meat and the manufacture of alcoholic beverages were man's first uses of fermentation. In those early days man considered fermentation as some sort of mystical process. He did not know that he was profiting from the activity of invisible microorganisms.

Without even knowing that these microorganisms existed, ancient man learned to put them to work. The ancient art of cheese-making involves the fermentation of milk or cream. For thousands of years, the soy sauces of China and Japan have been made from fermented beans. For centuries, the Balkan peoples have enjoyed fermented milk, or yogurt, and Central Asian tribesmen have found equal pleasure in sour camel's milk, or kumiss. Bread, which has been known almost as long as agriculture itself, involves a yeast fermentation. Loaves of bread have been found in Egyptian pyramids built six thousand years ago.

The discovery of fruit fermentation was made so long ago that the ancient Greeks believed wine had been invented by one of their gods, Dionysus. The manufacture of beer is only slightly less ancient than that of wine. A Mesopotamian clay tablet written in Sumerian-Akkadian about five hundred years before Christ tells us that brewing was a well established profession fifteen hundred years earlier. An Assyrian tablet of 2000 B.C. lists beer among the commodities that Noah took aboard his ark. Egyptian documents dating back to the Fourth Dynasty, about 2500 B.C., describe the malting of barley and the fermentation of beer. Kui, a Chinese rice beer, has been traced back to 2300 B.C. When Columbus landed in America, he found that the Indians drank a beer made from corn. More than three thousand years ago, the Chinese used moldy soybean curd to clear up skin infections, and primitive Central American Indians used fungi to treat infected wounds.

During the Middle Ages, experimenters learned how to improve the taste of wine, bread, beer, and cheese. Yet, after thousands of years of experience, men still did not realize that in fermentations he was dealing with a form of life. Man remained in the dark about the true cause of fermentation until the latter half of the nineteenth century.

A French scientist, L. J. Thenard, announced in 1803 that the yeasts used by wine makers were alive and were responsible for the formation of alcohol. Thenard's findings were rejected by supporters of the more conventional notion that fermentation was a chemical action in which living things played no role. It remained for Louis Pasteur to prove that Thenard was right. In 1857, Pasteur proved that alcoholic fermentation was brought about by yeasts and that yeasts were living cells. In addition, Pasteur showed that certain diseases were caused by microorganisms. This discovery was a turning point in medical history and the birth of microbiology.

Other observations of Pasteur's indicated that certain disease-producing microorganisms survived for only a few hours when introduced into soil. He concluded from this that certain microbes were killed by others in the soil. He also found that the bacillus which causes anthrax in cattle could thrive in the tissues of cattle but appeared to be inhibited by the presence of certain air-borne microbes. This prompted Pasteur to suggest that human disease could be cured by marshaling microbe against microbe.

To avoid the risk inherent in fighting one disease with another, medical workers looked for a chemical agent elaborated from a microbe innocuous to man which would be able to destroy disease-causing microorganisms. In 1901, Rudolf Emmerich and Oscar Low, of the University of Munich, isolated pyocyanase from *Pseudomonas aeruginosa*, a bacterium. Several hundred patients were treated quite successfully with pyocyanase, the world's first antibiotic. But pyocyanase was ahead of its time. No techniques existed to guarantee that each batch of the substance would be equally effective. The quality controls now common to pharmaceutical manufacturing were more than forty years in the future. Standardization was impossible, and pyocyanase was abandoned as too hazardous.

During this time, the inheritors of Pasteur's knowledge encountered better luck when they moved outside the field of medicine and sought to use microbes as production workers in industry. The production of baker's yeast in deep, aerated tanks was developed towards the end of the nineteenth century and in the early twentieth century. During World War I, Chaim Weismann almost singlehandedly rescued Britain from a serious ammunition shortage. He did it by using a bacterial cousin of the tetanus microbe to convert maize mash into acetone, which is essential in the manufacture of the explosive cordite. In 1923, Pfizer opened the world's first successful plant for citric acid fermentation. The process involved a fermentation utilizing the mold *Aspergillus niger* whereby ordinary sugar was transformed into citric acid.

Other industrial chemicals produced by fermentation were found subsequently, and the processes reduced to commercial practice. These included butanol, acetic acid, oxalic acid, gluconic acid, fumaric acid, and many more.

Practically nothing was done with antibiotics until 1928. It was in this year that Alexander Fleming, working with *Staphylococcus aureus*, a bacterium that causes boils, observed a strange fact. A mold of the *Penicillium* family grew as a contaminant on a Petri dish inoculated with *Staphylococcus aureus;* a clear zone was observed where the *Staphylococcus* organisms in the vicinity of the contaminating mold had been killed. Fleming nurtured the mold and then extracted a chemical from it which killed the bacteria. He named the extracted material penicillin and used most of his meager supply to clear up one infected wound.

Fleming's discovery received little notice as far as application was concerned until two Oxford University experimenters, under the stress of World War II, resolved to find an antibacterial agent of wider activity than the sulfa drugs. These two British workers, Dr. Howard Florey and Dr. Ernst Chain, were sure that earth or air could offer a yeast, mold, or fungus which, under the proper conditions, could be made to produce a therapeutic agent capable of saving the lives of war casualties. Their first candidate was the *Penicillium notatum* mold preserved from Fleming's studies. Penicillin turned out to be exactly what they were looking for; it could save thousands of lives and was needed immediately. Since all of Britain's production facilities were devoted to war work, Flory and Chain turned to the American pharmaceutical industry to help them solve their difficulties in mass-producing the antibiotic. Three American companies led the way—Merck, Pfizer, and Squibb—with the help of government laboratories.

Initially, the cultures were grown in flasks about the size of milk bottles. It was soon realized that factories larger in capacity than all the milk-bottling plants in the United States would be needed. A chance discovery in a Peoria market provided the major breakthrough. Here a government worker found a moldy cantaloupe on which was growing a new strain of penicillin, *Penicillium chrysogenum*, which would thrive when cultured in deep, aerated tanks and which gave two hundred times more penicillin than did Fleming's mold.

Other antibiotics were quick to appear. From the throat of a chicken Professor Selman A. Waksman of Rutgers University isolated an actinomycete, *Streptomyces griseus*, which elaborated a new antibiotic, streptomycin. This antibiotic was particularly effective against the causative organism of tuberculosis. The search was now on. Antibiotic prospectors combed the earth for organisms that produced different and more useful antibiotics. The list of these antibiotics is long today and includes such important antibiotics as chloramphenicol, the tetracyclines, bacitracin, erythromycin, novobiocin, nystatin, kanamycin, and many others.

Progress in fermentation is continuing at an ever-increasing pace. Each year new products are added to the list of compounds derived from fermentation. Several vitamins are now produced routinely employing fermentation steps in their synthesis. Outstanding examples are B-2 (riboflavin), B-12 (cyanocobalamin), and C (ascorbic acid). Some of the more interesting fermentation processes are the specific dehydrogenations and hydroxylations of the steroid nucleus. These chemical transformations are economical short cuts used in the manufacture of the anti-arthritic cortisone and its derivatives. Fermentative syntheses of the amino acids L-lysine and L-glutamic acid are also being carried out commercially. The fermentive production of nucleic acids is proving to be an important source of flavor-enhancing compounds. Important agricultural uses are being found for the new fermentation product gibberellin, a plant-growth regulator; and bacterial spores are being used as specific insecticides in another agricultural application. Microbial attack of crude oil promises to be an important source of feed materials as well as certain highly oxidized aromatic compounds for chemical synthesis. Research is in progress on chemical transformations utilizing fermentation techniques, new fermentative biosyntheses, continuous algal culture, and submerged mammalian-tissue culture. Fermentation processes may not only be tomorrow's source of chemotherapeutic agents, but may very well be the manner in which food is produced. Many scientists have predicted that hydroponics—the submerged culture of plant cells—is the farming of the future.

1.3. ROLE OF THE BIOCHEMICAL ENGINEER IN THE DEVELOPMENT OF MODERN FERMENTATION PROCESSES

Prior to the penicillin fermentation, pure-culture requirements of fermentation processes were not strictly controlled. Earlier processes such as those used in producing yeast, citric acid, and gluconic acid were favored by pH conditions unsuitable for contaminating organisms. In other processes, such as the production of sorbose, acetone and butanol and ethanol, the concentrations of ingredients and products were sufficiently high to suppress the growth of most contaminants. The latter two fermentations are also anaerobic. The problem facing the engineer in the development of the penicillin fermentation was the design and operation of an absolutely-pure-culture fermentation in deep, aerated fermentation vessels containing an ideal environment for the growth of contaminating organisms.

The engineer thus encountered a formidable problem—the prevention of contamination. Many fermentation plants were delayed in reaching their maximum productive capacities because of contamination problems. Perhaps the most notable contribution the engineer made was in the advancement of sterile techniques, or the "contaminant-proof" philosophy, in the design and operation of the fermentation vessel and its associated maze of piping. Firstly, sterility of the equipment and the fermentation medium had to be achieved. Next, inoculum had to be passed into the fermentor without contaminating it. The process then had to be maintained in a pure state by preventing the entry of contaminating organisms during the fermentation.

To accomplish these objectives, the engineer changed methods of vessel fabrication, revised gasketing, piping, and valve design, and devised new methods of steam-sealing possible points of contaminant entry. Methods for removing samples and adding materials aseptically to the fermentation vessel were also devised. Methods for sterilizing equipment, medium, and the large quantities of compressed air required during the fermentation were developed.

In addition to designing an aseptic fermentation operation, the engineer also had to design air-compression and delivery systems and efficient methods for agitating and aerating the fermentation. Heat evolved by the metabolic reactions of the microorganism had to be removed, and methods of maintaining the temperature within a narrow range were developed. Other instrumentation and process-control problems were also encountered and solved.

The ultimate success of any chemical process depends on its successful demonstration in pilot-plant equipment and its subsequent scale-up to the production stage. The engineer has made important contributions to this facet of fermentation technology.

The process is not complete until the product is finally isolated. Numerous problems hitherto not encountered faced the engineer in product recovery. Early commercial fermentations had only been used to produce relatively simple, stable chemicals in such high concentrations that their isolation was an easy matter. Concentrations of penicillin in early fermentation media, on the other hand, were extremely low. Also, penicillin could very easily be degraded to inactive material. Special isolation techniques involving filtration, extraction, adsorption, and concentration were developed to recover these small quantities in remarkably good yields. In some instances the product was contained in the cells and had to be extracted.

While the laboratory scientist—the microbiologist, the biochemist, and the microbial geneticist—continues to discover and advance desirable interactions between microorganisms and their environment, the biochemical engineer must control these interactions and translate laboratory results to production-scale operation in an economic manner. The biochemical engineer, therefore, must continue to develop, design, and scale-up new fermentation processes. Improvements in management, as well as in equipment, are needed to accomplish these aims. In addition, he must continue to operate his fermentation plant safely and efficiently, and he must see that his products meet the requirements of his customers and the standards set by his industry. Very likely, as in the past, complete engineering knowledge of a process with which he may be concerned will be unavailable at the time he needs it. Therefore, he must be prepared to offer engineering experience and judgment when needed. These latter qualities have been largely responsible for the important concepts and methods of biochemical engineering presented in this book.

1.4. STATUS OF BIOCHEMICAL ENGINEERING IN THE FERMENTATION INDUSTRY

The engineer's task in the development of the penicillin fermentation has already been described as a very important one. The outgrowth of this undertaking was the submerged pure culture technique, carried out in aerated and agitated deep-tank fermentors. This submerged technique, similar to its antecedent used for yeast propagation, introduced to the biochemical process industry refined fermentation equipment capable of being maintained under aseptic conditions even when vigorously aerated.

Development of processes for the production of other antibiotics naturally drew heavily upon the experience gained from the penicillin process. It was found that other antibiotic fermentations also could utilize the same deep-tank techniques. Hence, construction and expansion of fermentation plants to accommodate the rapidly rising production of these drugs tended to make use of standardized equipment. Even to the present time, the method of submerged culture has proven the most suitable way to cultivate microorganisms for commercial purposes, whether they be used in the production of antibiotics, steroids, amino acids, or industrial chemicals.

The equipment and operations used in different fermentation processes are similar to those used for chemical processes, and while the biochemical engineer was quick to recognize the features common to the two processes, at the same time he was well aware of the difference between them. As a consequence, fermentation process technology has been organized by many institutions of higher learning as a specialized branch of chemical engineering. Biochemical engineering, as it is usually called, is based on the unit-operation and unit-process concepts of the parent discipline, as well as the stoichiometric, kinetic, and thermodynamic principles which are its very foundation.

1.4.1. Development of unit operations

Fermentation processes have in common many of the familiar chemical-engineering unit operations. For example, aerobic fermentations involve the "mixing" of three heterogeneous phases—microorganisms, medium, and air. Other unit operations include "mass transfer" of oxygen from the air to the organisms, and "heat transfer" from the fermentation medium.

Analysis of fermentations by the unit-operation technique has added greatly to the understanding of their behavior. This understanding, however, is far from complete. The scale-up of fermentations, for instance, is still rather empirical. The mechanism of oxygen absorption in non-Newtonian fluids, which usually characterize fermentation broths, must be evaluated before rigorous scale-up procedures can be employed.

Of the operations auxiliary to those in the fermentor, sterilization of large volumes of media and supply of large quantities of sterile air have been major accomplishments of biochemical engineering. However, it was not until recently that an understanding of these operations evolved from a logical, theoretical basis. Application of this understanding still awaits actual use in many fermentation plants. Aside from media and air sterilizers, amazingly little development of auxiliary operations for the fermentation-process industry has been achieved.

1.4.2. Development of unit processes

A careful analysis of the many industrially significant fermentation processes shows that there are common reactions from a chemical as well as a physical viewpoint. Fermentation processes can be classified by the reaction mechanisms involved in conversion of raw materials into products. Among these are included reductions, simple and complex oxidations, substrate conversions, transformations, hydrolyses, polymerizations, and complex biosyntheses and cell formation.

Unit-process classification provides a ready catalog of the chemical activities and abilities of microorganisms for the biochemist. More importantly, to the biochemical engineer it offers a logical approach to an examination of fermentation reaction mechanisms.

1.4.3. Process design

A fermentation may be viewed as a catalyzed chemical reaction in which enzymes are the catalysts and cellular material the catalyst support. Therefore, fermentation-process design has required an understanding of stoichiometry and reaction kinetics. In batch-fermentation design, a consideration of the kinetics of the process has often not been necessary. However, as continuous fermentation has developed, these reaction kinetics have become increasingly important. At the present time, the biochemical engineer is making important contributions to the design of practical continuous-fermentation systems, based upon chemical-reaction kinetics.

Successful process design depends, of course, on successful process control. Although certain process variables such as temperatures, air flow, and agitation were controlled in even the earliest deep-tank fermentations, other variables have remained untouched because of the difficulties, usually from an aseptic viewpoint, that they presented. Only recently have sterilizable and stable pH probes been developed. Under active investigation are detectors for the measurement and control of dissolved oxygen, oxygen uptake, dissolved carbon dioxide, redox potential, nutrient concentration, etc. Successful development of these control devices will permit greater economy in substrate utilization, power, and aeration.

1.4.4. Process economics

The recent trend toward greater competition among fermentation products, and the ever-present threat of replacement by chemical synthesis, are producing an increasing interest in process economics. Equipment, plant, and process design are all receiving a more thorough evaluation. Advanced instrumentation and process-control techniques are beginning to be used in new process designs to maximize product yields. Equipment and plant are continually being modernized in efforts to operate more efficiently. Also, greater cognizance is being taken of money spent for research and development of new fermentation processes and improvements of established processes. This has given rise to the use of statistical design techniques in experimentation. Economy has always been an important engineering consideration in any process industry. Because of the diversity of operations, the value of products, and the complexity of equipment, it is an especially important consideration in fermentation operations. However, because of the ever-changing spectrum of fermentation products, process equipment must be versatile. This feature often complicates the economic considerations.

1.5. FERMENTATION PRODUCTS

1.5.1. Antibiotics

Fermentation processes are the prime source of over a hundred products for the food, chemical, and pharmaceutical industries. Once dominated by alcohol and solvent making, the fermentation industry now derives its primary income from antibiotics. The total world sales of antibiotics are in excess of one billion dollars per year. A list of the more common antibiotics is given below.

TABLE 1.1

SOME IMPORTANT FERMENTATION-MADE ANTIBIOTICS.

Aterrimin	Hygromycin	Ristocetin
Amphotericin	Kanamycin	Streptomycin
Bacitracin	Leucomycin	Tetracyclines
Blasticidin-S	Neomycin	Thiostrepton
Colistin	Novobiocin	Tricomycin
Chloramphenicol	Nystatin	Tyrocidine
Cycloheximide	Oleandomycin	Tyrothricin
Cycloserine	Paromomycin	Tylosin
Erythromycin	Penicillins	Vancomycin
Fumagillin	Polymyxin	Viomycin
Gramicidin		

Despite the emergence of many new antibiotics, derivatives of penicillin and streptomycin represent over sixty percent of the total antibiotic production. More than two million pounds of penicillins and streptomycins are produced annually.

1.5.2. Steroids

Another important source of fermentation revenue is the transformation of steroids; this includes the introduction of hydroxyls in the 11α, 11β, and 16α positions, dehydrogenation of the 1, 2 positions, and hydrolysis of esters of the 3 hydroxyl group. Table 1.2 lists key steroids in microbial processes.

TABLE 1.2

KEY STEROIDS IN MICROBIAL TRANSFORMATION PROCESSES.

Cortisone
Hydrocortisone
Prednisolone
9α-fluoro-16α-methylprednisolone
9α-fluoro-16β-methylprednisolone
6α-methylprednisolone

1.5.3. Enzymes

Many companies are involved in the production of enzymes. For the most part, enzymes are used in small quantities for special purposes; only amylases, pectinases, proteases, and cellulases are tonnage items. Many of the enzymes find application as analytical agents. A list of important industrial enzymes is given in Table 1.3.

TABLE 1.3

IMPORTANT INDUSTRIAL ENZYMES.

γ-amino butyric transaminase
amylase
catalase
cellulase
collagenase
glucose oxidase
glutamic acid decarboxylase
hemicellulase
invertase
lipase
pectinase
penicillinase
proteases
streptokinase-streptodornase

1.5.4. Organic acids

Manufacturers using fermentation processes for production of organic acids have found themselves generally squeezed by new developments in chemical synthesis. Of the various organic acids that can be produced by fermentation, only lysine, glutamic, citric, isoascorbic, and gluconic acids have not been challenged by chemical synthesis. Table 1.4 indicates the use and approximate annual production of important fermentation organic acids.

TABLE 1.4

ORGANIC ACIDS.

Acid	Use	Approximate Annual Production in Millions of Pounds
Citric	Food acidulant	100
Lactic	Food acidulant	20
Gluconic	Sequestrant	10
Fumaric	Plasticizer	—
Itaconic	Plasticizer	—
Lysine	Food supplementation	—
Glutamic	Food flavoring	200
5′-nucleotides	Food flavoring	—
Isoascorbic	Reducing agent	0.5

1.5.5. Vitamins and growth factors

Fermentations have been used to produce growth factors for many years. Nearly one million pounds of riboflavin are produced by fermentation each year and used in pharmaceutical products and animal feeds; nearly two thousand pounds of B_{12} are sold each year for similar purposes, all synthesized by microorganisms. Gibberellin, used in germinating barley and ripening fruit, is worth a million dollars annually. Xanthophylls, produced by algal culture, is added to chicken feed to give color to egg yolks and chicken meat. Torula yeast, used in animal feeds as a source of the "B" vitamins, is derived by fermentation of waste liquors from the paper industry.

1.5.6. Solvents

Historically, solvents have been an important segment of the fermentation industry. Prior to the 1940's, fermentation was an important source of alcohol, acetic acid, acetone, butanol, and propanol. Today these chemicals are almost totally produced by synthetic processes.

1.5.7. Polymers

Microbial polymers have not been fully exploited to date. Dextran is the only substance in actual production on a fairly large scale. It has been used as a blood extender and food thickener. Many biological polymers, mostly carbohydrate in character, are awaiting investigation. A promising lipid polymer appears to be that derived from β-hydroxybutyric-acid.

1.5.8. Miscellaneous

Among the miscellaneous fermentations may be found processes for the production of sorbose (as an intermediate in ascorbic-acid manufacture) fructose (a liquid sweetener), dihydroxyacetone (a sun-tanning agent), and phenylacetylcarbinol (an intermediate in L-ephedrin synthesis). None of these is a large volume item. The use of microorganisms as insecticides is one of the more novel fermentation developments. For example, spores of *Bacillus thuringiensis* have found application as an insecticide for chickens.

Numerous other fermentations products have been developed. For the most part the cost of producing these chemicals by fermentation is prohibitive or else there is no large market for them. Kojic and α-keto glutaric acids are examples of fermentation products awaiting the development of large markets.

To help the reader appreciate the value of fermentation products, a price list of the more important products is given in Table 1.5. A rough index of the economic potential of a fermentation can be obtained from this table if the rule-of-thumb guide used by fermentation technologists is applied. This guide says that for a fermentation to be profitable, the broth must have a value of at least 25 cents per liter.

TABLE 1.5

PRICES OF SOME CHEMICALS PRODUCED BY FERMENTATION PROCESSES.*

Alcohols and Solvents		Amino Acids	
Acetone	0.065	Monosodium glutamate	0.57
Butanol	0.135	L-lysine HC1	3.90
Ethanol	0.078	DL-methionine	3.00
Fusel Oil	0.155	L-tryptophane	45.00
Glycerol	0.155		
Acids		Antibiotics	
Citric acid	0.295	Bacitracin	590.00
Fumaric acid	0.185	Gramicidin	1,930.00
Gluconic acid	0.155	Neomycin	40.86
Itaconic acid	0.295	Penicillin	10.15
Lactic acid	0.155	Streptomycin	11.82
Oxalic acid	0.185	Tyrothricin	227.00
Tartaric acid	0.365		
Miscellaneous		Vitamins	
Brewers Yeast	0.27	Ascorbic acid	1.86
Diacetyl	3.30	Cyanocobalamin	20,400.00
Dihydroxyacetone	3.64	Riboflavin	14.54
Ephedrine	10.88		
Ergot	1.85		
Erythorbic acid	1.84		

* Based on prices listed in *Oil Paint & Drug Reporter* and *Chemical & Engineering News* (1964). Prices listed in dollars/lb (USA).

1.6.   POSSIBLE FUTURE TRENDS IN FERMENTATIONS

The products of fermentation processes that are likely to be of expanding importance are those which are complex and hard to make. For the most part, fermentive production of simple compounds has been displaced by chemical synthesis. It appears, therefore, that the complex products hold the real opportunity for future growth.

Some interesting complex molecules that can be produced by fermentation are nucleic acids and alkaloids. Since a significant amount of research into the application of these compounds has only been under way for a short time, it is difficult to predict where the future may lie. Most likely these complex compounds will find use as drugs for physiological regulation. An interesting question is whether purine and pyrimidine compounds can be obtained from microorganisms in significant quantities and at a low price. If so, it is possible that fermentations may open the way to new fields of purine and pyrimidine chemistry.

The transformation of complex chemicals is also an area of fermentation that is likely to increase in activity. Considerable research has been done on steroid transformations because there has been a demand for the product. Recently, researchers have studied microbial oxidation, hydroxylation, and reduction of various aromatic compounds. This work is uncovering a host of complex chemicals. The development of these fermentations on an industrial scale will be dependent solely upon finding applications for the products.

As pointed out in the previous section, numerous microbial polymers have been uncovered. Many are carbohydrate in character. Some polypeptides and polyhydroxy acids also are produced by microbial action. These polymers exhibit a range of properties including high viscosity, low viscosity, elasticity, and film formation. Just what the future holds in this area remains to be seen as most of the microbial polymers have not yet been investigated. Certain unsaturated, dibasic acids produced by fermentation have a potential use in polymerization reactions. Likely candidates are itaconic, muconic, and ketoadipic acids, as well as the various dibasic acids that can be produced by "di-terminal" oxidation of alkanes and alkenes.

Over the long term, microbial cultivation will have an impact on problems of feeding the world population. Every forty years the population is doubling. Although some countries have agricultural surpluses, in others starvation conditions prevail. Even in the agriculturally well-off countries, surpluses are expected to disappear in the next twenty to thirty years unless population increases are checked. That microorganisms will play an important role is shown by Table 1.6 in which the mass-doubling times of various agricultural products are compared. The important point to note is that some microorganisms have as much as a 500-fold growth rate advantage over crops and 10,000-fold advantage over cattle. The primary limitations of microbial foods are taste and texture.

TABLE 1.6

DOUBLING TIMES OF PLANTS AND ANIMALS.

Organism	Doubling time
Yeast and bacteria	20 – 120 minutes
Complex microorganisms such as algae	2 – 48 hours
Crops such as grass and alfalfa	1 – 2 weeks
Chickens	2 – 4 weeks
Hogs	4 – 6 weeks
Cattle	1 – 2 months

Research will, of course, greatly affect the development of future processes. Important researches are under way involving (1) the "tailoring" of microorganisms to perform special jobs—the elucidation of the genetic code may be a significant factor here—and (2) the use of cheaper carbon sources, particularly hydrocarbons and natural gas, for biosynthesis. The full potential of these researches is yet to be assessed. Certainly the long-range outlook for fermentation processes is indeed bright.

REFERENCES

1. ANONYMOUS (1947). "The case of biochemical engineering." *Chem. Eng.* May, p. 106.
2. GADEN, E. L., JR. (1960). "Microbiological process discussion; Bioengineering and fermentation." *Appl. Microbiol.* **8**, 123.
3. HARTLEY, H. (1958). "The principles of biochemical engineering." *Biochemical Engineering* (Ed.). STEEL, R., p. 11, Heywood, London.
4. HASTINGS, J. J. H. (1954). "Problems of biochemical engineering." *Tran. Instn. Chem. Engrs.* **32**, 11.

CHAPTER 2

THE CHARACTERISTICS OF BIOLOGICAL MATERIAL

2.1. TYPES OF MICROORGANISMS

Microorganisms are chemically very similar to higher animal cells, and they can perform many of the same biochemical reactions. Generally, microorganisms exist as single cells, or at most in relatively unspecialized multicellular colonies, with no capacity to control cellular temperature. While mammalian cells need to be supplied with substances like the B-group vitamins and aromatic amino acids from the diet, many microorganisms can make their requirements for growth from inorganic salts alone or from inorganic salts supplemented by a simple hexose.

The purpose of this chapter is to provide a brief introduction to the microbes which the biochemical engineer may use either to produce cell mass or some by-product of cell metabolism. Emphasis will be placed on those characteristics and properties that are significant in attaining these ends. For this discussion micro-organisms will be considered in four main groups:

1. Bacteria
2. Viruses including bacteriophages
3. Fungi including yeasts and Actinomycetes
4. Protozoa including algae

2.1.1. Bacteria

Typically, bacteria are single cells, either cocci, rods, or spirals, which are capable of growth independent of living cells. Coccal forms vary from 0.5 to 4μ in diameter, rods are from 0.5 to 20μ long and 0.5 to 4μ wide, and spirals may be greater than 10μ long and about 0.5μ wide.

Table 2.1 lists the various parts of bacteria that can be seen in electron micrographs, with some comments on their composition and functions; Fig. 2.1 shows diagramatically a transverse section of a bacterium.

Bacteria are ubiquitous in nature, in aerobic and anaerobic environments containing water. Among the genera, synthetic abilities range from those of the autotrophic species, which require only inorganic compounds for growth, to those of heterotrophic species, which may have considerable synthetic ability or so little that they must be grown in tissue culture. Similarly, there is an enormous range of degradative ability, from species which may use native protein and complex chitins, to those that cannot degrade large molecules and so require amino acids and hexoses supplied as such. Because of these diverse capacities, bacteria have been exploited

17

TABLE 2.1

COMPOSITION OF THE VARIOUS PARTS OF BACTERIA.

Part	Size	Composition and Comments
Slime Layer		
i) Microcapsule	5 – 10 mμ	Protein-polysaccharide-lipid complex responsible for the specific antigens of enteric bacteria and of other species.
ii) Capsule	0.5 - 2.0μ	Mainly polysaccharides (e.g., *Streptococcus*) sometimes polypeptides (e.g., *Bacillus anthracis*)
iii) Slime	Indefinite	Mainly polysaccharides (e.g., *Leuconostoc*) sometimes polypeptides (e.g., *Bacillus subtilis*)
Cell Wall		Confers shape and rigidity to the cell.
i) Gram positive species	10 – 20 mμ	20% dry weight of the cell. Consists mainly of macromolecules of a mixed polymer of N-acetyl muramic-peptide, teichoic acids and polysaccharides.
ii) Gram negative species	10 – 20 mμ	Consists mostly of a protein-polysaccharide-lipid complex with a small amount of the muramic polymer.
Cell Membrane	5 – 10 mμ	Semi-permeable barrier to nutrients. 5-10% dry weight of the cell, consisting of protein 50%, lipid 28%, and carbohydrate 15-20% in a double-layered membrane.
Flagellum	10 – 20 mμ by 4 – 12μ	Protein of the myosin-keratin-fibrinogen class, M. W. 40,000. Arises from the cell membrane and is responsible for motility.
Inclusions		
i) Spore	1.0 – 1.5μ by 1.6 - 2.0μ	One spore is formed per cell intracellularly. Spores show great resistance to heat, dryness, and antibacterial agents. Spore walls are rich in dipicolinic acid.
ii) Storage granules	0.5 - 2.0μ	Glycogen-like, sulphur, or lipid granules may be found in some species.
iii) Chromatophores	50 – 100 mμ	Organelles in photosynthetic species. *Rhodospirillum rubrum* contains about 6,000 per cell.
iv) Ribosomes	10 – 30 mμ	Organelles for synthesis of protein. About 1,000 ribosomes per cell. They contain 63% RNA and 37% protein.
v) Volutin	0.5 - 1.0μ	Inorganic polymetaphosphates which stain metachromatically.
Nuclear Material	About half cell volume	Composed of DNA which functions genetically as if the genes were arranged linearly on a single endless chromosome but which appears by light microscopy as irregular patches with no nuclear membrane or distinguishable chromosomes. Autoradiography confirms the linear arrangement of DNA and suggests a M.W. of at least $1,000 \times 10^6$.

industrially to accumulate both intermediate and end products of metabolism. They are also a rich source of both synthetic and degradative enzymes; but the exploitation of bacteria in this field is still at an early phase of development.

TABLE 2.2

PROPERTIES OF TYPICAL VIRUSES.

Type of Virus	Size (mμ)	Shape, Composition and Comments
Animal		
i) Cubic Symmetry		
Poliomyelitis	30	Consists of 1 molecule RNA (M.W. 2×10^6) in a spiral, surrounded by protein macromolecules 6 mμ diam. arranged as an icosahedron with no retaining membrane. Particle M.W. 10×10^6.
ii) Helical symmetry		
Influenza	100	Consists of 1 molecule RNA (M.W. 2×10^6) as a nucleo-protein macromolecule arranged in a helix, the whole coiled and enclosed in a lipo-protein sheath. Particle M.W. 100×10^6.
Plant		
i) Rods		
Tobacco mosaic	300×15	The whole virus particle is rod-shaped and consists of 1 molecule RNA (M.W. 2×10^6) associated with protein macro-molecules arranged in a helix. Particle M.W. 39×10^6.
ii) Sphere		
Tomato bushy stunt	30	An icosahedron consisting of 16% RNA (M.W. 1.6×10^6) and protein. Particle M.W. 9×10^6.
Insect	280×40	The actual virus is rod-shaped. DNA constitutes about 8% of dry weight but *in vivo* the virus rods are embedded in poly-hedral crystalline aggregates of protein $0.5–15\mu$ diameter.
Silkworm		
Bacteriophages		
i) Double stranded DNA		
T-even of *E. coli*	Head: 90×60 Tail: 100×25 Tail fibrils: 130×2.5	A tadpole-shaped phage with DNA (M.W. 130×10^6) confined to the head. The tail is protein some of which is contractile; long tail fibrils are involved in attachment to the host cell. Particle M.W. 250×10^6.
ii) Single strand DNA		
ϕX174 of *E. coli*	22	A dodecahedron with 12 subunits. DNA (M.W. 1.6×10^6) 25% dry weight. Particle M.W. 6.2×10^6.
iii) RNA	20	A polyhedron containing RNA (3×10^{-12} μg/virus) and protein. Nucleic acid content is probably similar to that of ϕX174.
f2 of *E. coli*		

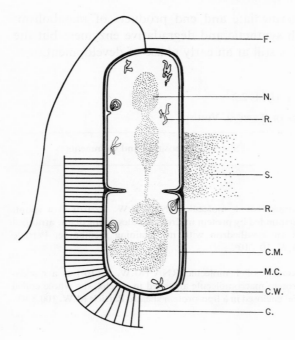

FIG. 2.1.　Diagram to show the structure of bacteria and the formation of a new cell wall and a new cell membrane as the cell divides.

F.	= flagellum
N.	= nuclear material
R.	= reticulum (or mesosome)
S.	= loose, extracellular slime
C.M.	= cell membrane
M.C.	= microcapsule
C.W.	= cell wall
C.	= true capsule

2.1.2.　Viruses

Viruses are the smallest microbes; they are obligate intracellular parasites of animals, plants, insects, fungi, algae, or bacteria. Some of their properties have been listed in Table 2.2. They contain no water and have little or no synthetic or metabolic activity in themselves. Growth and multiplication take place intracellularly, where the virus directs the host cell to synthesize a new virus; this frequently results in the cell's damage and death. The genetic material of viruses may be either ribonucleic acid (RNA) or deoxyribonucleic acid (DNA). Many plant and animal viruses consist of a single molecule of RNA, associated with protein subunits arranged in a polyhedron showing cubic symmetry. The myxoviruses show helical symmetry, with the nucleoprotein helix enclosed by a lipoprotein sheath. Viruses vary in diameter from $10 \, m\mu$ (foot-and-mouth virus) to $300 \, m\mu$ (vaccinia virus).

Viruses that are parasitic on bacteria are called bacteriophages; some are tadpole-shaped with a hexagonal head (c. $90 \times 60 \, m\mu$) and a tail (c. $100 \times 25 \, m\mu$); a few phages have no tail. Bacteriophages are highly specific to the strain of host bacterium they will attack. If the phage has a tail, the tip attaches to the cell wall; some phages have tail fibrils ($3 \text{ to } 5 \times 150 \, m\mu$) which are also concerned in attachment. The cell wall is altered by the phage to allow the nuclear material from the phage head (either DNA or RNA) to enter the bacterium, leaving the empty phage shell outside. The entry of nucleic acid is associated in some phages with contraction of the tail protein; but not all phages have contractile tails. Once inside the bacterium, the phage nucleic acid directs bacterial metabolism to the formation of new phage material. Phage particles are released after lysis and death of the bacterium. In some cases, phage DNA may actually be incorporated into bacterial DNA; bacteria so infected continue to metabolize and multiply normally in what is called the lysogenic state. Occasionally the phage DNA dissociates from the host DNA and the phage then directs the host cell to make phage material; such host cells die and the phage particles are released.

Phages are important industrially as possible contaminants of bacterial fermentations, notably streptococcal cultures used in cheese-making, clostridia for acetone-butanol production, and pseudomonads for organic-acid production. The cultivation of animal viruses to test antiviral drugs and for vaccine production is also an important undertaking, although on a relatively small scale.

2.1.3. Fungi

Fungi are widely spread in nature in environments of lower relative humidity than those which favor bacteria. The metabolism of fungi is essentially aerobic; they form long filamentous, nucleated cells (hyphae) 4 to 20μ wide, which are much branched and which may or may not have cross walls. In Table 2.3 is a summary of some of the properties of fungal hyphae, while Fig. 2.2 shows diagramatically a cross section of a hypha.

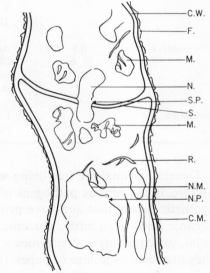

FIG. 2.2.   Diagram to show the structure of septate fungal hyphae with a nucleus migrating from one cell to the next.

C.W. = cell wall
F. = fibrous layer
M. = mitochondrion
N. = nucleus
S.P. = pore in the septum
S. = septum
R. = reticulum
N.M. = nuclear membrane
N.P. = pore in the nuclear membrane
C.M. = cell membrane

Many species of fungi have complicated life cycles during which both sexual and asexual spores are formed, these spores being often carried on special fruiting bodies. The hyphal mass (mycelium) on a solid surface may be only a couple of millimeters wide, or as much as two meters, depending on the species and the growth medium.

TABLE 2.3

PROPERTIES OF FUNGAL HYPHAE.

Part	Size	Comments
Outer Fibrous Layer	100 – 500 mμ	Very electron-dense material.
Cell Wall	100 – 250 mμ	*Zygomycetes, Ascomycetes,* and *Basidiomycetes* contain chitin in amounts varying from 2 to 26% of dry weight. *Oomycetes* contain cellulose not chitin, while the yeast cell contains glucan (29%), mannan (31%), protein (13%), and lipid (8.5%).
Cell Membrane	7 – 10 mμ	Much-folded, double-layered membrane; semi-permeable to nutrients.
Endoplasmic Reticulum	7 – 10 mμ	Highly invaginated membrane or set of tubules, probably connected with both the cell membrane and the nuclear membrane and concerned in protein synthesis and probably other metabolic functions.
Nucleus	0.7 – 3 μ	Surrounded by a double membrane (10 mμ), containing pores 40 to 70 mμ wide. Nucleus is flexible and contains cytologically distinguishable chromosomes. Nucleolus about 3 mμ. In Actinomycetes there is no nuclear membrane. The nucleus is capable of migration.
Mitochondria	0.5 – 1.2μ by 0.7 – 2μ	Analogous to those in animal and plant cells, containing the electron transport enzymes and bounded by an outer membrane and an inner one forming cristae. They probably develop by division from pre-existing mitochondria.
Inclusions		Lipid and glycogen-like granules are found in some fungi and ribosomes have been seen in all fungi examined.

Generally, fungi are free-living saprophytes, but a few are parasitic on animals and many are serious pathogens of plants. They have very wide degradative and synthetic capabilities and have proved a fruitful source of industrially important organic acids (e.g., citric, gluconic, gibberellic), numerous antibiotics (e.g., penicillin, griseofulvin) and enzymes (e.g., cellulase, protease, amylase). In addition, they may cause spoilage of paper, fabrics, and food, particularly in high humidity.

Some yeasts form elliptical cells 8 to 15μ by 3 to 5μ, others are almost spherical. Asexual spores are rarely observed, but they form sexual spores in the same way as *Ascomycetes*, and are therefore classified with them. Yeasts differ from most fungi, however, in that vegetative growth is by budding so that long hyphae are rarely formed, their cell wall contains mannans and glucans, not chitin or cellulose as is common in fungi, and they are capable of both aerobic and anaerobic growth.

Growth of yeast on solid medium resembles a bacterial colony. They are industri-ally important in making beverage alcohol and baker's yeast and in producing protein for a stock feed or human use.

Actinomycetes are a group of organisms intermediate in properties between bacteria and true fungi. They form long, much-branched hyphae with no cross walls, spores are budded from the tip of aerial hyphae, and they can form hetero-karyons (cells with discrete nuclei derived from different parents, co-existing in a common cytoplasm). In these characteristics they are similar to true fungi. On the other hand, the cells are smaller, being only 0.5 to 1.4μ wide; the cell wall polymer contains N-acetyl muramic-peptide, including diamino pimelic acid; the nuclear material is not enclosed in a nuclear membrane; and the cells are lysed by lysozyme and attacked by specific phages. In these properties and in the small cell width, Actinomycetes resemble bacteria.

Industrially, the group is extremely important as a source of powerful antibiotics for the control of microbial infections of man, animals, and plants. Their growth in fermentation tanks is very similar to that of fungal fermentations; for this reason they have been grouped with the fungi in this discussion.

2.1.4. Protozoa

Protozoa are widely distributed in fresh and salt water, in soil, and in animals. Some authorities separate them into two distinct groups: the algae, which are largely photosynthetic and resemble primitive plants, and the protozoa, which are not photosynthetic and resemble primitive animals.

Protozoa may be unicellular or multicellular and exhibit a wide variety of morphological forms; some are non-motile, some are motile with flagella, some are motile with cilia, some are amoeboid; some are parasitic, others are symbiotic. Many genera of flagellated protozoa contain chloroplasts and are photosynthetic, like *Euglena*, with very simple requirements for growth; others have complex growth requirements. Some flagellated species are free living cells, others form co-lonies of cells; other flagellates, like the trypanosomes, are parasitic on animals.

Paramecium and *Vorticella* are typical ciliates. The true amoebae may be para-sitic or saprophytic. Some members of the *Sarcodina* (which includes the true amoebae) form calacareous exoskeletons, e.g., *Foraminifera*, whose bodies may accumulate to form large chalk deposits. The malaria organism, *Plasmodium*, is a typical obligate parasite with a complex life cycle involving the mosquito and man.

The algae may be either uni- or multi-cellular. Some species have complex life cycles; all are capable of photosynthesis and contain chlorophyll a. Associated with the photosynthetic pigments are many other pigments, such as carotenoids, xanthophylls, and phycocyanins, which give different colors to the algae. Some species are capable of heterotrophic growth; the blue-green algae are important in the fixation of gaseous nitrogen. Some species of diatoms have siliceous exo-skeletons; diatomaceous earth, a useful filter aid, is composed of diatom bodies.

ırgest of the algae are the multicellular seaweeds; the brown ones, often
ł kelp, have a highly differentiated thallus.

ırotozoa have not been grown to any extent on an industrial scale, although
Chlorella (a unicellular alga) was grown as a protein supplement on a semi-
industrial scale in Japan after World War II. Seaweeds, of course, are gathered
in large quantities from natural sources providing an important human food in
Asia and a source of agar and alginates; but, so far, seaweeds have not been
cultivated on an industrial scale.

2.2. CHEMICAL COMPOSITION

Complete detailed analyses of microorganisms are not often made and would
be of little use. There is abundant evidence that the amount of any particular
component found depends greatly on the composition of the growth medium,
the age of the culture, and its rate of growth. The data in Table 2.4 merely indicate
gross differences in the composition of the different groups of organisms and give
some concept of the numbers and the dry weight of the population likely to be
achieved in culture.

TABLE 2.4

CHEMICAL ANALYSES, DRY WEIGHTS, AND THE POPULATIONS OF DIFFERENT MICROORGANISMS
OBTAINED IN CULTURE.

Organism	Composition (% Dry Weight)			Population in Culture Numbers/ml	Dry Weight of this culture g/100 ml	Comments
	Protein	Nucleic Acid	Lipid			
Viruses	50 – 90	5 – 50	<1	$10^8 – 10^9$	0.0005*	Viruses with a lipo-protein sheath may contain 25% lipid.
Bacteria	40 – 50	13 – 25	10 – 15	$2 \times 10^8 – 2 \times 10^{11}$	0.02 – 2.9	*Mycobacterium* may contain 30% lipid.
Filamentous fungi	10 – 25	1 – 3	2 – 7		3 – 5	Some *Aspergillus* and *Penicillium* sp. contain 50% lipid.
Yeast	40 – 50	4 – 10	1 – 6	$1 – 4 \times 10^8$	1 – 5	Some *Rhodotorula* and *Candida* sp. contain 50% lipid.
Small unicellular algae	10 – 60 (50)	1 – 5 (3)	4 – 80 (10)	$4 – 8 \times 10^7$	0.4 – 0.9	Figure ( ) is a commonly found value but the composition varies with the growth conditions.

* For a virus 200 mμ diam.

Table 2.4 shows that while some viruses consist entirely of nucleoprotein, others contain some lipid. In general, viruses have no enzymic activity; but it seems that all phages contain an enzyme, which alters the bacterial cell wall to allow entry of the phage nucleic acid. Adenosine triphosphate (ATP), which is important for contraction of muscle in higher animals, has been detected in those phages which have contractile tail protein.

All microorganisms, except viruses, contain about 80% water; bacteria, yeast, and unicellular algae are very similar in protein content—about 50% of the dry weight; the protein is largely enzymatic. It is estimated that *Escherichia coli* has about 2,000 different enzymes, as well as the genetic potential to form many more should suitable environmental conditions be supplied.

Structurally more complex organisms, like fungi and seaweeds, contain less of the metabolically active proteins and nucleic acids, while the inert polysaccharide components of the cell walls constitute a larger proportion of the total dry weight. As an approximation, about 10% of the dry weight of yeasts, bacteria, and unicellular algae is nitrogen, but nitrogen comprises only 5% of the dry weight of fungi.

Lipids are essential components of all organisms, except for some viruses, and, although they are vital to the structure of semi-permeable membranes and cell walls, they are not usually a major component of the dry weight. There are a few exceptions however; among bacteria, *Mycobacterium* species may contain 30% mycolic acid; *Rhodospirillum rubrum*, during growth on acetate, may synthesize a polymer of β-OH-butyric acid constituting about 20% of its dry weight. Lipid inclusions are common among the fungi and, in certain yeasts and *Ascomycetes*, may constitute 50% of dry weight under special conditions. The fatty acid content of the lipid is variable, but it is rich in C_{16} and C_{18} fatty acids, particularly palmitic, oleic, and stearic acids.

2.3. REQUIREMENTS FOR GROWTH AND FORMULATION OF MEDIA

2.3.1. Requirements for growth

It is important to appreciate that the cultural conditions that achieve maximum cell mass may not necessarily be those that give maximum yield of some product of metabolism. For example, *Aspergillus niger* gives best yields of citric acid when growth is restricted in media by semi-starvation concentrations of nitrogen, phosphorus, and trace metals, but a high concentration of sugar.

The best temperature for cultivation varies with the species, but organisms naturally occurring in soil, air, or water usually grow best at from 25° to 30°C, while those isolated from animals grow best at 37°C. Some organisms are in fact thermophilic; some of industrial importance, like lactobacilli, cellulose digesters, and methane producers, grow best at 40° to 45°C. Organisms with high temperature optima offer the technical advantage that contaminants usually grow better at lower temperatures, thus the growth of contaminants is likely to be inhibited at the temperature of the fermentation. In fermentations where growth and product formation are not concurrent, it might well be profitable to test different temperatures for the growth and product-forming stages.

The products of microbial metabolism often cause major shifts in pH; hence to maintain rapid growth, the pH must be kept close to the optimum for the particular organism. For many organisms this is close to pH 7. As with the thermophilic organisms, however, it is useful to take advantage of any tolerance of extremes of pH which an organism may happen to possess. For example, yeast and lacto-bacilli grow well at pH 4.5; while many fungi and the thiobacilli readily tolerate pH 2. Fermentations maintained at these pH levels are relatively free from contamination by other organisms. The pH for optimum product formation may be different from that for optimum growth, as is the case with *Clostridium aceto-butylicum*, which gives very low yields of solvents if the pH is maintained near neutrality, although at this pH growth is rapid.

When acid by-products accumulate in the medium, causing an unwanted fall in pH, it is sometimes possible to feed ammonia slowly to the culture, so supplying nitrogen for growth while controlling pH. Calcium carbonate may also be used for pH control, but this is only practicable if the required product is water soluble. When cell mass or some insoluble metabolite is required, acid end-products are most conveniently neutralized by adding sodium hydroxide as required.

Microorganisms vary in their need for oxygen. Fungi, algae, and a few bacteria are obligate aerobes, a few bacteria are strict anaerobes, while yeasts and many bacteria can grow in both situations (facultative aerobes). If organisms are capable of facultative growth, a substrate that is metabolized aerobically gives a much larger cell yield than the same weight of substrate fermented anaerobically (see Section 2.3.2.2, Source of carbon). When a product of anaerobic metabolism is required, it may be profitable to grow a dense population of cells aerobically and then allow them to metabolize the remainder of the substrate anaerobically. The turnover of substrate to product is thus achieved much faster than when the cells are grown slowly under completely anaerobic conditions. This principle has been successfully exploited in the production of ethanol by yeast.

The obligate anaerobes and facultative aerobes, grown for some product of anaerobic metabolism, can be cultivated in very large tanks provided with adequate mixing of the nutrients with the organisms. Obligate aerobes or facultative aerobes, grown aerobically, require a much more complicated plant. The details of air sterilization, and the problems of design and aeration of cultures, are fully discussed in Chapters 6 and 9.

Heterotrophs often fix carbon dioxide during growth, but normal air usually supplies sufficient carbon dioxide for this purpose. Autotrophs depend on carbon dioxide for their main source of carbon; improved growth of autotrophs has been found in an atmosphere enriched with carbon dioxide.

2.3.2. Formulation of media

Detailed investigation will be required in order to establish the most economic medium for any particular fermentation, but certain basic requirements must be met by any growth medium; these will be discussed below.

2.3.2.1.　*Source of energy*

Growth processes are endergonic, so that energy for growth must come from either the oxidation of medium components or from light. Adenosine triphosphate is the most important compound in energy transformations in cells. The coupling of ATP to thermodynamically unfavorable reactions enables them to proceed at a useful rate. Photosynthetic bacteria and algae can utilize the energy from light for ATP formation; autotrophic bacteria can generate ATP from the oxidation of inorganic compounds; while heterotrophic bacteria, yeasts, and fungi form ATP while oxidizing organic compounds.

In present-day industrial fermentations, the commonest source of energy is starch or molasses; but the growing world population and the increasing cost of plant products may force a change in this pattern; the autotrophic microorganisms and those which can oxidize cheap hydrocarbon substrates like alkanes for energy are therefore of potential industrial interest.

2.3.2.2.　*Source of carbon*

Frequently, the carbon needs of a cell are supplied with the energy source, but the autotrophic and photosynthetic bacteria use carbon dioxide. The pathway by which heterotrophs metabolize substrate carbon is important in determining the amount of carbon converted to cell material. It is found that facultative organisms incorporate about 10% of substrate carbon in cell material when metabolizing anaerobically, but 50–55% of substrate carbon is converted to cells with fully aerobic metabolism. Since 50% of the dry weight of cells is carbon, it is possible to calculate how much carbon must be supplied in the medium in order to give any particular weight of cells. For example, if 40 grams per liter dry weight of cells are required, and metabolism is aerobic, then the carbon required in the medium equals $40/2 \times 100/50 = 40$ g carbon. If this is supplied as a hexose, then $40 \times 180/72 = 100$ g per liter of hexose are required.

2.3.2.3.　*Source of nitrogen*

This can be supplied for most industrially important organisms by ammonia or ammonium salts, although growth may be faster when using organic nitrogen. Certain organisms, however, have absolute requirements for organic nitrogen. These requirements vary from single amino acids to the entire range of amino acids, as well as purines, pyrimidines, and vitamins. Some organisms have complex, unknown requirements, which can be met only by crude animal or plant extracts; but it is impossible to supply the needs of viruses in cell-free systems. When products with a high nitrogen content are required, the greater the amount of nitrogen that can be assimilated by the organism, the greater the chance of a high yield of product, provided the organism has the genetic potential to produce the product.

Organic nitrogen compounds suitable for media are relatively expensive. The cheapest forms are soy bean, peanut, fish, or meat meals, malt combings, yeast extract, whey, casein, and various enzyme digests of protein-rich materials. Plant by-products, like molasses and corn steep liquor, can often provide the small amounts of growth factors that are either essential for growth or greatly accelerate the rate of growth.

Nitrogen constitutes 10% of the dry weight of most organisms, so that the minimum nitrogen content of the medium can be calculated for a desired cell yield; but the form in which it is supplied will depend on the organism, the cost and the purpose of the fermentation.

2.3.2.4. *Source of minerals*

Phosphorus and magnesium are particularly important constituents in the medium, since they are concerned in all energy-transfer reactions involving adenosine triphosphate. Calcium, potassium, sulphur, and sodium are found in significant quantities in most cells, and so must also be supplied in the medium. The trace metals iron, cobalt, copper, and zinc are essential but are usually present as impurities in other medium ingredients.

2.4. REPRODUCTIVE CYCLES IN MICROORGANISMS

Different microorganisms multiply in different ways; it is therefore important to know how this is achieved, in order to understand variability in fermentations, to maintain stock cultures without deterioration, and to breed strains for particular purposes.

2.4.1. Bacteria

Bacteria divide vegetatively by fission. Growing cells increase in mass in a continuous process, the cell wall and cell membrane extending as the protoplasm increases. As the cell mass increases, the membrane, followed by the cell wall, begins to grow inwards, until the membrane and cell wall from the circumference meet in the center. At the same time the nuclear material elongates, and forms dumbbell-shaped masses with the narrow part at the site of the future wall. The cytoplasm and nuclear material separate equally between the two cells, with no indication that one cell is the mother and the other the daughter. After the cell wall and membrane have been laid down between the two cells, in some species they detach immediately, but often a bacterium which appears by simple stain to be one cell has several cross walls and several sets of nuclear material.

Some bacterial species (e.g., *Escherichia coli* and *Pseudomonas aeruginosa*), show a primitive system of sexual reproduction between positive and negative strains. The nuclear material of a bacterium contains only one chromosome with one set of genes (the units of genetic information which fix its characters) which are contained in one double-stranded DNA polymer, the whole polymer constituting one chromosome. The nucleus of other microbes may contain more than one chromosome; when a nucleus has only one set of chromosomes it is haploid, when it has pairs of similar chromosomes it is diploid. In sexual reproduction in higher plants and animals, haploid nuclei derived from different diploid parents combine to form a zygòte, which develops into a diploid offspring. In conjugation between positive and negative strains of bacteria, only some of the genes from the positive strain enter the negative strain; this results in the formation of a partial diploid. The characters of the offspring of the cross show, however, that there has been a mixing and recombining of the genes from both parents, in the same way as occurs in the nuclei from higher cells; but there is only one offspring from the cross, as an incomplete chromosome cannot give rise to a viable cell.

2.4.2. Viruses

Animal viruses are adsorbed to the host cell, penetrate the wall, and shed their protein sub-units, thus exposing the viral nucleic acid. The virus suppresses in the host cell processes that are directed to host requirements, and directs metabolism to the formation of viral constituents. New viral nucleic acid and protein sub-units are assembled into macromolecules, which, in viruses with cubic symmetry, are cytologically identifiable intracellularly as complete virus particles. Viruses having a lipo-protein sheath acquire this as they leave the cell.

For phages, the process of multiplication is very similar to that of animal viruses, except that only the phage nucleic acid enters the bacterium; the phage nucleic acid then directs the formation and assembly of new phage material; the bacterium then lyses, so that phage particles are released. This cycle of multiplication is known as a lytic cycle, but phage and bacteria can form a different type of association. The so-called temperate phages adsorb to the host cell, and their DNA penetrates the host cytoplasm just as with lytic phages, but instead of directing the cell to form new phage particles, the viral DNA becomes attached to the bacterial DNA. The mixed DNA complex replicates as a unit, and divides with the host bacterium. This cycle is called a lysogenic cycle and can be repeated through hundreds of cell divisions.

The lysogenic cycle may change to a lytic cycle spontaneously at a low rate of frequency. When this occurs, the viral DNA becomes detached from bacterial DNA and directs the host metabolism to the formation of phage particles. As the phage DNA leaves the bacterial DNA, it sometimes takes with it a piece of bacterial DNA. If such a phage enters another bacterium and becomes lysogenic, the DNA from the first bacterium is incorporated into the DNA of the second bacterium, with the possibility that the second bacterium may acquire new characters. This process is known as transduction.

In bacteria that are capable of entering the lysogenic state, but without sexual reproduction, transduction could provide a rational approach to the problem of breeding strains of bacteria with desirable fermentation characters. So far, however, this technique has mainly been used in academic research.

2.4.3. Fungi

Vegetative growth of filamentous fungi and Actinomycetes is by simple extension of the hyphae and asexual division of the nuclei. As the hyphae elongate, the older parts of the mycelium become extensively vacuolated and inactive in nutrient absorption. Cross-walls are formed in all fungi except members of the *Oomycetes* and *Zygomycetes*, but the cross-wall has a pore through which cytoplasm and nuclei can pass from cell to cell. This situation is quite different from that in plants and animals, where nuclei are confined to their respective cells. Asexual spores are budded from the tip of hyphae and may be either uni- or multi-nucleate.

Sexual spores are produced following conjugation of two haploid nuclei. In the *Ascomycetes*, the zygote divides immediately to form four or eight haploid ascospores enclosed in a special sack or ascus. In the *Basidiomycetes*, the zygote is formed inside a special cell or basidium and divides to form four haploid nuclei which migrate to outgrowths of the basidium. The mature basidiospores are discharged from these outgrowths.

Yeasts grow vegetatively by budding from the mother cell, or by fission. During bud formation, the cytoplasm of the bud is continuous with that of the mother cell and is bounded by a typical cell membrane and cell wall. Most workers consider that nuclear division does not involve cytologically recognizable chromosomes. The mother nucleus enlarges and migrates in the direction of the bud; the nuclear membrane constricts the nucleus, so that one-half remains in the bud and the other in the mother cell; the cell membrane is then completed between the bud and the mother cell, and the cell wall is laid down. The readiness with which the bud is detached from the mother cell is a characteristic of the species, and the site of the former bud can be seen as a bud scar. One cell may have as many as 100 daughter cells. When sexual spores are produced in yeast, two haploid nuclei fuse, and the diploid zygote divides to give four haploid ascospores inside the original vegetative yeast cell.

This very brief outline of the ways in which microorganisms divide is to serve as an introduction to a discussion of variability encountered in fermentations and of the rationale behind strain-breeding programs.

2.5. VARIATION IN MICROORGANISMS

It is a common problem that one cannot always predict the behavior of biological material. Variation in behavior may be associated with genetic change or with some effect of the environment.

From the previous section it is clear that some microorganisms multiply asexually only, while others have both asexual and sexual phases of reproduction. To assist in understanding how variation in both types of organisms is possible, the next section will outline the process of nuclear division and will indicate how changes in properties might arise during growth and so become a permanent property of the organism.

2.5.1. Changes due to genetic alteration

The nucleus of all organisms contains nucleic acid, which consists of two pentose-phosphate chains linked together from the pentose number 1 carbon by pairs of bases. Adenine and guanine (purines) and cytosine and thymine (pyrimidines) are the bases in DNA, while uracil replaces thymine in RNA. In DNA, the arrangement of the two base-pairs is such that adenine is always paired to thymine, and guanine to cytosine; the actual number of each base-pair, and the order in which the pairs are fitted in the helical macro-molecule, are characteristic of each species. It is thought that each gene determining a particular property corresponds to a section of the nucleotide polymer, and that the difference between genes is due to differences in the sequence of the bases in the polymer.

When a nucleus divides, the hydrogen bonds, linking the purines to the pyrimidines, break; the two halves of the molecule then serve as templates onto which a complementary half can be assembled from purines, pyrimidines, deoxyribose, and phosphate in the cytoplasm. Fig. 2.3 indicates the arrangement of nucleotides in part of a DNA molecule and shows the plane of cleavage in DNA replication.

If errors in making the new half of the DNA molecule should occur, a nucleus with altered genetic information would be created. If the error is gross, the cell may die, but, in about 1 in 10^6 replications, an error occurs such that a living but different individual results, i.e., a mutant. It is clear that in haploid organisms like bacteria, a mutation to a different gene will be expressed immediately. In algae and in those fungi and yeasts that are diploid, a mutation may not be expressed immediately, as the change is unlikely to occur in both sets of genes simultaneously. Mutant forms which are dominant over the normal have been observed; in a diploid organism, such a mutation is, of course, expressed immediately.

Since a mutation in some gene of the nucleus occurs naturally with a frequency of 1 in 10^6 replications, it follows that there will have been about 10^9 mutations in a 1,000 liter tank containing 10^9 bacteria per ml at the end of the fermentation. Many of these mutants will be non-viable, and many will be less fit to survive than the

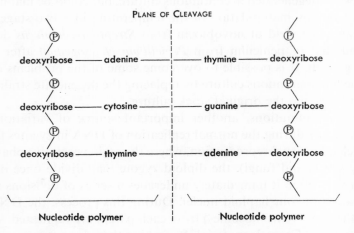

FIG. 2.3.   Diagram of part of a DNA molecule showing the plane of cleavage during DNA replication.
Ⓟ=phosphate

parents, but some may have changed to a faster growth rate and so will tend to overgrow the original culture. If the fermentation is aimed solely at cell mass, such mutants could be industrially desirable; but when some by-product of growth is wanted, it could be that the growth rate has been increased at the expense of product formation.

These undesirable mutants can be a serious problem, particularly if the faster-growing mutant arises in the seed tank early in inoculum build-up. If the mutation occurs late in the growth cycle of the main fermentation, the yield may not be seriously affected; provided the finished fermentation is not used as the inoculum for the next batch, no great harm results. The practice of inoculating a new fermentation from the previous one is to be avoided, as it tends to perpetuate mutations. The inoculum for each fermentation should be built up from a stock culture that has been maintained with the minimum opportunity for nuclear variation (see section 2.5.3.).

Growth in continuous culture presents a special problem. Theoretically, it offers infinite time for the selection of mutants arising spontaneously during growth, and the very nature of the apparatus automatically selects the fastest-growing individuals. Hence marginal advantages in growth rate, which would never be significant in batch growth, could be significant in prolonged continuous culture.

Relatively little work has so far been carried out on the genetic stability of industrially important organisms in continuous culture. The production of fodder yeasts from sulphite-waste liquors has been highly successful in continuous cultivation, but the selection of the faster growers imposed by the method of cultivation is also in the best interests of the process.

At the pilot-plant stage of investigation, *Aerobacter aerogenes* was reported to give high yields of 2,3-butylene glycol after two months of continuous growth, while *Salmonella typhimurium* showed no change in antigenic potency after 14 days. *Pasteurella pestis* degenerated in continuous culture, but could be maintained at full antigenic potency by manipulation of the temperature in a two-stage system. On the other hand, the yield of novobiocin from *Streptomyces niveus* declined after 28 days, and that of penicillin from *Penicillium chrysogenum* after 25 days, of continuous growth. It is possible to overcome some of the problems of decline in antibiotic yield in continuous culture by replacing the degenerate strain with a new inoculum grown from the original stock culture.

In addition to mutations, another important source of variation in genetic constitution occurs during the normal replication of DNA in zygotes formed from different nuclei. In sexual reproduction, where the main vegetative phase is haploid (as in many yeasts and fungi), the diploid zygote may divide once or twice as a diploid; but very often it immediately undergoes a series of divisions which result in the formation of four haploid nuclei. During this process, the DNA polymers containing the genes (chromosomes) from each parent are replicated, so that in all there are four sets of genetic material. In making these long macro-molecules, the strands become twisted on each other, break and rejoin, but not necessarily with their original parts. In this way, a crossing over and recombining of the genes from the two parents occurs. Some of the haploid nuclei from the cross will then have different characters from those of either parent. Crossing over and recombination occur at every sexual cycle of reproduction. Fig.2.4 shows diagrammatically how two different strains of an organism having one chromosome per nucleus could conjugate and produce offspring whose genetic make up is not identical with that of either parent. It is thus possible that recombinant types will arise from every sexual mating. Although the new types come from a reassorting of the existing genes of the two parents, this could result in individuals with small differences (either desirable or undesirable from the point of view of the biochemical engineer) which might influence the outcome of the fermentation.

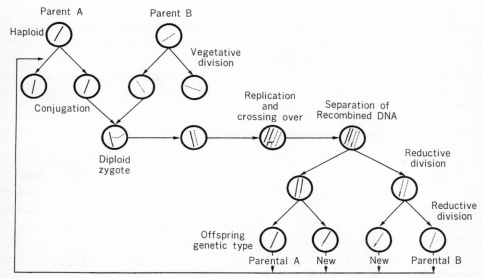

FIG. 2.4. Sexual reproduction between two different strains, A (chromosome, a solid line) and B (chromosome, a dotted line), of a haploid organism. For simplicity, only one chromosome is shown, though a haploid nucleus often contains more than one chromosome. The haploid nuclei fuse to form a diploid zygote; the DNA of the two chromosomes replicates, but during replication the DNA chains break and recombine so that some of the chromosomes of the diploid are different from those of either of the original parents A and B. The offspring of the zygote nucleus may, therefore, be either like their parents or new genetic types called recombinants.

2.5.2. Strain breeding

It is well known that while mutations in nature take place with a frequency of about 1 in 10^6 nuclei, this rate can be greatly increased by mutagens. Irradiation of organisms with ultraviolet light, X-rays, or gamma rays, treatment with nitrogen-mustard gas, camphor vapor, manganous chloride, or nitrous acid all increase mutation rates and are very useful in providing large numbers of mutants from which to select desirable strains.

From a genetic study of organisms that form zygotes, it is possible to cross two parents, each with a desirable property, and look among the progeny of the cross for those which have acquired, by recombination during nuclear division, the desirable properties from both parents.

2.5.3. Maintenance of stock cultures

In all the industrially important bacteria and fungi, except some yeasts, the main vegetative phase of growth is haploid, so that variation in genetic material arises only from mutations, provided transduction does not occur in bacteria, and provided sexual spores are not formed in fungi. In maintaining stock cultures, genetic change must be minimized; this is best achieved by preventing nuclear divisions, since most mutations occur as errors in DNA replication. Spores of fungi or bacteria, which are formed asexually, provide the best form in which to maintain stock cultures.

Freeze-drying (lyophilization) of vegetative organisms and spores has proved a very successful method of storage; the very low temperatures achieved by immersion in liquid nitrogen, or maintenance at $-15°C$ in deep-freeze cabinets, also permit little change. Storage at $0°$ to $4°C$ is better than storage at higher temperatures; though growth proceeds slowly at these temperatures and mutation is nevertheless possible.

2.5.4. Changes due to alteration in environment

Extremes of pH, temperature, and osmotic pressure, or the presence of sub-lethal concentrations of inhibitory substances, can cause aberrant morphology, metabolic malfunction, and slow growth rates. Proper management and design of plant should avoid such gross changes; but conditions that allow reasonable growth rates allow considerable latitude in the choice of cultural conditions. In industrial fermentations, it is important to control the environment so that conversion of nutrients to product is obtained. Some of the factors which affect cell composition and efficiency will now be discussed.

2.5.4.1. *Changes in the composition of cells with age and with growth rate*

This discussion will draw largely on studies of bacterial populations, since this group has been best studied; but isolated observations on fungi and Actinomycetes suggest that the findings for bacteria probably apply in principle to these groups also.

In traditional batch methods of growing cells, the developing population passes through a number of phases:

1. Lag phase, in which cell mass increases but no division occurs.
2. Logarithmic (log) phase, in which cell numbers increase at a constant growth rate.
3. Stationary phase, when cells are alive but not dividing owing to lack of some nutrient.
4. Decline phase, when the cells begin to die.

In addition, phases of increased and decreased rates of growth occur for a brief time at the beginning and end of the log phase.

It is important to appreciate that, in a batch system, the environmental conditions are not constant, even during the phase of constant growth rate. When the composition of bacteria from different stages of batch cultivation was examined, some very significant differences were found. These observations have been collated by Herbert from his own data and from those of other workers and are presented in slightly idealized form in Fig. 2.5. Ordinates on the left of the figure represent (on a logarithmic scale) the numbers and the dry weight of cells per ml, while the ordinates on the right represent (on an arithmetic scale) the weight of individual cells and their content of RNA and of DNA. All scales have arbitrary units chosen so that each initial value is 1.0.

When resting cells are inoculated into a fresh culture medium with complex nutrients, the cell weight increases logarithmically immediately and is accompanied by a sharp increase in the RNA content per cell. The individual cell weight and the RNA content rise to a certain level, indicated at time a in the figure, then both cell numbers and cell mass increase logarithmically. The period from inoculation to time a is the time required for each individual cell to initiate cell division, that is, the lag phase.

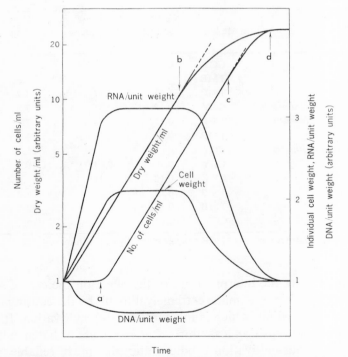

Time

FIG. 2.5.   Schematic representation of changes in cell size and chemical composition during growth of bacteria in batch culture.

(from HERBERT, D. (1961). *11th Symposium of the Society for General Microbiology* p. 395)

During the exponential growth phase, the values of RNA per unit cell weight and the individual cell mass remain relatively constant. When some nutrient in the medium is exhausted, the individual cell weight falls, at time b in the figure. The RNA content per cell and the individual cell weight also begin to fall at b, since exponential cell division continues until time c, while the rate of synthesis of RNA decreases during this period. At time c, the rate of cell division declines, eventually entering a resting stage, shown at d in the figure. When the amount of DNA per unit cell weight is measured at these different stages of cultivation, the shape of the curve obtained is the reverse of that for changes in the RNA content of the cells, although the actual changes in DNA are much less marked. These results show that data about cell composition and cell size which are not accompanied by information about the conditions of growth have little meaning; this is clearly illustrated by reference to Table 2.5, where the cell mass and the RNA content of several species of bacteria harvested from the resting and log phases of growth are listed.

TABLE 2.5

MASS AND RNA CONTENT OF CELLS OF A NUMBER OF BACTERIAL SPECIES.
(from HERBERT, D. (1961). *11th Symposium of the Society for General Microbiology* p. 394)

Organism	Medium*	Cell Mass ($\times 10^{-12}$g)		RNA content (%)	
		Resting cells	Log phase cells	Resting cells	Log phase cells
Aerobacter aerogenes	CCY	0.11	0.40	4.4	26.6
Bacillus anthracis	TMB	—	—	1.5	24.0
Bacillus cereus	TMB	1.97	3.77	3.9	31.5
Chromobacterium prodigiosum	CCY	0.12	0.35	7.8	32.1
Chromobacterium violaceum	TMB	0.17	0.56	7.2	30.3
Clostridium welchii	TMB	0.91	2.19	32.2	42.2
Corynebacterium hofmannii	CCY	—	—	25.4	51.0
Salmonella typhi	CCY	0.19	0.34	10.5	35.9
Escherichia coli	CCY	0.12	0.41	15.5	37.0
Pasteurella pestis	TMB	0.13	0.15	5.9	20.1
Proteus vulgaris	TMB	0.18	0.36	12.6	35.0
Staphylococcus aureus	CCY	0.19	0.24	5.2	10.0

* CCY, casein-yeast extract medium; TMB, tryptic meat digest medium.

In batch cultivation, the interpretation of the effect on the cell of some change in experimental conditions is made extremely difficult by the continually changing composition of the medium which is inherent in batch cultivation. It is clear that the cell changes in composition least during the log phase of batch culture, but the data from continuous-cultivation studies offer the most reliable information about the effect of environmental conditions on the composition of cells, because such cells grow at all times at a constant rate in a constant environment.

Herbert observed *Aerobacter aerogenes* growing at different rates in continuous culture in a mineral-salts medium with glycerol as the growth-limiting substrate; the specific rate of growth (μ) was controlled by changing the dilution rate. The mean cell mass and the percentages of RNA, DNA, and protein per unit dry weight were measured and these are shown in Fig. 2.6. The percentages of protein and DNA changed very little with specific growth rate but both mean cell mass and the percentage of RNA increased markedly with increase in growth rate. Similar changes in RNA, DNA, protein, and cell mass were observed if the substrate limiting growth was changed from glycerol to ammonium ion; this implies that the specific growth rate was important in determining the composition and mass of cells and that this was independent of the nutrient limiting growth. Essentially similar effects were observed following changes in the rate of growth of *Bacillus megaterium* in continuous culture.

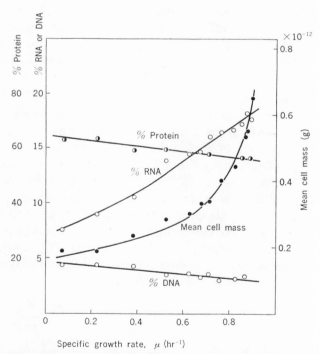

FIG. 2.6.   Effect of different rates of growth on the cell mass and chemical composition of *Aerobacter aerogenes* maintained in continuous culture.
(from HERBERT, D. (1961). *11th Symposium of the Society for General Microbiology* p. 401)

While these studies suggest that cell mass and composition are directly related to the specific growth rate and virtually independent of the factor that caused the change in growth rate, there are too few studies available for this statement to be made dogmatically. Nevertheless, these preliminary studies have important implications for biochemical engineering.

There is no doubt that the formation of product and of cell mass is closely related to the amount of RNA present in the cell, and it appears that the RNA
content of individual cells of a batch culture begins to fall about halfway through
the log phase. This means that more than half of the cells of a batch fermentation
have less than their maximum amount of RNA. From a biochemical engineer's
point of view, cells with a low content of RNA are inferior for producing either
cell mass or a product that is related to cell mass. As has been seen, variation in
the composition of cells is an intrinsic feature of the batch system of growth;
such variation can only be avoided by growing organisms at steady state in continuous culture in defined media. Continuous culture has the great advantage,
biochemically, that it is possible to produce cells of a particular type and to maintain them indefinitely at the particular growth rate and with the particular composition which is known to give maximum productivity.

This method of cultivation has not been fully exploited on an industrial scale,
and while it seems to hold much promise, serious problems have yet to be solved;
they are found both at the level of technology and in the organisms themselves,
where genetic variation is likely to be encountered during prolonged cultivation.
Apparatus for continuous cultivation of microorganisms and the theoretical bases
of its use will be discussed fully in Chapter 5.

2.5.4.2.   *Variation in the enzyme content of cells*

Although the nucleus of an organism may contain the genetic information to
produce a wide variety of enzymes, only some enzymes are produced at all times
irrespective of the presence of their substrate (constitutive). The concentration
of others is greatly influenced by the presence of their respective substrates (inducible). With inducible enzymes in the absence of an inducing substrate, the
enzyme-synthesizing system is inhibited, but this inhibition is reversed by the
inducing substance. Besides this control by the inducer, the end product of the
series of reactions may also exercise control over the amount of enzyme produced.
This system can best be illustrated by reference to Fig. 2.7, in which a series of
biosynthetic reactions, A to D, each controlled by a different enzyme, E_a, E_b, etc.,
is shown leading to an amino acid end product.

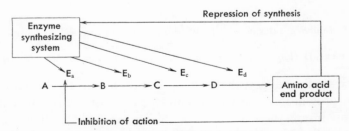

FIG. 2.7. System for the control of the formation and action of the
inducible enzymes involved in the biosynthesis of an amino acid.

If the amino acid is formed faster than needed for protein synthesis, its concentration rises; this inhibits the first enzyme (E_a) peculiar to the formation of the amino acid. This effect is immediate and tends to decrease the formation of end product. It is freely reversible should the concentration of amino acid fall. Further, the amino acid also represses the formation of all the enzymes of the series. This effect will be slow in action, since the existing enzymes will remain in the cell until they are either diluted out by cell division or destroyed in normal protein turnover.

These processes allow the cell to regulate its enzyme content in direct response to the composition of the environment. They also enable the most economic use of nutrients, as they prevent synthesis both of end products already present in excess of the need for synthesis, and of superfluous enzyme protein. Genetic studies have established that the regulatory mechanism itself is under genetic control. If mutations occur leading to loss of regulator genes, the mutants may be useful industrially in allowing the accumulation of large amounts of some compound, like an amino acid or a purine, which would normally be present in very small amounts intracellularly.

Regulatory mechanisms can be exploited in another way to cause accumulation of intermediates or to build up a high concentration of inducible enzymes in cells. If a mutant blocked in a biosynthetic pathway is grown in a limiting concentration of the end product of synthesis, exhaustion of the end product releases the repression of the enzyme synthesizing system; large amounts of enzymes on the blocked pathway will then be synthesized. Such cells can be used to accumulate intermediates of the blocked pathway in media that do not permit growth, or can be used as a source of the enzymes themselves (see Fig. 2.8).

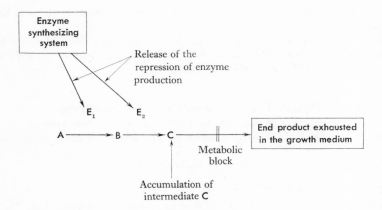

FIG. 2.8.   Diagram to show the release of control mechanisms which occurs when a series of biosynthetic reactions is blocked and the cells are grown in a limiting concentration of the end product of synthesis; this allows the accumulation of an intermediate of the pathway. The block could result from a mutation to a defective enzyme or could be created by adding an enzyme inhibitor to normal cells.

NOMENCLATURE

ATP = Adenosine triphosphate
DNA = Deoxyribonucleic acid
M.W. = Molecular weight
ⓟ = Phosphate
RNA = Ribonucleic acid
μ = Specific growth rate

TEXTBOOKS AND ARTICLES FOR FURTHER READING
AND AS A SOURCE OF REFERENCES

Introductory Texts

HAWKER, L. E., LINTON, A. H., FOLKES, B. F., and CARLILE, M. J. (1960). *An Introduction to the Biology of Micro-organisms* Arnold, London.

STANIER, R. Y., DOUDOROFF, M., and ADELBERG, E. A. (1963). *General Microbiology* 2nd ed. Macmillan, London.

Cytology and Structure

BRIEGER, E. M. (1963). *Structure and Ultrastructure of Microorganisms* Academic Press, N. Y.

GUNSALUS, I. C., and STANIER, R. Y. (1960). (Eds.). *The Bacteria* Vol. I: *Structure* Academic Press, N. Y.

VALENTINE, R. C. (1962). (Ed.). *Electron Microscopy Brit. Med. Bull.* **18**, p. 179-245. British Council, London.

Classification and Taxonomy

ALEXOPOULOS, C. J. (1962). *Introductory Mycology* 2nd ed. Wiley, London.

AINSWORTH, G. C. (1961). *Dictionary of the Fungi* 5th ed. Commonwealth Mycol. Inst., Kew, Surrey.

BREED, R. S., MURRAY, E. G. D., and SMITH, N. R. (1957). *Bergey's Manual of Determinative Bacteriology* 7th ed. Williams & Wilkins, Baltimore.

SKERMAN, V. B. D. (1959). *A Guide to the Identification of the Genera of Bacteria* Williams & Wilkins, Baltimore.

SMITH, G. M. (1955). *Cryptogamic Botany* 2nd ed. Vol. I: *Algae and Fungi* McGraw-Hill, N. Y.

WAKSMAN, S. A. (1961). *The Actinomycetes* Vol. II *Classification, Identification and Descriptions of Genera and Species* Williams & Wilkins, Baltimore.

Genetics and Reproduction

FINCHAM, J. R. S., and DAY, P. R. (1963). *Fungal Genetics* Blackwell, Oxford.

HAYES, W. (1963). *The Genetics of Bacteria and Their Viruses* Blackwell, Oxford.

JACOB, F., and WOLLMAN, E. L. (1961). *Sexuality and the Genetics of Bacteria* Academic Press, N. Y.

SAGER, R., and RYAN, F. J. (1961). *Cell Heredity* Wiley, N. Y.

Growth Requirements and Composition of Cells

COOK, A. H. (1958). (Ed.). *The Chemistry and Biology of Yeasts* Academic Press, N. Y.

FOSTER, J. W. (1949). *Chemical Activities of Fungi* Academic Press, N. Y.

GUNSALUS, I. C., and STANIER, R. Y. (1960, 1962). (Eds.). *The Bacteria* Vol. I: *Structure* Vol. IV: *The Physiology of Growth* Academic Press, N. Y.

HERBERT, D. (1961). "The Chemical Composition of Micro-organisms as a Function of their Environment." *Microbial Reaction to Environment Symp. Soc. gen. Microbiol.* **11**, 391. Camb. Univ. Press.

LEWIN, R. A. (1962). (Ed.). *Physiology and Biochemistry of Algae* Academic Press, N. Y.

Regulatory Mechanisms

JACOB, F., and MONOD, J. (1961). "Genetic Regulatory Mechanisms in the Synthesis of Proteins." *J. molec. Biol.* **3**, 318.

PARDEE, A. B. (1961). "Response of Enzyme Synthesis and Activity to Environment." *Microbial Reaction to Environment Symp. Soc. gen. Microbiol.* **11**, 19. Camb. Univ. Press.

PARDEE, A. B. (1962). "The Synthesis of Enzymes." *The Bacteria* Vol. III: *Biosynthesis* p. 577. (Eds.). GUNSALUS, I. C., and STANIER, R. Y. Academic Press, N. Y.

CHAPTER 3

THE FERMENTATION PATHWAYS

It would be completely out of place in this text to attempt to cover what is known of the very diverse metabolic activities of microorganisms. References at the end of this chapter will provide a starting point for those who want detailed discussions of this subject.

The purpose of this chapter is to give an account of basic physiological reactions, to show how microorganisms oxidize substrates, how they obtain energy for biosynthesis, and how they couple energy-yielding reactions with energy-requiring reactions. It is intended also to outline those sequences of reactions that are common to many microorganisms and to show how conditions in a fermentation might be manipulated to achieve an improved yield of product or to direct metabolism from its normal course. It is important for biochemical engineers to be aware of what is known about the chemical activities of biological material, of what questions might profitably be asked of expert biochemists, and to appreciate which factors in the environment are likely to be important in obtaining good results in fermentation processes and, therefore, which factors must be controlled with precision.

3.1. BIOLOGICAL OXIDATIONS AND THE TRANSFER OF ENERGY

Living material gets energy for growth from oxidations or from light. The energy released on the removal of hydrogen or electrons from a substrate is partly dissipated as heat, but some is used for the formation of organic compounds with so-called "high energy" bonds. These compounds contain sulphur or phosphate in one of the configurations set out below.

$$
\begin{array}{cc}
\underset{\underset{R}{\overset{\parallel}{C}}}{-C}-O\sim\underset{\underset{OH}{\overset{\parallel}{O}}}{P}-OH
&
-N-\underset{\underset{N}{\overset{\parallel}{C}}}{C}-N\sim\underset{\underset{OH}{\overset{\parallel}{O}}}{P}-OH
\\[2em]
\underset{\underset{OH}{\overset{\parallel}{O}}}{-P}-O\sim\underset{\underset{OH}{\overset{\parallel}{O}}}{P}-O\sim\underset{\underset{OH}{\overset{\parallel}{O}}}{P}-OH
&
\underset{\overset{\parallel}{O}}{-C}\sim S-
\end{array}
$$

$\sim$ = bond which releases a large amount of energy on hydrolysis

Adenosine triphosphate (ATP) is one of the most important "high energy" compounds in the metabolism of the cell since ATP formed during oxidations can be coupled to endergonic reactions that will not proceed unless energy is supplied.

When the two terminal phosphate groups of ATP are hydrolysed, 12,000 cal are released per phosphate, but hydrolysis of adenosine monophosphate yields only 1,500 cal.* Although ATP contains two "high energy" phosphate bonds, it is common (though not always so) for the terminal phosphate only to be involved in reactions.

Adenosine monophosphate (AMP)

Adenosine diphosphate (ADP)

Adenosine triphosphate (ATP)

During cellular oxidations, protons and electrons from the substrate often pass through a system of enzymes, the individual members of which are successively reduced and reoxidized until some substance acts as a final electron acceptor. The order of reactions is determined by their oxidation/reduction potential (E_0'). In biological systems, the oxidation/reduction scale is based on the hydrogen couple with an $E_0' = -0.41$ V and the oxygen/water couple with an $E_0' = +0.82$ V, with the hydrogen carriers ranging in between.

The enzymes that are concerned in the removal of protons and electrons from the substrate are called dehydrogenases, each one being specific for the substrate it will oxidize; the enzymes that react directly with oxygen are called oxidases. The part of the dehydrogenase that reacts with the protons and electrons from the substrate is called the prosthetic group; it is either a pyridine nucleotide or a flavin nucleotide; the reactions for the oxidation and reduction of these two prosthetic groups are set out below.

---

* The amounts of energy released on hydrolysis of ATP are dependent upon the conditions of hydrolysis, particularly on the pH and the concentration of reactants. Under physiological conditions, it is thought that the number of calories released on hydrolysis of the phosphate groups is of the order given in the text.

When R = ribose-phosphate-phosphate-ribose-adenine, the prosthetic group is nicotinamide adenine
          dinucleotide (NAD)

When R = ribose-phosphate-phosphate-ribose, 2-phosphate-adenine, the prosthetic group is nicotina-
          mide adenine dinucleotide phosphate (NADP)

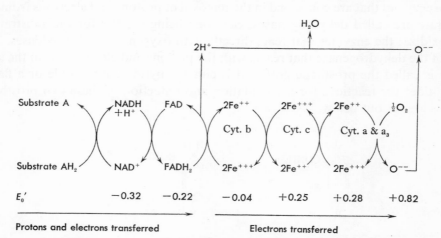

When R = ribose-phosphate, the prosthetic group is flavin mononucleotide (FMN)

When R = ribose-phosphate-phosphate-adenine, the prosthetic group is flavin adenine dinucleotide
          (FAD)

Many fungi, yeasts, algae, and bacteria can use oxygen as the final electron acceptor; a typical sequence of oxidation reactions following the removal of hydrogen
from a substrate is set out in Fig. 3.1. The reduced pyridine nucleotide of the dehydrogenase is reoxidized by transferring protons and electrons to a flavoprotein.
In its turn, the reduced flavoprotein is oxidized by passing two electrons to two iron-
containing prosthetic groups of cytochrome b and releasing two hydrogen ions into
the medium. The electrons then pass from cytochrome b to cytochrome c and so to
cytochrome a and a_3; cytochrome a and a_3 is the enzyme system that transfers
electrons to molecular oxygen. The activated oxygen then combines with hydrogen
ions released earlier, to form water. The E_0' values applying in the reaction sequence
just outlined are shown in Fig. 3.1.

The relationship between the change in free energy and the change in potential

FIG. 3.1.   Terminal electron transport pathway showing the oxidation/reduction potential of the reactants involved in substrate oxidation via a dehydrogenase, a flavoprotein, and cytochromes b, c, a and a_3
with oxygen as the final electron acceptor.

difference which occurs when electrons pass from one system to another can be expressed as follows:

$$\Delta F^\circ = -nF\Delta E_0$$

where,

ΔF° = free energy change (cal/mole) at standard state
n = number of electrons transferred
ΔE_0 = potential difference (volts)
F = faraday (23,063 cal/volt equivalent)

For biological systems, n is generally two and F° is replaced by F' as conditions are not at standard state. Then,

$$\Delta F' = -46,126 \times \Delta E_0'$$

If the potential difference of a system before and after oxidation is known, from the above equation it is possible to calculate the amount of energy released during an oxidation. For example, if electrons pass from $NADH+H^+$ to oxygen, the $\Delta E_0' = 1.14$ volt and so $\Delta F' = -52,000$ cal. Theoretically, this would allow the synthesis of 4 "high energy" phosphate bonds. When these reactions are studied in mitochondria (organelles in which the enzymes concerned in electron transport are situated) which have been isolated from mammals, yeasts, or fungi, it is found that such an oxidation involves the uptake of only 3 moles of inorganic phosphate and the formation of 3 moles of ATP per mole of oxygen used during the oxidation, which means that the system is about 70% efficient. Although all the enzymes for the process are present in bacteria, the amount of phosphate taken up per molecule of oxygen used suggests that only 1 mole of ATP is formed instead of the 3 found with higher cells carrying out the same oxidation. The explanation of this difference is not clear. It may be that the extracts tested are not fully active. On the other hand, bacteria do not have cytologically recognizable mitochondria like those in higher cells. It is possible that the reactions between enzymes and substrates are less efficient in bacteria because of a less favorable spatial arrangement of the enzymes in the bacterial cell compared with the arrangement in a mitochondrion.

Table 3.1 shows the E_0 of some oxidizable and reducible systems of biological importance. It also indicates the energy calculated to be released when electrons from substances at the E_0' of α-ketoglutarate pass, via NAD and the cytochrome system, to oxygen. It also indicates the number of $\sim P$ bonds that are known to be synthesized in mitochondria during such oxidations; it is clear that not all of the energy released by oxidations is transferred to "high energy" bonds. While some of the energy of oxidation which is not in the form of "high energy" bonds may be useful to the cell, most of it is dissipated as heat. In large industrial fermentations, it is essential to install cooling coils in tanks to remove this heat, as the temperature would otherwise rise to levels inhibitory to growth.

Although some microorganisms have all the terminal electron transport enzymes, others do not. For example, the lactobacilli and clostridia have no cytochromes,

TABLE 3.1

THE OXIDATION/REDUCTION POTENTIALS OF SOME BIOLOGICALLY IMPORTANT COMPOUNDS ARE SHOWN ON THE LEFT. THE CALCULATED CHANGES IN POTENTIAL AND FREE ENERGY WHICH OCCUR WHEN A COMPOUND AT THE E_0' OF X IS OXIDIZED TO THE E_0' OF OXYGEN VIA TWO INTERMEDIATES, Y AND Z, IS SHOWN ON THE RIGHT. THE NUMBER OF "HIGH ENERGY" PHOSPHATE BONDS OBSERVED TO BE FORMED IN MITOCHONDRIA IN SOME OF THE OXIDATION STEPS IS ALSO INDICATED.

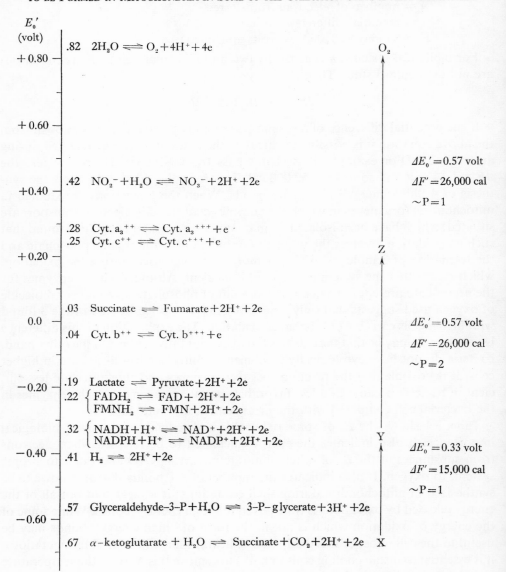

Table 3.1 was compiled from data presented by DOLIN, M. I. (1961). *The Bacteria* (Eds.). GUNSALUS, I. C., and STANIER, R. Y. Vol. II: *Metabolism* p. 319, "Microbial electron transport mechanisms." Academic Press, London.

although they have enzymes with pyridine nucleotide and flavoprotein prosthetic groups. The lactobacilli contain flavoprotein oxidases which can use oxygen as a terminal electron acceptor, but, in the presence of oxygen, they form hydrogen peroxide instead of water. Some species of *Streptococcus*, *Acetobacter*, *Pseudomonas*, and yeast have peroxidases that can reoxidize reduced substrates (for example, reduced cytochrome c or reduced NAD) in the presence of peroxides and hydrogen ions; the products of this reaction are oxidized substrate and water.

Oxygen cannot act as the hydrogen acceptor for facultative aerobes grown anaerobically or for strict anaerobes. These organisms must have an alternative method of reoxidizing their reduced hydrogen carriers. This is frequently achieved by coupling the oxidation of one substrate with the reduction of another, and often the reduced compound accumulates as an end product. For example, under anaerobic conditions, the lactobacilli reoxidize dehydrogenases reduced during glycolysis, by passing the hydrogen to pyruvate to form lactate.

$$CH_3 \cdot CO \cdot COOH + NADH + H^+ \rightleftharpoons CH_3 \cdot CHOH \cdot COOH + NAD^+$$

The species of clostridia that ferment hexoses anaerobically reoxidize their reduced-hydrogen carriers by reducing aceto-acetate (as the coenzyme A complex) to butyric acid or butanol; yeast reduces acetaldehyde to ethanol; some enteric bacteria reduce the dicarboxylic acids oxalacetic, malic, and fumaric to succinic acid; and acetoin is reduced to 2,3-butylene glycol in order to oxidize reduced flavin and nicotinamide carriers. A few species of *Pseudomonas* and a *Thiobacillus* can use nitrate as an electron acceptor, reducing the nitrate to gaseous nitrogen in the process; many species of bacteria and fungi can reduce nitrate to nitrite; and a few species of bacteria reduce sulphate to sulphide as a means of oxidizing hydrogen carriers.

It can be seen that microorganisms, and particularly bacteria, can reoxidize hydrogen carriers in the absence of oxygen in a number of different ways. The early industrial fermentations exploited these anaerobic methods of growth to accumulate useful products.

3.2. BREAKDOWN OF CARBOHYDRATE

3.2.1. Anaerobic fermentations

The biochemistry of the alcohol and lactic-acid fermentations has been extensively investigated and a good deal is known of the process, but it is not intended to discuss these reactions in detail. Rather it is proposed to outline the common pathways that exist among microorganisms metabolizing carbohydrates, to show that some species can metabolize hexoses by different pathways, to show how reduced-hydrogen carriers are reoxidized, to show how much energy is obtained from the process, and what application this knowledge has to biochemical engineering.

3.2.1.1. *Glycolysis*

The steps in the anaerobic breakdown of glucose to pyruvate via the glycolytic or Embden-Meyerhof-Parnas (EMP) pathway are outlined in Fig. 3.2. Points of importance in this sequence are listed below.

1. Activation of glucose with ATP; isomerization and a second phosphorylation to give fructose-1,6-diphosphate and 2 ADP.
2. Cleavage of fructose-1,6-diphosphate to give two molecules of triose-phosphate.
3. Oxidation of 3-phospho-glyceraldehyde with reduction of NAD and uptake of inorganic phosphate (i Ⓟ), resulting in the formation of a "high energy" bond in 1,3-diphospho-glycerate.
4. Transfer of the ∼P from 1,3-diphospho-glycerate to ADP.
5. Isomerization of 3-phospho-glycerate, followed by dehydration to form a ∼P in phospho-enol-pyruvate.
6. Transfer of the ∼P of phospho-enol-pyruvate to ADP and the formation of pyruvate and ATP.

There is thus a net gain of 2 moles of ATP per mole of glucose oxidized, and 2

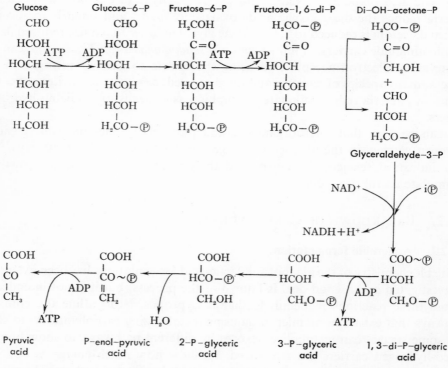

Summary: Glucose + 2ATP + 2NAD$^+$ ⇌ 2 Pyruvate + 4ATP + 2NADH + 2H$^+$

FIG. 3.2.   The reactions of glycolysis.   Ⓟ = H_2PO_3.

moles of NAD are reduced. The glycolytic pathway to pyruvate is widely distributed among all types of cells. Oxygen is not required for any of its reactions, but of course the reduced NAD must be regenerated by some mechanism. In the absence of oxygen, lactobacilli reduce pyruvate to lactate and yeast reduces acetaldehyde to ethanol.

$$CH_3 \cdot CO \cdot COOH \longrightarrow CH_3 \cdot CHO \longrightarrow CH_3 \cdot CH_2OH$$

$$CO_2 \qquad \begin{array}{c} NADH \\ +H^+ \end{array} \qquad NAD^+$$

Pyruvic acid   Acetaldehyde   Ethanol

3.2.1.2. *Entner-Doudoroff Pathway*

This pathway, which has some reactions in common with glycolysis, was found by Entner and Doudoroff when studying the oxidation of glucose by species of *Pseudomonas*. The pathway is outlined in Fig. 3.3.

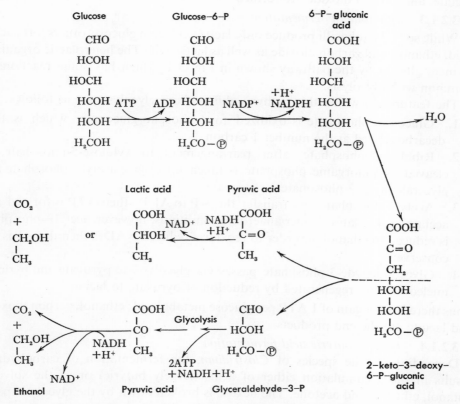

Summary: Glucose$+$ATP$+$NADP$^+$+NAD$^+$ $\rightleftharpoons$ 2Pyruvate$+$2ATP$+$NADPH$+$H$^+$+NADH$+$H$^+$

FIG. 3.3.   Reactions of the Entner-Doudoroff pathway. $\textcircled{P}$ $=$ H_2PO_3.

The essential features of the pathway are:

1.   Activation of glucose by ATP.
2.   Oxidation of the aldehyde group of glucose-6-phosphate to form 6-phospho-gluconate and the reduction of NADP.
3.   Dehydration of 6-phospho-gluconate to form 2-keto-3-deoxy-6-phospho-gluconate (KDPG).
4.   Cleavage by KDPG-aldolase to give pyruvate with one-half of the molecule and glyceraldehyde-3-phosphate with the other half.
5.   The triose-phosphate then passes via the glycolytic pathway to pyruvate and this provides 2 moles of ATP and 1 mole of reduced NAD per mole of triose-phosphate.

There is thus a net gain of 1 mole of ATP per mole of glucose metabolized, and 1 mole each of NADP and NAD are reduced. These are reoxidized in *Pseudomonas lindneri* by reducing the acetaldehyde formed after decarboxylation of 2 moles of pyruvate, to form 2 moles each of ethanol and carbon dioxide; in other pseudomonads, the hydrogen carriers are reoxidized while 1 mole each of ethanol, lactate, and carbon dioxide are formed.

3.2.1.3.   *Heterolactic fermentation*

While some lactobacilli produce only lactic acid from glucose, others form acetic acid, ethanol, and carbon dioxide as well as lactic acid. The heterolactic organisms ferment glucose by the pathway shown in Fig. 3.4, which has some reactions in common with glycolysis.

The features in which this pathway differs from glycolysis are as follows:

1.   Glucose-6-phosphate is oxidized to 6-phospho-gluconate, which is then decarboxylated at the number 1 carbon.
2.   Ribulose-5-phosphate, after rearrangement to xylulose-5-phosphate, is cleaved and inorganic phosphate is taken up to give acetyl~phosphate and glyceraldehyde-3-phosphate.
3.   Acetyl~phosphate can transfer the ~P to ADP; then ATP is formed and acetate accumulates. Under anaerobic conditions, however, acetyl~phosphate is reduced to ethanol, in order to reoxidize reduced NADP, then the ~P is not conserved.
4.   Glyceraldehyde-3-phosphate passes via glycolysis to pyruvate and pyridine nucleotides are regenerated by reduction of pyruvate to lactate.

Thus there is a net gain of 1 ATP per glucose metabolized; ethanol, carbon dioxide, and lactate are the end products.

3.2.1.4.   *Butanol-butyric acid fermentation*

Depending on the species of *Clostridium*, the fermentation of carbohydrate results in the accumulation either of acids (largely butyric) or of the solvents butanol, ethanol, and acetone. The hexose is broken down by the glycolytic pathway to pyruvate, then pyruvate is decarboxylated in the presence of coenzyme A (CoA) and NAD. Under these conditions, acetyl~SCoA and reduced NAD are formed. Acetyl~SCoA is a complex in which hydrolysis of the acetyl-sulphur linkage releases an amount of energy similar to that following hydrolysis of the "high energy" bonds of ATP. The metabolism of acetyl~SCoA by *Clostridium* species is outlined in Fig. 3.5.

The interesting features of this fermentation are the opportunities provided for the reoxidation of flavin and nicotinamide hydrogen carriers under strictly anaerobic conditions and the formation of "high energy" sulphur bonds. If the end

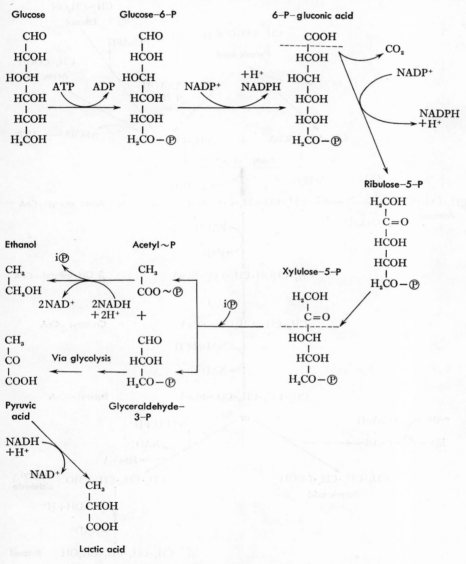

Summary: Glucose + ATP $\rightleftharpoons$ Ethanol + Lactic + CO_2 + 2ATP

FIG. 3.4.   Reactions of the heterolactic fermentation.   ℗ = H_2PO_3.

products of the fermentation are acids, it is possible for the energy of acetyl~SCoA
to be conserved for the cell, as follows:

$$\text{Acetyl} \sim \text{SCoA} + H_3PO_4 \rightleftharpoons \text{Acetyl} \sim \text{phosphate} + \text{HSCoA}$$
$$\text{Acetyl} \sim \text{phosphate} + \text{ADP} \rightleftharpoons \text{Acetic acid} + \text{ATP}$$

If the end products are fully reduced to alcohols, however, the "high energy"
bonds are used in the reductions. Hence, when a clostridium reduces glucose t

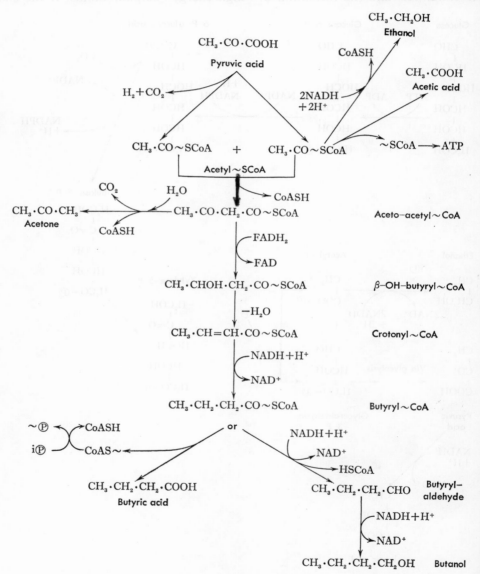

FIG. 3.5.   Fermentation of pyruvate by *Clostridium* species showing the formation of butyric and acetic
acids and of butanol, acetone, and ethanol.   ℗ = H_2PO_3.

butanol, ethanol, and acetone, the only gain of energy will be the 2 ATP derived
from the reactions of glycolysis.

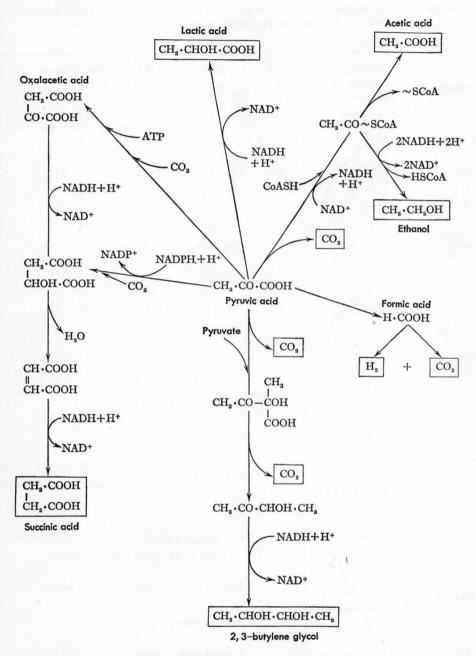

FIG. 3.6.   Metabolism of pyruvate by various enteric bacteria. The end products have been placed inside
squares.

TABLE 3.2

THE DISTRIBUTION OF THE CARBON ATOMS OF GLUCOSE IN THE PRODUCTS OF FERMENTATION AND THE YIELD OF ATP BY THE DIFFERENT PATHWAYS OF FERMENTATION.

Organism	Pattern of Cleavage of the Substrate Molecule	Yield of ATP (moles)	Distribution of the Carbon Atoms of Glucose in the End Products					
			C^1	C^2	C^3	C^4	C^5	C^6
Yeast		2	$CH_3 \cdot CH_2OH + CO_2 \ + \ CO_2 + \ CH_2OH \cdot CH_3$					
Homofermentative Lactobacilli		2	$CH_3 \cdot CHOH \cdot COOH + COOH \cdot CHOH \cdot CH_3$					
Heterofermentative Lactobacilli	a)	1	$CO_2 + CH_3 \cdot \quad CH_2OH + COOH \ \cdot CHOH \ \cdot CH_3$					
	b)	2	$CH_3 \cdot \quad COOH + COOH \cdot CHOH \cdot CH_3$					
Pseudomonas		1	$CO_2 + CH_2OH \cdot CH_3 \quad \begin{array}{l} COOH \cdot CHOH \cdot CH_3 \\ or \\ CO_2 \quad + CH_2OH \cdot CH_3 \end{array}$					
Clostridium			CO_2 derived from C^3 and C^4 ex pyruvate, and C^2 and C^6 ex aceto-acetyl-CoA. Butanol or butyric from C^1, C^2, C^5 and C^6. Acetone from C^1, C^2 and C^5 or C^1, C^5 and C^6. Ethanol from C^1 and C^2 or C^5 and C^6.					

3.2.1.5. *Mixed acid fermentation*

The bacteria of the enteric group ferment glucose via glycolysis to pyruvate, and then different species metabolize pyruvate differently. Fig. 3.6 shows that the organisms do not gain further energy from these reactions unless the "high energy" sulphur bond from acetyl~SCoA is conserved. Therefore, 2 moles of ATP per mole of glucose would be the minimum yield, plus 1 mole of ATP per mole of acetate formed via acetyl~SCoA. Although most of the reactions do not yield energy, they enable the cell to reoxidize hydrogen carriers.

Table 3.2 summarizes the pathways of glucose metabolism that have just been discussed and shows the distribution of the carbon atoms of glucose in the end products and the number of moles of ATP formed by each pathway. C_6, C_5, etc., indicates the number of carbon atoms in the molecule being metabolized; C^1, C^2, etc., refers to the numbering of the individual carbon atoms in the substrate molecule.

Over the past ten years, attempts have been made to relate the mass of cells formed to the amount of energy-producing substrate used and to the number of moles of ATP formed during the utilization of that substrate. It should be pointed out that these relationships are intended to apply in conditions where the substrate is used only for energy production, that is, the amino acids and other monomers needed for growth are pre-supplied in the medium. In such media, the yield has been expressed by different workers in the relationships which follow.

$$\text{Yield}_{\substack{\text{Energy Substrate} \\ \text{(e.g., Glucose)}}} = Y_G = \frac{\text{Dry Weight of Cells (g)}}{\text{Glucose Fermented (mole)}}$$

$$\text{Yield}_{\text{Adenosine triphosphate}} = Y_{ATP} = \frac{\text{Dry Weight of Cells (g)}}{\dfrac{\text{Number of Moles of ATP formed}}{\text{Mole of Substrate fermented}}}$$

In order to calculate Y_{ATP}, it is necessary to know the pathway by which the organism has fermented the substrate, as this will influence the number of moles of ATP which can, theoretically, be formed from each mole of substrate.

In describing the anaerobic breakdown of glucose in the previous sections, the number of moles of ATP formed by the different pathways has been stressed. The figure has been included in Table 3.3 along with the yield of cells per mole of energy substrate used. In addition, the yield of cells with *Desulfovibrio desulfuricans* growing on pyruvate for energy has been included in the table. The yield of cells per mole of ATP formed is about 10 g, suggesting that biosynthesis in all these cells is proceeding with the same efficiency despite wide differences in the substrate used for energy, the metabolic route used, and the organism. This constant appears to represent an important new concept in biological growth considerations. For example, it would be extremely useful when studying the biochemistry of unknown organisms to be able to calculate from the weight of cells formed and the amount of energy substrate used the number of moles of ATP that are likely to be formed. In addition, if the metabolic pathway is known, it is possible to calculate the mass of cells which will be obtained from any given weight of substrate used for energy.

TABLE 3.3

A COMPARISON OF THE YIELDS OF CELLS OBTAINED WHEN DIFFERENT ORGANISMS METABOLIZE SUBSTRATES BY DIFFERENT PATHWAYS.

Organisms	Energy Substrate Used	Pathway for Energy Production	Cell Yield	
			Y_s (g/mole of substrate)	Y_{ATP} (g/mole ATP)
Streptococcus faecalis	Glucose	Glycolysis	20	10
	Arginine	Arginine→ Ornithine + 1 ATP	10.5	10.5
Yeast	Glucose	Glycolysis	20	10
Pseudomonas lindneri	Glucose	Entner- Doudoroff	8.3	8.3
Leuconostoc mesenteroides	Glucose	Heterolactic	15*	15
Desulfovibrio desulfuricans	Pyruvate	†Pyruvate→ Acetyl ∼ P → ATP	9.5	9.5

* Estimated from optical density measurements.
† Based on pathway for energy metabolism proposed by SENEZ, J. C. (1963). *Bact. Rev.* **26**, 95.

It should be pointed out, however, that it is rather early to be certain that 10 g of cells will be obtained when all organisms synthesize one mole of ATP; Table 3.3 shows the Y_{ATP} for *Leuconostoc* to be 15 g. This may mean that the estimation of products is wrong or that knowledge of the biochemistry is incomplete. It may be that more than one mole of ATP is, in fact, formed; this would be the case if some of the acetyl∼phosphate, resulting from the cleavage of the pentose-phosphate, were converted to acetic acid instead of to ethanol. Then a further mole of ATP would be generated for every mole of acetic acid formed. On the other hand, if careful analyses and enzyme studies show the metabolic route to be consistent with formation of only one mole of ATP, then care must be taken before accepting that about 10 g of cells will always be obtained for each mole of ATP generated.

3.2.1.6. *Monophosphate oxidation*

Many organisms that metabolize glucose via the EMP pathway can also metabolize it by the monophosphate pathway. (This pathway is also known as the Warburg-Dickens or direct-oxidative pathway or as the monophosphate shunt.) The pathway comprises a rather complicated series of reactions; it has been set out in a

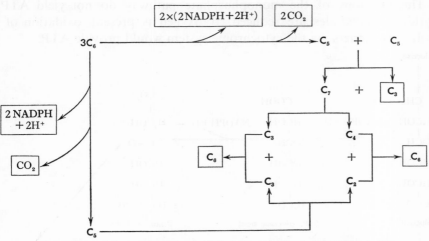

Summary: $3C_6 + 6NADP^+ \rightleftharpoons 2C_6 + C_3 + 3CO_2 + 6NADPH + 6H^+$

FIG. 3.7. Diagrammatic representation of the main reactions of the monophosphate oxidation of glucose, where C_6=hexose-6-P, C_5=pentose-5-P, C_7=sedoheptulose-7-P, C_4=erythrose-4-P, C_3= triose-3-P or a triose fragment, C_2=2-carbon fragment.

greatly simplified form in Fig. 3.7 and given in more detail in Fig. 3.8. The important features of the pathway are listed below.

1.   It provides a means of forming pentoses needed as part of nucleic acids and of the prosthetic groups of many enzymes.
2.   It leads to an understanding of the way in which cells transfer two-carbon and three-carbon fragments from one compound to another using the enzymes transketolase and transaldolase respectively.
3.   It provides the carbon skeletons needed as precursors for the formation of the aromatic amino acids and p-aminobenzoic acid, a vitamin for bacteria; erythrose-4-phosphate combines with phospho-enol-pyruvate to form a heptonic acid phosphate which is a precursor of tyrosine, phenylalanine, tryptophan, and p-aminobenzoic acid.
4.   The decarboxylation of 6-phospho-gluconate in this pathway explains how glucose labeled in the number 1 carbon can yield carbon dioxide containing radioactivity. This would not be expected if glucose were metabolized solely via the EMP route. The reactions of the monophosphate pathway also explain how preparations poisoned with fluoride or iodoacetate can continue to ferment glucose. Iodoacetate blocks the oxidation of glyceraldehyde-3-phosphate and fluoride interferes with the conversion of 2-phospho-glycerate to phospho-enol-pyruvate; both reactions are essential for the operation of the EMP pathway. Glucose can still be metabolized, however, by the monophosphate pathway; carbon dioxide is then derived from the decarboxylation of 6-phospho-gluconate, see Fig. 3.9.

5. The reactions of the monophosphate pathway do not yield ATP, but
pyridine nucleotides are reduced. If oxygen is present, oxidation of these
hydrogen carriers via the cytochrome system would provide ATP.

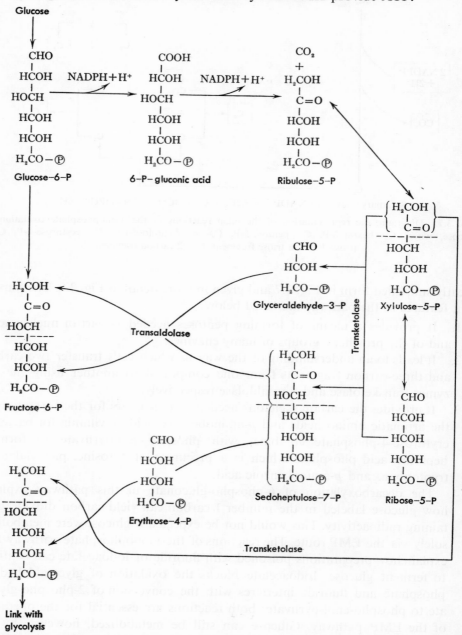

Summary: $3\text{Glucose} + 6\text{NADP}^+ \rightleftharpoons 2\text{Fructose-6-P} + \text{Glyceraldehyde-3-P} + 3CO_2 + 6\text{NADPH} + 6H^+$

FIG. 3.8.   Hexose monophosphate oxidation of glucose.   ⓟ = H_2PO_3.

6. The functioning of this cycle is of great importance to photosynthetic and chemosynthetic autotrophs; all their cellular carbon is derived by condensing carbon dioxide with ribulose-1,5-diphosphate, which is derived from ribulose-5-phosphate.

The pathways outlined in this section represent the ways different organisms have solved the problem of "life without air." While these differences in metabolism provide information of academic interest, they also offer interesting possibilities for the production of organic acids and solvents of industrial importance.

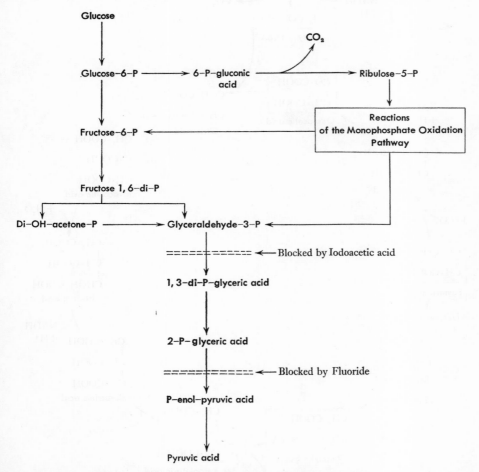

FIG. 3.9.   The links between glycolysis and the monophosphate oxidation pathway. The metabolic blocks caused by iodoacetate and fluoride are also shown; preparations poisoned with these inhibitors ferment glucose via the monophosphate pathway, liberating carbon dioxide from 6-P-gluconate.

3.2.2.   Aerobic oxidation of pyruvate

Although many species of bacteria are able to live by the anaerobic oxidation of substrates, most microorganisms, including bacteria, are able to use oxygen as the

final electron acceptor in oxidations. When oxygen is available, pyruvate is metabolized by many of these organisms via the tricarboxylic acid (TCA) cycle.

3.2.2.1. *Tricarboxylic acid cycle*
The reactions of the tricarboxylic acid cycle are set out in Fig. 3.10. This cycle is

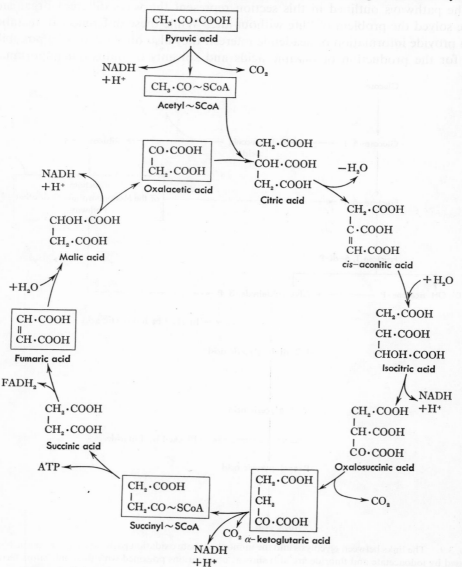

Summary: $CH_3 \cdot CO \cdot COOH + 4NAD^+ + FAD \rightleftharpoons 3CO_2 + 4NADH + 4H^+ + FADH_2$

Fig. 3.10. Tricarboxylic acid cycle. The compounds put inside squares are the starting compounds for
synthetic reactions; α-ketoglutaric, fumaric, oxalacetic, and pyruvic acids are all concerned in amino acid
formation, succinyl~SCoA is used for porphyrin synthesis, and acetyl~SCoA is needed for acetylation
reactions.

of the greatest importance in biosynthesis, as it provides both the carbon skeletons needed as starting materials and the energy needed for the reactions.

For most microorganisms, glutamate is the key amino acid synthesized *de novo* from ammonia and carbohydrate; it is formed by combining ammonia with α-ketoglutarate. Many bacteria, however, can combine ammonia with fumarate to form aspartate; by transamination, these amino acids act as amino-donors to α-keto acids such as pyruvic, oxalacetic, and α-ketoisovaleric to form other amino acids. Another important biosynthetic pathway begins when succinyl∼SCoA from the TCA cycle combines with glycine to form the pyrroles which are needed for the formation of porphyrins; the prosthetic groups of the cytochromes are iron-porphyrins, and a magnesium-porphyrin is the prosthetic group of chlorophyll.

Energy is derived from the operation of the TCA cycle during the reoxidation of reduced-hydrogen carriers. During the oxidation of one mole of pyruvate to carbon dioxide and water, four pairs of protons and electrons pass to dehydrogenases with nicotinamide prosthetic groups and one pair of protons and electrons passes to a dehydrogenase with a flavin prosthetic group; the cycle would halt quickly if the hydrogen carriers were not reoxidized. In the presence of oxygen, the series of oxidation/reduction reactions discussed in Section 3.1 takes place. As each pair of protons and electrons passes from the substrate to oxygen, ∼P bonds are formed; for fungi, yeasts and algae, 3 ATP are formed as each pair of protons and electrons

TABLE 3.4

AMOUNT OF ENERGY DERIVED BY MICROORGANISMS DURING THE OXIDATION OF GLUCOSE VIA
GLYCOLYSIS AND THE TRICARBOXYLIC ACID CYCLE.

Pathway	Number of moles of ATP Formed	
	Algae, Yeast and Fungi	Estimated for Bacteria
Glycolysis		
Glucose ⟶ 2 Pyruvate	2	2
Oxidation of: 2 NADH + 2 H⁺	$2 \times 3 =$ 6	$2 \times 1 =$ 2
TCA Cycle		
Pyruvate ⟶ 3 CO_2 + 3 H_2O		
Oxidation of: 4 NADH + 4 H⁺ 1 FADH₂	$4 \times 3 = 12$ $1 \times 2 = 2$	$4 \times 1 = 4$ 1
Succinyl∼SCoA ⟶ 1 ATP	1 ‾‾ 15	1 ‾ 6
2 Pyruvate ⟶ 6 CO_2 + 6 H_2O	$2 \times 15 =$ 30	$2 \times 6 =$ 12
Glucose + 3 O_2 ⟶ 6 CO_2 + 6 H_2O	38	16

passes from reduced NAD to oxygen. The number of moles of ATP formed during the oxidation of glucose to carbon dioxide and water via glycolysis and the TCA cycle is set out in Table 3.4. Even with bacteria, where the efficiency of formation of ATP is possibly less than for higher organisms, aerobic oxidation provides considerably more energy for the cell than anaerobic oxidation.

There are difficulties in attempting to calculate the Y_{ATP} for the aerobic oxidation of glucose. During aerobic growth, a significant amount of the carbon of the substrate is diverted from the TCA cycle for biosynthesis; this carbon is thus not oxidized to provide energy for the cell. Theoretically, aerobic metabolism gives 38 moles of ATP, while anaerobic fermentation gives 2 moles of ATP per mole of glucose, and it might be expected that the yield of cells would be in the same ratio; but, empirically, aerobic oxidation of glucose gives about five times as many yeast cells as does anaerobic fermentation of the same weight of glucose.

Since the TCA cycle provides many compounds used in biosynthetic reactions, it is clear that the cycle will be broken if intermediate compounds of this pathway are removed. Each complete turn of the cycle regenerates oxalacetate to condense with acetyl~SCoA to form citrate; when compounds are removed from the cycle, oxalacetate must be formed by some other route. This is achieved by fixing carbon dioxide to a three-carbon intermediate of glycolysis. Three reactions that fix carbon dioxide are widely spread among microorganisms:

$$COOH \cdot CO \cdot CH_3 + CO_2 + NADPH + H^+$$
$$\rightleftharpoons COOH \cdot CHOH \cdot CH_2 \cdot COOH + NADP^+$$

$$COOH \cdot \underset{\parallel}{C}O \sim \textcircled{P} + CO_2 + ADP \rightleftharpoons COOH \cdot CH_2 \cdot CO \cdot COOH + ATP$$
$$CH_2$$

$$COOH \cdot \underset{\parallel}{C}O \sim \textcircled{P} + CO_2 \rightleftharpoons COOH \cdot CH_2 \cdot CO \cdot COOH + H_3PO_4$$
$$CH_2$$

If malic acid is the end product of fixation, it is oxidized to oxalacetic acid by malic dehydrogenase.

$$COOH \cdot CHOH \cdot CH_2 \cdot COOH + NAD^+$$
$$\rightleftharpoons COOH \cdot CO \cdot CH_2 \cdot COOH + NADH + H^+$$

3.2.2.2. *Glyoxylic acid cycle*

Certain bacteria and fungi are able to grow when two-carbon substrates are supplied as the sole source of carbon. These organisms have all the enzymes for the operation of the TCA cycle but have, in addition, one enzyme which splits isocitrate to succinate and glyoxylate and a second enzyme which condenses glyoxylate and acetyl~SCoA to form malate. In the presence of "sparking" amounts of oxalacetate, the operation of these two enzymes enables the organism to synthesize dicarboxylic acids. When the dicarboxylic acids have been formed, the complete TCA cycle can operate. Fig. 3.11 shows the connections between the TCA and glyoxylic acid cycles. It also shows that the operation of these two cycles will allow the cell to make the α-ketoglutarate required for biosynthesis. In addition, by decarboxylating malate to form phospho-enol-pyruvate and reversing the reactions of glycolysis and the monophosphate oxidation pathway, the organism can form the hexoses and pentoses which it needs for growth but which are not provided by the two-carbon substrate itself.

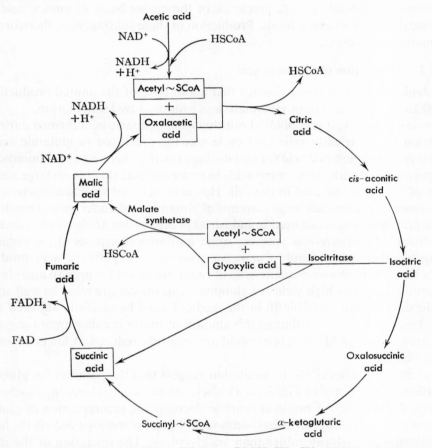

Summary: $2CH_3 \cdot COOH + 2NAD^+ + 2H_2O \rightleftharpoons COOH \cdot CH_2 \cdot CH_2 \cdot COOH + 2NADH + 2H^+$

FIG. 3.11.   Glyoxylic acid and tricarboxylic acid cycles. The compounds in squares are important intermediates in the reactions of the glyoxylic acid cycle.

3.3.   ACCUMULATION OF AMINO ACIDS

Many microorganisms have the capacity to make all the amino acids needed for growth from inorganic salts and simple carbohydrates. Man and animals cannot synthesize some of these amino acids; they must be supplied in the diet. Diets rich in cereals and low in animal proteins frequently have a low content of amino acids, particularly lysine, methionine, and tryptophan. The production of amino acids by fermentation could provide a means of supplementing such marginal diets. Fermentation processes have an advantage over non-biological methods of producing amino acids; the amino acids formed by fermentation are in the L-form, where as chemical processes give a D-L mixture; only the L-form is used by mammals. Investigations of the chemical basis of food flavor has shown that monosodium glutamate and inosinic acid (a precursor of the purine bases of nucleic acids) accentuate the flavor of many foods. Production of these substances is, therefore, also of commercial interest.

3.3.1. Production of glutamic acid

In Japan in 1963, it was estimated that about 60% of the annual production of 35,000 tons of monosodium glutamate was produced by fermentation.

In Section 3.2.2.1, it was pointed out that α-ketoglutaric acid formed during the operation of the tricarboxylic acid cycle was the precursor of glutamic acid. In normal cells, the glutamic acid formed during growth either acts as an amino-donor or is polymerized with other amino acids to make protein; there is no large accumulation of free glutamic acid in the cell. However, selected strains of bacteria have been shown to accumulate large amounts of glutamic acid under special conditions.

The principal organisms used in industrial processes are *Micrococcus glutamicus* and various *Brevibacterium* species; some authorities consider these organisms belong together in the family *Corynebacteriaceae*. The glutamic acid producing strains have the common characteristic of requiring biotin for growth and glutamic acid production. For high yields of glutamic acid, the culture must be well aerated and the concentrations of biotin in the medium must be carefully adjusted to between 1 μg and 5 μg/liter, although this amount of biotin is suboptimal for growth. Both growth and yield of glutamic acid are seriously reduced at lower concentrations of biotin.

Biochemical studies of the fermentation suggest that the pathway for glutamate formation is as outlined in Fig. 3.12. This scheme has some interesting biochemical features. A deficiency of biotin appears to decrease the incorporation of glutamic acid into protein; it also increases the amount of glucose metabolized via the hexose monophosphate pathway rather than via glycolysis. The operation of the monophosphate pathway produces reduced NADP. This can be reoxidized by the reductive amination of α-ketoglutaric acid and by the fixation of carbon dioxide via the malic enzyme, since both of these reaction systems require reduced NADP. From Fig. 3.12, it is clear that these two reactions are important for the formation of large amounts of glutamate.

Either a high biotin content in the medium or poor aeration gives a low yield of glutamic acid and causes the accumulation of lactic and succinic acids, which are reduced compounds whose formation provides an alternative means of reoxidizing reduced hydrogen carriers; some acetic acid may also be formed. Although it is well known that the concentration of biotin in the medium affects the yield of glutamic acid, the exact role of biotin in this fermentation is still uncertain.

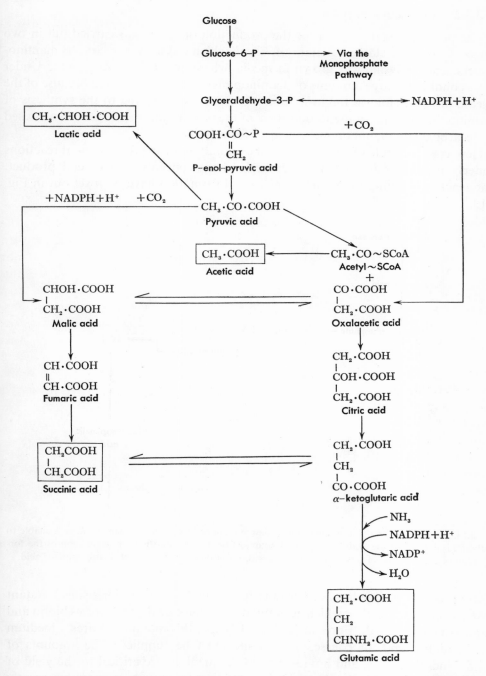

FIG. 3.12.   Pathway for glutamic acid formation in *Micrococcus glutamicus*. When aeration is poor or the biotin content of the medium is high, lactic, acetic, and succinic acids accumulate instead of glutamic acid.

3.3.2. Production of lysine

The process first developed for the production of lysine was carried out in two stages. In the first stage, a mutant of *E. coli* which was unable to convert diamino-pimelic acid to lysine was grown in media where lysine limited growth. Under these conditions, large amounts of diaminopimelic acid accumulated because of the release of repression on the formation of the enzymes leading to the synthesis of diaminopimelic acid. In the second stage of the process, another organism was used to decarboxylate diaminopimelic acid to form lysine.

Here is an example of the commercial exploitation of the fundamental reactions underlying cellular control of biosynthesis by the concentration of end product. The reactions leading to diaminopimelic acid formation have been set out in Fig. 3.13.

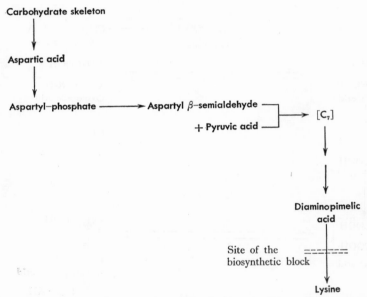

FIG. 3.13. Reactions for the accumulation of diaminopimelic acid with a mutant of *E. coli* unable to synthesize lysine. When the medium contains amounts of lysine that limit growth, repression of the formation of the enzymes of this sequence is released, resulting in high yields of diaminopimelic acid.

More recently, lysine has been produced in a single fermentation using a mutant of *Micrococcus glutamicus* which accumulates glutamic acid and requires biotin and homoserine for growth. For a high yield of lysine, this mutant requires a medium rich in biotin, and, of course, homoserine must be supplied. The amounts of methionine, threonine, and homoserine in the medium are critical to the yield of lysine. If any one of these amino acids is supplied in large amount, growth is greatly stimulated but the yield of lysine is very low. A suggested sequence of reactions leading to the accumulation of lysine is indicated in Fig. 3.14; the possible sites of

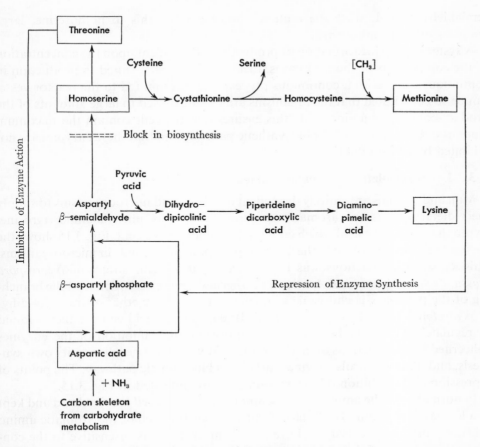

FIG. 3.14. Biosynthesis of lysine, threonine, and methionine in a mutant of *Micrococcus glutamicus* requiring homoserine and biotin. Excess methionine and threonine actuate feed-back mechanisms which decrease the conversion of carbohydrate to lysine.

the regulatory action (feed-back control) of these end products of biosynthesis are shown.

When methionine is present in excess of the immediate needs of growth, it represses the formation of the enzymes that convert aspartic acid to aspartyl β-semialdehyde. This reduces the amount of carbohydrate directed via aspartic acid to lysine. Threonine probably acts either by inhibiting the action of aspartyl kinase or of aspartyl β-semialdehyde dehydrase. The effect of excess threonine on lysine formation will be similar to the effect of excess methionine. When homoserine is supplied in excess, feed-back regulation, either by inhibition or repression or both, also reduces the amount of lysine formed. When all three amino acids are present in low concentration, enzyme formation is not repressed and enzyme activity is not inhibited, and so large amounts of aspartic acid are converted to aspartyl β-semialdehyde, and, since the mutant cannot convert this to homoserine, large amounts of lysine are formed.

A system where the formation of product is so dependent upon the concentration of the components of the medium is, theoretically, ideally suited to production in continuous culture. In a continuous process, the medium fed to the reactor vessel can be so constituted that the organisms are never exposed to large amounts of the product-controlling amino acid; this ensures that the cells contain the maximum amount of the enzymes of the biosynthetic pathway and that these enzymes are not inhibited by end product.

3.3.3. Accumulation of aromatic amino acids

Man and animals are entirely dependent on plants and microorganisms to supply their dietary needs for aromatic compounds such as phenylalanine, tyrosine, tryptophan, and folic acid which contains *p*-aminobenzoic acid. Fig. 3.15 shows the biosynthetic steps involved in the formation of these compounds in microorganisms. This sequence of reactions was established using mutant strains of *Neurospora crassa, Escherichia coli*, and *Aerobacter aerogenes*. The key compound at the branching of the pathways is chorismic acid (the 3-enol-pyruvic ether of trans-3,4-dihy-droxy*cyclo*hexa-1, 5-diene carboxylic acid); each amino acid end product is found to regulate its own synthesis by both repression and inhibition of the enzymes concerned in the reactions after chorismic acid which are peculiar to its own synthesis, and it also controls enzymes early in its biosynthetic pathway. The points of repression and inhibition of enzyme function are indicated in Fig. 3.15.

In normal cells, the amounts of free amino acids in the cell are regulated and kept at a low concentration. To develop fermentations for each of the aromatic amino acids, it would be necessary to have an organism that was insensitive to the concentration of one of the end products of biosynthesis, as was found in strains of *Micrococcus glutamicus* accumulating glutamate. Such a defective organism could be treated with mutagens, and a mutant selected which had deficiencies in the synthesis of, say, phenylalanine and tyrosine. A mutant with these multiple deficiencies could be used to produce tryptophan. The composition of the medium for the fermentation would need to be carefully controlled so that phenylalanine and tyrosine were supplied at concentrations that limited growth; any regulatory function that these compounds have on the intermediates common to all the aromatic compounds would then not operate. This would have the effect of increasing the amount of substrate carbon directed towards the aromatic biosynthetic pathway; but since the pathways to two of the end products are blocked, the third compound (in this example, tryptophan) would be produced in large amounts.

3.4. OBSERVATIONS OF FERMENTATION CYCLES

The most ancient fermentations were haphazard affairs where the operator did little more than expose the substrate to chance infection; he partially controlled the

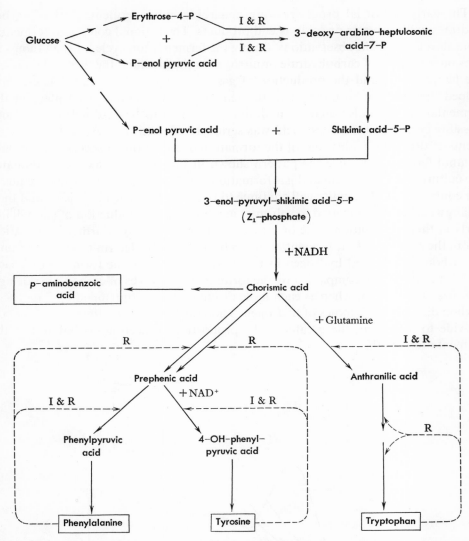

FIG. 3.15.   An abridged scheme of the pathway found in coliform bacteria for the formation of various aromatic amino acids. The conversion of chorismate to prephenate is achieved by two enzymes each under the specific control of either phenylalanine or tyrosine. In the same way, these two compounds exercise control over a pair of enzymes that condense phospho-enol-pyruvate and erythrose-4-phosphate to form 3-deoxy-arabino-heptulosonic acid-7-phosphate.

I = Inhibition of enzyme action
R = Repression of enzyme synthesis

temperature and the access of oxygen to the material, but otherwise allowed the fermentation to take its own course. When fermentation processes ceased to be cottage crafts and became industrial processes, a completely different approach was necessary.

The early industrial processes were anaerobic batch fermentations of carbohydrates, with solvents or acids as end products. The rational control of fermentations developed from observations, during the fermentation cycle, of such things as
the concentration of carbohydrate or nitrogen in the medium, the titratable acidity,
the temperature, and the production of gas and other end products. These data
helped the operator to understand the sequence of reactions taking place in the
fermentation; they also enabled undesirable changes to be detected quickly, and
possibly corrected before the yield was seriously affected. For example, measurements of titratable acidity and of the formation of gas during a successful acetone-
butanol fermentation give the pattern shown in Fig. 3.16. If phage contaminates
the culture, the rate of acid and gas formation will be very slow; if a lactobacillus is
the contaminant, the acidity will continue to rise steadily, instead of rising and then
falling as acids are converted to solvents; in addition, the production of gas will fall
early in the fermentation cycle or may even stop completely. Further information
about the products of the fermentation can be obtained by determining the amounts
of carbon dioxide and hydrogen in the gas evolved, since the formation of each
mole of acetone is accompanied by the formation of 3 moles of carbon dioxide and
2 moles of hydrogen, whereas each mole of butanol is accompanied by 2 moles of
carbon dioxide and 2 moles of hydrogen. Therefore, the greater the ratio of carbon
dioxide to hydrogen, the greater is the proportion of acetone to butanol in the
fermentation broth.

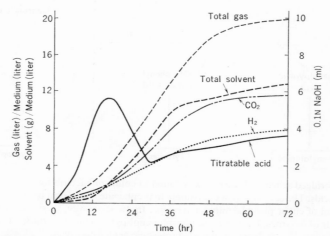

FIG. 3.16.   Formation of carbon dioxide, hydrogen, total solvent, total gas and titratable acid during the
production of acetone and butanol by *Clostridium acetobutylicum.*
Redrawn from the data of PETERSON, W. H., and FRED, E. B. (1932). *Ind. Eng. Chem.* **24,** 237.

With information of this kind it is possible to predict early in the fermentation
cycle whether the yield of product will be satisfactory, and to be alerted to any
abnormalities in the process.

Measurements made during fermentations assist greatly in management and control, and from a study of the kinetics of the processes, useful generalizations can be made. These generalizations will help to improve the yield from batch processes and assist in transferring information from batch to continuous processes. A study of the rates of growth, of utilization of substrate, and of formation of product allow fermentations to be grouped into three broad classes.

1. Fermentations where the formation of product is stoichiometrically related to the utilization of the carbohydrate that supplies energy for growth; changes in the rate of carbohydrate utilization are parallel with changes in the rate of formation of product.
2. Fermentations where the formation of product is related to the utilization of the carbohydrate supplying energy for growth, but the association is less direct; the formation of product is not stoichiometrically related to the utilization of carbohydrate at all times during the fermentation.
3. Fermentations where no clear relation exists between the rate of formation of the product and the rate of utilizaton of the substrate providing energy for growth.

The production of ethanol by yeast and the production of lactic acid by homofermentative lactobacilli are two anaerobic fermentations that illustrate clearly the first type of process. Growth is completely dependent upon the capacity of the organism to obtain energy from glycolysis; glycolysis can only continue while the pyridine nucleotides reduced during glycolysis are reoxidized. This is achieved in yeast by reducing acetaldehyde to ethanol, and in lactobacilli by reducing pyruvate to lactate; growth and formation of product are parallel processes when the cells are growing anaerobically. In the presence of oxygen a new system operates; the substrate is metabolized by a different pathway to yield completely different products; with yeast grown aerobically, the major product of the utilization of substrate is cell mass. Hence, in the manufacture of baker's yeast, the rate of utilization of substrate and the rate of formation of cell mass are parallel, so the aerobic growth of yeast also belongs to the first class of fermentations. In general, fermentations of this first class, when carried out in a batch process, require conditions that allow the maximum rate of utilization of the energy substrate throughout the process. If the process is continuous, a single vessel only will be needed, though it may well be profitable, in an anaerobic process with the relatively slow rate of growth, to feed back some of the cells to the reactor vessel.

In fermentations of the second class, the growth of the organism is separated in time from the formation of product, although the same carbohydrate is supplying the energy for growth and the carbon for the formation of product. The uptake of carbohydrate is rapid during two periods of the fermentation cycle, one corresponding with the period of maximum growth and the other with the period of maximum formation of product. The production of citric acid by *Aspergillus niger* follows the general pattern just outlined. The mould is provided with a large amount of carbohydrate but little nitrogen, phosphorus, or trace metals; early in the fermentation, carbohydrate is used for growth until other nutrients are exhausted; it is then metabolized so that the amount of citric acid accumulating is related to the amount of carbohydrate used; this process gives a small yield of energy. There is evidence of an increase in cell mass during the stage of rapid formation of product, but it seems probable that this increase is due to the formation of metabolically inactive material, such as polysaccharides, since other nutrients are limiting growth after 40 to 60 hours. The management of this type of fermentation in a batch system clearly offers opportunities for changing the environment during the process to provide the best conditions for each stage; in continuous culture, at least two vessels would be desirable, with the sizes of the vessels arranged to give the correct time of residence in the environment that is best for each stage of the process.

Fermentations of the third class show no close relation at any time between the rate of utilization of the substrate supplying energy and the rate of formation of product; fermentations for antibiotics, vitamins, and enzymes are typical of this class. Antibiotics, for example, are not secreted from the cells until growth is complete, or nearly so, and the rate of utilization of the substrate is very slow.

In these fermentations, as with fermentations of the second class, it may be desirable to provide different environmental conditions for different stages of the process; but unlike the second class of fermentations, carbohydrate supplied in excess of the needs for cellular carbon and energy is not converted to product. In studies of the effect of environment on the yield of antibiotic, it has been shown with two different species of *Streptomyces*, that the mycelium has only a limited period when a very large amount of oxygen is essential to obtaining a good yield of antibiotic. If less oxygen is available at other times in the fermentation, the yield of antibiotic is not affected. In practice, this means that aeration costs can be considerably reduced without decreasing the yield of product, provided the critical period of demand for oxygen is satisfied.

Since the products of fermentations of this class are often complex molecules, yields are likely to be improved by supplying the cells, at the right time, with substances that are on the pathway to the formation of the product but which are synthesized by the cell with difficulty. For example, the addition of phenyl acetate to the broth after 48 hours in penicillin fermentations greatly increases the yield of penicillin G, although it does not stimulate growth.

Since growth and the formation of product are separated in time, it would seem worth investigating the effect of providing in the medium during the product-forming phase of the cycle a pH, oxygen tension, temperature, or carbon-to-nitrogen ratio that differs from that supplied during the growth phase. The choice of the particular components of the environment to be changed should be made after a study of the biochemistry of the process; it would be highly desirable to know the optimum conditions for the enzymes involved in the formation of product so that these conditions could be supplied during the product-forming stage. It might be expected that these conditions would not be identical with those for optimum growth. It follows that in continuous culture, this class of fermentation would probably require more than one vessel with different conditions provided for each stage of the process.

Although it is obvious that there is still much to be learnt about the metabolism of substrates by microorganisms, it is now possible to use organisms to produce specific compounds efficiently. The understanding of biosynthetic processes in cells and their regulation is far from satisfactory; but it is in this field that future advances in fermentations seem likely to lie. For example, the parts played by DNA and the various types of RNA in the synthesis of protein from amino acids have only recently been appreciated; this offers the exciting prospect that, in the future, it may be possible to direct organisms to make proteins "to order."

Setting such speculations aside, our present knowledge of metabolism is not applied as effectively as it could be, because insufficient account is taken of conditions in the fermentation vessel, as they affect the gross form of the microbial cells; this is particularly true of organisms that form hyphae or aggregate into clumps. It has been noted by many observers that the gross morphology of microorganisms is influenced by factors like the quantity and type of inoculum, the degree of agitation in the fermentation vessel, the duration of periods of vigorous agitation, and by the composition of the growth medium; but in the past there has been little appreciation by biochemical engineers of the great importance of the gross form of the microbial growth. Great trouble is taken to adjust pH, temperature, and the concentrations of oxygen and nutrients in the bulk of the medium, making the assumption that these conditions apply uniformly at the surface of all cells; this is manifestly not true for pellets of hyphae or large clumps of cells. Biochemical information can suggest the environment that gives increases in yield and faster rates of growth, but this information applies to single cells or enzyme preparations where diffusion is not a limiting factor. While the favorable environment can be carefully maintained in the bulk of the medium, its effect may be partly lost if the microclimate at the surface of a large proportion of the cells is unfavorable.

It is suggested, therefore, that research directed to controlling the gross form of microbial growth should always accompany biochemical investigations.

NOMENCLATURE

ADP = Adenosine diphosphate
ATP = Adenosine triphosphate
$\text{CoAS}\sim$ = Coenzyme A in the "high energy" form
CoASH = Reduced coenzyme A
DNA = Deoxyribonucleic acid
E_0' = Oxidation/reduction potential
EMP = Embden-Meyerhof-Parnas pathway
FAD = Flavin adenine dinucleotide
FMN = Flavin mononucleotide
NAD = Nicotinamide adenine dinucleotide

NADP = Nicotinamide adenine dinucleotide phosphate
$\sim$P = "High energy" phosphate
i $\circledP$ = Inorganic phosphate
RNA = Ribonucleic acid
TCA = Tricarboxylic acid cycle
$$Y_{ATP} = \frac{\text{mass of cells formed (g)}}{\text{number of moles of ATP formed/mole of substrate fermented}}$$
$$Y_G = \frac{\text{mass of cells formed (g)}}{\text{glucose fermented (mole)}}$$

TEXTBOOKS AND ARTICLES FOR FURTHER READING
AND AS A SOURCE OF REFERENCES

General Texts of Biochemistry

CONN, E. E., and STUMPF, P. K. (1963). *Outlines of Biochemistry* Wiley, N. Y.

FRUTON, J. S., and SIMMONDS, S. (1958). *General Biochemistry* 2nd ed. Wiley, N. Y.

WEST, E. S., and TODD, W. R. (1961). *Textbook of Biochemistry* 3rd ed. Macmillan, London.

Metabolism of Carbohydrates and the Yield of Energy

BAUCHOP, T., and ELSDEN, S. R. (1960). "The growth of microorganisms in relation to their energy supply." *J. gen. Microbiol.* **23**, 457.

GADEN, E. L., JR. (1959). "Fermentation process kinetics." *J. Biochem. Microbiol. Tech. & Eng.* **1**, 413.

GUNSALUS, I. C., and STANIER, R. Y. (1961). (Eds.). *The Bacteria* Vol. II: *Metabolism* Academic Press, London.

KORNBERG, H. L. (1959). "Aspects of terminal respiration in microorganisms." *Ann. Rev. Microbiol.* **13**, 49.

RAINBOW, C., and ROSE, A. H. (1963). (Eds.). *Biochemistry of Industrial Microorganisms* Academic Press, London.

SENEZ, J. C. (1962). "Some considerations on the energetics of bacterial growth." *Bact. Rev.* **26**, 95.

Accumulation of Amino Acids and Other Metabolites

GIBSON, M. I., and GIBSON, F. (1964). "Preliminary studies on the isolation and metabolism of an intermediate in aromatic biosynthesis: chorismic acid." *Biochem. J.* **90**, 248.

GORINI, L. (1963). "Control by repression of a biochemical pathway." *Bact. Rev.* **27**, 182.

KAPLAN, N. O. (1963). "Multiple forms of enzymes." *Bact. Rev.* **27**, 155.

KINOSHITA, S. (1959). "The production of amino acids by fermentation processes." *Adv. Appl. Microbiol.* **1**, 201.

MOAT, A. G., and FRIEDMAN, H. (1960). "The biosynthesis and interconversions of purines and their derivatives." *Bact. Rev.* **24**, 309.

STADTMAN, E. R. (1963). "Enzyme multiplicity and function in the regulation of divergent metabolic pathways." *Bact. Rev.* **27**, 170.

UMBARGER, E., and DAVIS, B. D. (1962). *The Bacteria* Vol. IV: *Biosynthesis* p. 167, (Eds.). GUNSALUS, I. C., and STANIER, R. Y. Academic Press, London.

CHAPTER 4

KINETICS

PRELIMINARY REMARKS ON FERMENTATION KINETICS

Kinetic studies are necessary to gain a basic understanding of any fermentation; however, for the most part, they have been neglected.[7,13] As the name implies, fermentation kinetics is concerned with the rates of production of cells and/or of products of fermentation and the effect of environment on these rates. Kinetic studies are not necessarily limited to growing systems. They also may include dying cells.

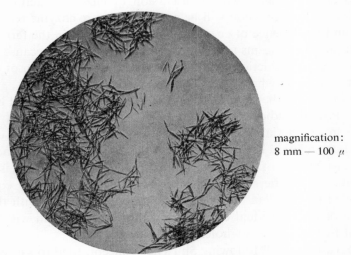

magnification:
8 mm — 100 μ

FIG. 4.1.   Photo-micrograph of amylo-1,4-glucosidase extracted and purified from the broth of *Aspergillus oryzae.*
(*Courtesy* Dr. T. Sawasaki, *Institute of Physical and Chemical Research, Tokyo.*) For the purification procedure of the enzyme see SAWASAKI, T. (1960). "Purification of amylo-1,4-glucosidase with *Aspergillus oryzae.*" *Repts. Inst. Phys. & Chem. Research* **36**, 584.

Needless to say, most people who are engaged in the study of fermentations do measure the effects of temperature, pH values, and nutrients on the fermentation course to determine the most appropriate cultural conditions. Far too often, however, these effects are not related to the basic reactions involved in the fermentation processes. One reason for this is the variety of conditions that occur in a batch fermentation.

In a typical batch fermentation, the microbial growth pattern exhibits different phases—lag, logarithmic (log), decline, and resting phases as were discussed in Chapter 2 (The characteristics of biological material). Chapter 8 (Media sterilization) deals with the effect of heat on the rate of denaturation of microbial protein as applied to the engineering problem of designing heat sterilizers. Continuous fermentation (Chapter 5) has been advocated by many people as a tool for the study of fermentation kinetics principally because of the fact that the environmental conditions can be kept constant. Because of this, the factors limiting growth or product formation for a particular fermentation can be sought and studied more readily. It will be appreciated, therefore, that studies of continuous fermentation and of fermentation kinetics are closely linked. In addition, mechanisms associated with the production of specific materials in fermentations have been discussed in Chapter 3 (The fermentation pathways); such information will help one construct the fermentation kinetics. From this, it is clear that subjects with important bearings on kinetics have been, or will be, discussed in other chapters rather than here in Chapter 4.

This chapter begins with a discussion of enzyme reaction patterns and rate equations. The discussion will be confined to pure enzyme reactions; this may be far from the sequence of enzyme reactions involved in the fermentation industry, but this approach seems to be worthy of a short review, because the study of single enzyme reaction kinetics is fundamental to the construction of the kinetics of the fermentation as a whole.

A number of other approaches to fermentation kinetics will be referred to here briefly. Powell studied experimentally and theoretically the distribution of the age of cells in a bacterial population.[17] Although his study was not especially oriented to the inter-relation between the age of the cell and its enzyme activity, knowledge of the distribution of cell generation times in a growing system is important to any fermentation kinetic study. Recently, Shu introduced a new concept of age. He attempted to correlate the rate of formation of product with the distribution of the age of the individual cells of the culture, rather than with the physiological state of the culture as a whole.[19]

Kobayashi et al.,[10] following Shu's age concept, tried to assess the cultural conditions of yeast with an "apparent age." In addition, the term "mean cumulative age," which was introduced by Aiba et al., will be useful in relating the enzyme activities of multicellular systems to the kinetics of the formation of product (see Chapter 5). In the future, reorganization and expansion of fermentation kinetics to embrace some concept of microbial age appears worthy of attention, though the definition of microbial age seems to be in a semantic turmoil.

Next in this chapter, the absolute reaction rate theory, as applied to the microbial system, will be discussed. Unfortunately, only a few papers have been published based on the absolute rate theory. This theory, when applied to the analysis of batch, as well as continuous fermentations, may become a powerful tool in analyzing substantial features of fermentation kinetics.

In the last sections, the rate patterns found in various fermentations and the expressions for the kinetic parameter of unicellular growth will be briefly reviewed. Different ways of classifying these fermentation patterns have been proposed. Gaden suggested that fermentations could be broadly divided into those where the rates of growth and of formation of product are closely associated (growth associated), and those where there is no close relationship (non-growth associated).[6] Luedeking and Piret studied the kinetics of the lactic acid fermentation and established that the formation of product was both growth associated and non-growth associated.[12] Deindoerfer proposed five types of fermentation—simple, simultaneous, consecutive, step-wise and complex.[2] Such a classification, although helpful, is only a gross simplification of the fermentation kinetics. It refers only to macro-effects and behavior.

Although the microbial system is complicated by involved sequences of enzymic reactions, biochemical research is elaborating these sequences. In the near future, there will be sufficient knowledge to place fermentation kinetics on a firmer basis, thus permitting the application of kinetics to the management of industrial fermentations, and allowing quantitative generalizations to be made about factors which affect the fermentation. With such information, the considerable number of shaken-flask experiments required to develop a fermentation process may be reduced. The biochemical engineer may then do much of his experimentation on the computer. The problems discussed in this chapter indicate the relatively primitive state of our knowledge of the kinetics of industrial fermentations, and it is hoped that readers of this book, recognizing the importance of this subject, will be motivated to contribute to the development of this aspect of biochemical engineering.

4.1. Enzyme Reaction Kinetics

4.1.1. Michaelis-Menten equation[3, 11]

One of the most widely accepted models of enzyme kinetics is that of Michaelis-Menten. These workers represented the reaction of enzyme with substrate as follows:

$$E+S \underset{k_{-1}}{\overset{k_{+1}}{\rightleftarrows}} E\text{-}S$$

$$E\text{-}S \overset{k_{+2}}{\longrightarrow} E+P \tag{4.1}$$

where

$$E = \text{enzyme}$$
$$S = \text{substrate}$$
$$E\text{-}S = \text{enzyme-substrate complex}$$
$$P = \text{product}$$

k_{+1} = forward reaction rate constant

k_{-1} = reverse reaction rate constant

k_{+2} = reaction rate constant

Denoting e, S, and c as the concentrations of total enzyme, substrate, and enzyme-substrate complex, respectively, the rate of change, dc/dt, will be:

$$\frac{dc}{dt} = k_{+1}(e-c)S - k_{-1}c - k_{+2}c \qquad (4.2)$$

It is assumed in Eq. (4.2) that the value of S is considerably greater than that of e. The left-hand side of Eq. (4.2) becomes zero in steady state. Then,

$$c = \frac{eS}{\dfrac{k_{-1}+k_{+2}}{k_{+1}}+S} \qquad (4.3)$$

The rate of product formation, v, in the enzyme reaction shown by Eq. (4.1) is given by:

$$v = k_{+2}c = \frac{k_{+2}eS}{\dfrac{k_{-1}+k_{+2}}{k_{+1}}+S} = \frac{VS}{K_s+\dfrac{k_{+2}}{k_{+1}}+S}$$

$$= \frac{VS}{K_m+S} \qquad (4.4)$$

where

$V = ek_{+2}$ = maximum rate of production; all of the enzyme forms the enzyme-substrate complex

$K_s = k_{-1}/k_{+1}$ = equilibrium constant in the dissociation of the enzyme-substrate complex, E-S

$K_m = K_s + k_{+2}/k_{+1} \qquad (4.5)$

If the value of k_{+2} is far less than that of k_{+1}, i.e., if the rate of product formation is controlled by the specific rate, k_{+2}, in the sequence of reactions expressed by Eq. (4.1), Eq. (4.5) reduces to:

$$K_m = K_s \qquad (4.6)$$

Eq. (4.4) is called the Michaelis-Menten equation. The term, K_m, is called the Michaelis-Menten constant. This constant is equal to the equilibrium constant, K_s, only when the value of $k_{+2} \ll k_{+1}$. When $K_m = K_s$, the value of K_m is inversely proportional to the chemical affinity of enzyme for the substrate. The smaller the value of K_m, the greater the affinity of enzyme for the substrate. In passing it should be noted that the Michaelis-Menten equation is analogous to the Monod's equation for microbial growth.[13] In Monod's equation, the values of V and v in Eq. (4.4) are replaced with μ_{max} (maximum value of specific growth rate) and μ (specific growth rate) respectively, as will be shown later.

Fig. 4.2 is a graphic representation of Eq. (4.4). It is apparent from Eq. (4.4) that the value of K_m is that value of S when the reaction proceeds at one-half the maximum reaction rate. The Michaelis-Menten equation can also be derived from Langmuir's isothermal adsorption theory.[7]

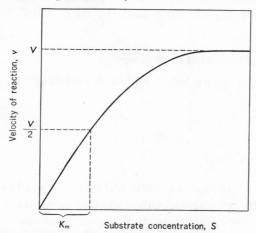

Fig. 4.2.   Graphic representation of the Michaelis-Menten equation, Eq. (4.4). The velocity of reaction, v, is plotted against the substrate concentration, S. The value of V is the maximum reaction rate, and K_m in the abscissa represents the Michaelis-Menten constant.

4.1.2.   Lineweaver-Burk plot [3,11]

It is seen in Fig. 4.2 that the value of V cannot be determined accurately by plotting the values of v against S, because the maximum value of V is the limit of an asymptote of the curve as shown in Fig. 4.2. However, taking reciprocals of both sides of Eq. (4.4),

$$\frac{1}{v} = \frac{K_m}{V}\frac{1}{S} + \frac{1}{V} \qquad (4.7)$$

If the value of $1/v$ is plotted against that of $1/S$, a straight line will be obtained as shown in Fig. 4.3. The intersection of this straight line with the ordinate represents $1/V$, while that with the abscissa is equal to $(-1/K_m)$. The characteristic

Fig. 4.3.   Graphic representation of the Lineweaver-Burk plot; the reciprocal of the reaction rate, $1/v$, is plotted against the reciprocal of the substrate concentration, $1/S$. The terms, K_m and V, in the figure are the Michaelis-Menten constant and the maximum reaction rate, respectively.

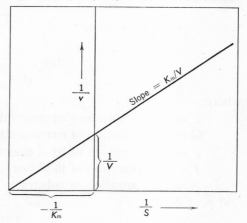

constants (V, K_m) can then be determined from the experimental data (v, S), as plotted in Fig. 4.3, following Eq. (4.7). This procedure of determining the values of V and K_m from the experimental data (v, S) is called the Lineweaver-Burk plot (1934).

4.1.3. Competitive inhibition of enzymes[3, 11]

The enzyme reaction shown below will be considered:

$$E+S \underset{k_{-1}}{\overset{k_{+1} \quad (K_s)}{\rightleftharpoons}} E\text{-}S \overset{k_{+2}}{\longrightarrow} E+P$$

$$E+I \underset{k_{-3}}{\overset{k_{+3} \quad (K_i)}{\rightleftharpoons}} E\text{-}I \tag{4.8}$$

It is assumed that two different equilibria will be established in the above sequence of reactions—one between enzyme, substrate, and substrate-enzyme complex, and the other between enzyme, inhibitor, and enzyme-inhibitor complex, where

     k_{+1} = forward reaction rate constant between enzyme and substrate
     k_{-1} = reverse reaction rate constant between enzyme and substrate
     k_{+2} = forward reaction rate constant in the dissociation of enzyme-substrate complex
     k_{+3} = forward reaction rate constant between enzyme and inhibitor
     k_{-3} = reverse reaction rate constant between enzyme and inhibitor
     I = inhibitor
     K_s = equilibrium constant in the reaction between E and S
     K_i = equilibrium constant in the reaction between E and I

Part of the enzyme is supposed to combine with inhibitor, forming an enzyme-inhibitor complex; the enzyme is then supposed to lose partially its capability to form the product, P. Equilibrium constants regarding the above sequence of reactions are:

$$K_s = \frac{(e-c-d)S}{c} = \frac{k_{-1}}{k_{+1}} \tag{4.9}$$

$$K_i = \frac{(e-c-d)i}{d} = \frac{k_{-3}}{k_{+3}} \tag{4.10}$$

where

     c = concentration of enzyme-substrate complex
     d = concentration of enzyme-inhibitor complex
     e = concentration of total enzyme
     i = concentration of inhibitor
     S = concentration of substrate

and provided:

$$S \gg e \text{ and } i \gg d$$

Cancelling the term, d, from Equations (4.9) and (4.10),

$$c = \frac{eSK_i}{K_sK_i+K_si+SK_i} \tag{4.11}$$

The rate of reaction (product formation), v, will then become:

$$v = k_{+2}c = \frac{k_{+2}eSK_i}{K_sK_i+K_si+SK_i}$$

$$= \frac{VSK_i}{K_sK_i+K_si+SK_i}$$

$$= \frac{VS}{K_s+S+\dfrac{K_s}{K_i}i}$$

$$= \frac{VS}{K_m+S+\dfrac{K_m}{K_i}i} \tag{4.12}$$

provided:

$$V = k_{+2}e \text{ (maximum rate of reaction)}$$
$$k_{+2} \ll k_{+1} \text{ (see Equations (4.5) and (4.6))}$$

Rearranging Eq. (4.12),

$$\frac{1}{v} = \frac{K_m}{V}\left(1+\frac{i}{K_i}\right)\frac{1}{S}+\frac{1}{V} \tag{4.13}$$

provided:

$$k_{+2} \ll k_{+1} \text{ (see Equations (4.5) and (4.6))}$$

Eq. (4.13) is shown in Fig. 4.4 by a straight line; the slope and intersection with

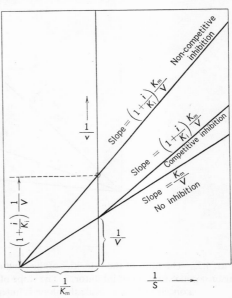

FIG. 4.4. Eq. (4.13) for the competitive inhibition of enzymes is shown graphically by the Lineweaver-Burk plot; the value of K_i is assumed to be independent of the values of S; see the middle straight line. The lower straight line in the figure represents Eq. (4.7) (no inhibition). It is apparent that the slope of the straight line for competitive inhibition is $\left(1+\dfrac{i}{K_i}\right)\dfrac{K_m}{V}$, whereas the intersection of the line with the ordinate is $1/V$. Regarding the upper line for non-competitive inhibition, the intersections of the ordinate and the abscissa are $\left(1+\dfrac{i}{K_i}\right)\dfrac{1}{V}$ and $(-1/K_m)$, respectively (see the next section).

the ordinate are $\left(1+\dfrac{i}{K_i}\right)\dfrac{K_m}{V}$ and $1/V$, respectively, provided the value of K_i is independent of S.

Comparison of Eq. (4.12) with Eq. (4.4) (Michaelis-Menten equation—no inhibition) suggests that the enzyme reaction rate, v, of Eq. (4.12), based on the sequence of reaction shown in Eq. (4.8), is affected both by the values of S and of i. The rate of enzyme reaction varies with the concentration of i, since there is competition between i and S for a place on the enzyme surface; this is called competitive inhibition of enzyme action. This point of terminology will be elaborated later in this section.

If v_i, the rate of enzyme reaction in the presence of inhibitor, is substituted for v in Eq. (4.13), and this equation is combined with Eq. (4.4), then Eq. (4.14) is obtained.

$$\frac{v}{v_i} = 1+\frac{K_m}{K_i}\left(\frac{1}{K_m+S}\right)i \tag{4.14}$$

If the term, v/v_i, from Eq. (4.14) is plotted against the inhibitor concentration, i, a straight line with a slope of $\dfrac{K_m}{K_i}\left(\dfrac{1}{K_m+S}\right)$ is obtained (see Fig. 4.5). It is evident from Eq. (4.14) and Fig. 4.5 that the slope of the line for competitive inhibition depends on the value of S.

If the term, $1/v_i$, is plotted against the inhibitor concentration, i, with the substrate concentration, S, as the parameter, competitive enzyme inhibition exhibits the straight line relationships shown in Fig. 4.6. It is seen from Eq. (4.13) that the abscissa value of the intersection of these straight lines (for S_1, S_2 and—) is $(-K_i)$.

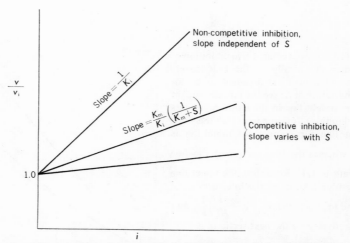

FIG. 4.5.   The ratio of the velocities of the reaction in the absence and presence of inhibitor, v/v_i, plotted against concentration of inhibitor, i. The slope of the line for competitive inhibition varies with substrate concentration, S, while the slope is independent of S for non-competitive inhibition.

At the abscissa reading, i, where the two straight lines regarding S_1 and S_2 intersect,

$$\frac{K_m}{V}\left(1+\frac{i}{K_i}\right)\frac{1}{S_1} = \frac{K_m}{V}\left(1+\frac{i}{K_i}\right)\frac{1}{S_2} \tag{4.15}$$

To satisfy the above equation,

$$i = -K_i \quad (S_1 \neq S_2) \tag{4.16}$$

The intersection of a straight line with the abscissa of Fig. 4.6 will be:

$$i = -K_i\left(1+\frac{S}{K_m}\right) \tag{4.17}$$

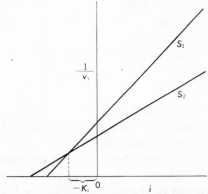

FIG. 4.6. $1/v_i$ vs. i; parameter$=S$; it is evident from Eq. (4.13) that the competitive inhibition of enzyme reaction yields straight lines and that the abscissa reading of the intersection of these straight lines is $(-K_i)$, the equilibrium constant of the dissociation of enzyme-inhibitor complex.

Figs. 4.4 to 4.6 are useful in differentiating between the various enzyme reaction patterns: no inhibition, competitive inhibition, and non-competitive inhibition (for non-competitive inhibition, see the next section). Experimental data can be analyzed by plotting them as was done in these figures, and so determine the enzyme reaction pattern; the values of K_m, K_i and V for a specific enzyme system can also be determined (see example of calculation later).

4.1.4. Non-competitive inhibition of enzymes

The following sequence of enzyme reactions will be considered. Unless otherwise noted, the nomenclature used in Eq. (4.18) is the same as in Equations (4.1) and (4.8). The complexes E-S and E-I are in equilibrium with enzyme and substrate and with enzyme and inhibitor, respectively. In addition, another complex, E-S-I, is present. The concentration of this triple complex is in equilibrium with E-S+I and E-I+S, respectively, as shown in Eq. (4.18).

$$E+S \underset{K_s}{\rightleftharpoons} E\text{-}S \xrightarrow{k_{+2}} E+P$$

$$E+I \underset{\longleftarrow}{\overset{K_i}{\rightleftarrows}} E\text{-}I$$

$$E\text{-}S+I \underset{\longleftarrow}{\overset{K_i'}{\rightleftarrows}} E\text{-}S\text{-}I$$

$$E\text{-}I+S \underset{\longleftarrow}{\overset{K_s'}{\rightleftarrows}} E\text{-}S\text{-}I \tag{4.18}$$

where

K_i' and $K' =$ equilibrium constants in the dissociations of E-S-I into E-$S+I$ and E-$I+S$, respectively

The equilibrium constants in the above enzyme reactions will be:

$$K_s = \frac{(e-c-d-f)S}{c}, \qquad K_i = \frac{(e-c-d-f)i}{d}$$

$$K_i' = \frac{ci}{f}, \qquad K_s' = \frac{dS}{f} \tag{4.19}$$

where

$e =$ concentration of enzyme, E

$c =$ concentration of enzyme-substrate complex, E-S

$d =$ concentration of enzyme-inhibitor complex, E-I

$f =$ concentration of enzyme-substrate-inhibitor complex, E-S-I

$S =$ concentration of substrate

$K_s =$ equilibrium constant of the reaction between $E+S$ and E-S

$K =$ equilibrium constant of the reaction between $E+I$ and E-I

$K_i' =$ equilibrium constant of the reaction between E-$S+I$ and E-S-I

$K_s' =$ equilibrium constant of the reaction between E-$I+S$ and E-S-I

and provided:

$$S \gg e \text{ and } i \gg d, f$$

If $K_s=K_s'$ and $K_i=K_i'$ (Eq. (4.20)) are assumed in the above sequence of enzyme reactions, Eq. (4.20)' is obtained from Eq. (4.19). Eq. (4.20) means that neither the substrate nor the inhibitor affects the affinity of the enzyme for the inhibitor or for the substrate; that is, the affinity of the pure enzyme for its substrate is unaffected by the existence of the enzyme-inhibitor complex, E-I.

$$K_s = K_s', \qquad K = K_i' \tag{4.20}$$

$$f = \frac{ci}{K_i} = \frac{dS}{K_s}, \qquad d = \left(\frac{K_s}{K_i}\right)ci\left(\frac{1}{S}\right) \tag{4.20}'$$

Substituting Eq. (4.20)' into K_s in Eq. (4.19),

$$c = \frac{eSK_i}{(K_s+S)(K_i+i)} \tag{4.21}$$

The rate, v, of producing a specific material, P, will be:

$$v = \frac{k_{+2}e\,SK_i}{(K_s+S)(K_i+i)}$$

$$= \frac{VSK_i}{(K_s+S)(K_i+i)}$$

$$= \frac{VS}{(K_m+S)\left(1+\dfrac{i}{K_i}\right)} \qquad (4.22)$$

where

$K_s = K_m$ (see Eq. (4.5) or Eq. (4.6))

$V = k_{+2}e$

Eq. (4.22) suggests that the rate of reaction, v, in this situation is less than that found with both Equations (4.4) (no inhibition) and (4.12) (competitive inhibition). It is characteristic of this type of inhibition that neither the substrate nor the inhibitor is competitive and the enzyme affinity for these substances is unchanged regardless of whether the enzyme exists as a pure enzyme, an enzyme-inhibitor complex, or as an enzyme-substrate complex. Eq. (4.22) thus represents the enzyme reaction rate equation for the non-competitive system.

From Eq. (4.22),

$$\frac{1}{v} = \left\{\frac{1}{V}+\left(\frac{K_m}{V}\right)\frac{1}{S}\right\}\left(1+\frac{i}{K_i}\right)$$

$$= \left(1+\frac{i}{K_i}\right)\left(\frac{K_m}{V}\right)\frac{1}{S}+\left(1+\frac{i}{K_i}\right)\frac{1}{V} \qquad (4.23)$$

Eq. (4.23) shows that the Lineweaver-Burk plot of non-competitive inhibition data yields a straight line whose slope is $\left(1+\dfrac{i}{K_i}\right)\dfrac{K_m}{V}$, whose intersection with the ordinate is $\left(1+\dfrac{i}{K_i}\right)\dfrac{1}{V}$, and with the abscissa $(-1/K_m)$ (see Fig. 4.4).

If v, the rate of reaction of an enzyme showing non-competitive inhibition, is substituted in Eq. (4.22) for v, and this equation is combined with Eq. (4.4) then,

$$\frac{v}{v_i} = 1+\frac{i}{K_i} \qquad (4.24)$$

Eq. (4.24) suggests that a straight line in a plot of v/v_i vs. i has a slope of $1/K_i$, the slope being independent of substrate concentration, S (see Fig. 4.5).

If a plot of $1/v_i$ vs. i is made with Eq. (4.23) selecting S as the parameter, straight lines are obtained (see Fig. 4.7), and at the intersections of these lines with the abscissa ($1/v=0$ in Eq. (4.23)),

$$\left(1+\frac{i}{K_i}\right)\left(\frac{K_m}{V}\right)\frac{1}{S_1} = \left(1+\frac{i}{K_i}\right)\left(\frac{K_m}{V}\right)\frac{1}{S_2} \qquad (4.25)$$

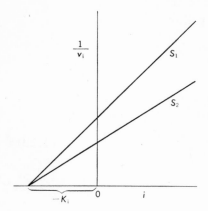

FIG. 4.7. $1/v_i$ vs. i; parameter$=S$; for the non-competitive inhibition of enzyme reaction, the reading of intersections of straight lines with the abscissa is $(-K_i)$ (see Eq. (4.23)).

Eq. (4.25) is satisfied if $i=-K_i$ $(S_1 \neq S_2)$. Straight lines in Fig. 4.7 then coincide at $i=-K_i$ on the abscissa. Equations (4.22) to (4.25) and Figs. 4.4, 4.5, and 4.7 are useful in deciding whether an enzyme reaction pattern exhibits non-competitive inhibition and also in determining the values of K_m, K_i and V.

4.1.5. Example of calculation for determining the type of enzyme reaction and the characteristic constants of the reaction

Experimental data on the hydrolysis of starch with α-amylase are given in Table 4.1.[3] The sequence of enzyme reactions is as follows:

$$\text{Starch} \longrightarrow \alpha\text{-dextrin} \longrightarrow \text{limit dextrin} \longrightarrow \text{maltose}$$

It is desired to determine the values of the Michaelis-Menten constant, K_m; the equilibrium constant for the dissociation of the enzyme-inhibitor complex, K_i; the maximum reaction rate, V; and the types of inhibition involved in the above sequence of reactions.

Solution

The experimental data are plotted as shown in Fig. 4.8 in terms of $1/v$ vs. $1/S$. Fig. 4.8 shows that limit dextrin and maltose exhibited non-competitive inhibition patterns, while the inhibition by α-dextrin was competitive (*cf*. Fig. 4.4).

However, Fig. 4.8 shows that inhibition by limit dextrin (non-competitive) and by α-dextrin (competitive) was clearly revealed when the substrate concentration was below 4 and 10 mg/ml, respectively.

For no inhibition in Fig. 4.8,

$$-1/K_m = -0.290 \text{ (the abscissa reading for } 1/v=0) \text{ (see Fig. 4.4)}$$
$$K_m = 3.45 \text{ mg/ml}$$

$$1/V = 0.0078 \text{ (the ordinate reading for } 1/S=0) \text{ (see Fig. 4.4)}$$
$$V = 128 \text{ (relative hydrolysis reaction rate)}$$

Maltose (non-competitive inhibition)
$$i = 12.7 \text{ mg/ml}$$

TABLE 4.1

DATA ON THE HYDROLYSIS OF STARCH.[3]

Inhibitor	Inhibitor concentration mg/ml	Substrate concentration mg/ml	Relative hydrolysis velocity
None	0.00	12.56 11.24 9.00 8.12 6.33 5.61 4.28 3.56 2.34 1.00	101 98.2 92.4 90.0 82.7 79.1 70.9 65.0 51.7 28.8
Maltose	12.7	10.00 7.70 5.26 4.55 3.33 2.04 1.89 1.67	77.0 71.4 62.5 58.9 51.4 38.9 37.0 34.2
Limit dextrin	13.35	10.00 7.15 6.25 5.00 4.17 3.77 3.14 2.39 2.10 1.75	95.3 87.0 83.4 75.9 47.6 45.5 41.7 35.7 33.0 29.4
α-dextrin	3.34	33.30 20.0 12.9 10.0 6.06 3.64 2.82 1.84 1.60 1.43	116 109 102 85.5 71.5 55.6 47.6 35.6 32.2 29.5

Slope of the Lineweaver-Burk plot in Fig. 4.8 for maltose,

$$\frac{0.0063}{0.190} = \left(1 + \frac{12.7}{K_i}\right)\left(\frac{3.45}{128}\right)$$

$$K_i = 56 \text{ mg/ml} \qquad \text{(see Fig. 4.4)}$$

Limit dextrin (non-competitive inhibition)

$$i = 13.35 \text{ mg/ml}$$

Slope of the straight line for the limit dextrin in Fig. 4.8,

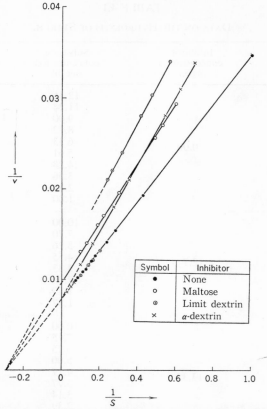

FIG. 4.8.   Plot of $1/v$ vs. $1/S$ using the data given in Table 4.1 as an example of calculation.

$$\frac{0.0053}{0.135} = \left(1+\frac{13.35}{K_i}\right)\left(\frac{3.45}{128}\right)$$

$$K_i = 29 \text{ mg/ml}$$

α-dextrin (competitive)

$$i = 3.34 \text{ mg/ml}$$

Slope of the straight line for the α-dextrin in Fig. 4.8,

$$\frac{0.0038}{0.1} = \left(1+\frac{3.34}{K_i}\right)\left(\frac{3.45}{128}\right)$$

$$K_i = 8.16 \text{ mg/ml}$$

4.2.   ABSOLUTE REACTION RATE THEORY AS APPLIED TO KINETICS

4.2.1.   Absolute reaction rate theory as applied to the biological system

The discussion in this section is another approach to fermentation kinetics. The ideas regarding the absolute reaction rate theory, while not inconsistent with the Michaelis-Menten theory, represent a different view; namely, that the transition state described in Fig. 4.9 is not necessarily the same as the enzyme-substrate complex.

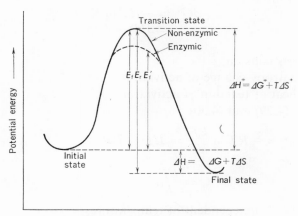

FIG. 4.9.   Potential energy model in the absolute reaction rate theory;[3] enzyme reaction reduces the energy barrier from E_f to E_f'.

The schematic diagram of Fig. 4.9 shows that the enzyme reduces the barrier of potential energy for forward and reverse reactions; the reduction is from E_f to E_f' for the forward reaction in the figure.

$$A + B \rightleftharpoons \text{Transition state} \longrightarrow \text{Product} \qquad (4.26)$$

The reaction is formulated in Eq. (4.26). The value of $\Delta E = E_f - E_r$ in the biological system is approximately equal to the value of ΔH (heat of reaction) (see later).

The equilibrium constant, K, for the formation of the transition state is described from Eq. (4.26) as follows:

$$K^* = \frac{c^*}{c_A c_B} \qquad (4.27)$$

where

$c^* =$ concentration of the transient material

$c_A, c_B =$ concentrations of A and B in Eq. (4.26)

It has been shown from the absolute reaction rate theory that

$$k_r c_A c_B = \frac{c^* kT}{h} \qquad (4.28)$$

where

$T =$ absolute temperature

$k_r =$ specific reaction rate to form the product

$k =$ Boltzmann constant

$h =$ Planck's constant

From Equations (4.27) and (4.28),

$$k_r = \frac{kT}{h}\frac{c^*}{c_A c_B} = \frac{kT}{h}K^* \tag{4.29}$$

The equilibrium constant, K^*, is related, on the other hand, to the free energy change, ΔG^*, as follows:

$$\Delta G^* = -RT \ln K^*$$
$$= \Delta H^* - T\Delta S^* \tag{4.30}$$

where

R = gas constant
ΔS^* = entropy change of activation
ΔH^* = heat of reaction of activation

From Equations (4.29) and (4.30),

$$\Delta G^* = -RT \ln \frac{k_r h}{kT} = \Delta H^* - T\Delta S^* \tag{4.31}$$

$$k_r = \frac{kT}{h} e^{\Delta S^*/R} e^{-\Delta H^*/RT} \tag{4.32}$$

Assuming that ΔS^* is independent of temperature,

$$\frac{d \ln k_r}{dT} = \frac{\Delta H^*}{RT^2} + \frac{1}{T} = \frac{\Delta H^* + RT}{RT^2} \tag{4.33}$$

$$\Delta H^* + RT = E \tag{4.34}$$

where

E = activation energy defined by the Arrhenius equation, which relates the change of specific rate of reaction with temperature, namely,

$$\frac{d \ln k_r}{dT} = \frac{E}{RT^2} \tag{4.35}$$

An error, due to the fact that ΔH^* in Eq. (4.32) is made approximately equal to E, must be considered. But this error is not necessarily so grave because in most biological systems at about 300 °K, the value of $RT = 1.987 \times 300 \doteq 600$ calories/mole and, moreover, ΔH^* is usually more than 10,000 calories/mole. Then, from Eq. (4.32),

$$k_r = \frac{kT}{h} e^{\Delta S^*/R} e^{-E/RT} \tag{4.36}$$

The values of k_r in Eq. (4.36) in a biological system reveal an over-all picture of the activities of the enzymes involved in a biological reaction. By measuring the change of k_r values with temperature, either the values of E or ΔS^* can be estimated. The values of E or ΔS^* thus determined with a specific biological reaction may give further insight into the kinetics of the whole system.

4.2.2. Example 1: Catalytic breakdown of hydrogen peroxide

Sizer has studied the activation and inactivation of the crystalline catalase-hydrogen peroxide system by changing the temperature of the reaction.[21] The catalase he used was extracted from beef liver and recrystalized. The activity of the enzyme was expressed by the rate of oxygen evolution (converted to standard temperature) from the catalase-hydrogen peroxide system. The rate was measured with the Warburg-Barcroft manometer at temperatures ranging from 0 °C to 60°C.

The experimental data are shown in Fig. 4.10, the ordinate of which represents the log rate of oxygen evolution, mm³/min, while the abscissa is reciprocal of the absolute temperature. Although a definite temperature at which the rate of oxygen evolution was maximized could not be determined by the experiment, it is apparent from Fig. 4.10 that the data points fall into two groups, one of which was related to the activation of the enzyme in a temperature range up to 53 °C, while the other dealt with inactivation of the enzyme at the higher temperatures.

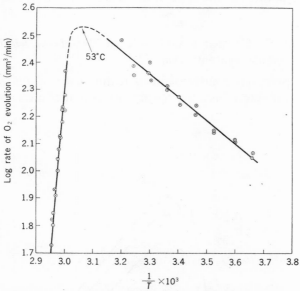

FIG. 4.10. Catalytic breakdown rate of H_2O_2 depending on temperature.[21]

Assuming that the k_r values in Eq. (4.35) can be represented by the rate of oxygen evolution,

$$E = \frac{2.303R \log \frac{k_{r_2}}{k_{r_1}}}{\frac{1}{T_1} - \frac{1}{T_2}} \doteqdot \frac{4.6 \log \frac{k_{r_2}}{k_{r_1}}}{\frac{1}{T_1} - \frac{1}{T_2}} \qquad (4.37)$$

where

k_{r_2} = specific activity of enzyme measured with the rate of oxygen evolution at T_2

k_{r_1} = specific activity of enzyme at T_1

From the slopes of solid lines drawn through the data points in Fig. 4.10 and with Eq. (4.37),

$$E_1 = 4,200 \text{ calories/mole (below 53°C)}$$
$$E_2 = 51,000 \text{ calories/mole (above 53°C)}$$

The former value is the energy required for enzyme activation, while the sum of E_1 and E_2 (55,000 calories/mole) represents the energy for the thermal inactivation of the enzyme.

Sizer calculated the value of ΔS^* from Eq. (4.36). According to his calculation, the values of ΔS^* in enzyme activation and inactivation were negative and positive, respectively. The negative values of ΔS^* meant that the randomness decreased due to reorientation of catalase and hydrogen peroxide molecules, presumably resulting from the formation of an enzyme-substrate complex in the temperature range of enzyme activation. The positive values of ΔS^* at the inactivation temperature apparently corresponded to the state of increased randomness of molecules during enzyme inactivation.

4.2.3. Example 2: Oxygen uptake rate of *Rhizobium trifolii* as affected by urethane concentration

Koffler *et al.* prepared a suspension of resting cells of *Rhizobium trifolii* in a buffer solution and determined the respiratory activities either with the Warburg

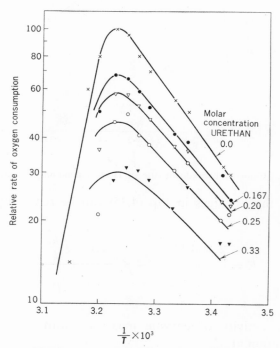

FIG. 4.11. Effects of temperature and urethane concentration on oxygen uptake rate of *Rhizobium trifolii*; the ordinate and the abscissa are the relative rate of oxygen consumption measured with the Warburg respirometer and the reciprocal of the absolute temperature, respectively; the parameter is the molar concentration of urethane (inhibitor).[9]

respirometer or by the methylene blue reduction rate.[9] They determined the respiratory activities of the bacteria at various temperatures in the presence or absence of urethane solution (inhibitor).

Their experimental results with the Warburg respirometer are shown in Fig. 4.11; the relative rate of oxygen uptake is plotted against the reciprocal of the absolute temperature. It is clear from Fig. 4.11 that the respiratory activity of the enzyme was inhibited markedly by urethane and that the enzyme, regardless of the presence or absence of the inhibitor was activated in a lower temperature range, approximately 19 °C to 37 °C ($1/T = 3.42 \times 10^{-3}$ to 3.23×10^{-3}). The denaturation became appreciable at temperatures above 37 °C ($1/T \leq 3.2 \times 10^{-3}$).

A curve based on the data obtained in the absence of urethane is shown in Fig. 4.11; the relation is represented by:

$$I' = \frac{\alpha T e^{-E_1/RT}}{1 + e^{-E_2/RT} e^{\Delta S^*/R}} \tag{4.38}$$

where

$$E_1, E_2 = \text{activation energies}$$
$$R = \text{gas constant}$$
$$T = \text{absolute temperature}$$
$$\Delta S^* = \text{entropy change of activation}$$
$$I' = \text{enzyme activity measured with the oxygen uptake rate}$$
$$\text{(the Warburg respirometer)}$$
$$\alpha = \text{proportionality constant}$$

The denaturation of the enzyme at higher temperatures was expressed by

$$I' = \frac{\alpha T}{1 + e^{-E_2/RT} e^{\Delta S^*/R}}$$

as can be seen from Fig. 4.11, while the activity, I', was equated to $\alpha T e^{-E_1/RT}$ in the lower temperature range; the numerator of the enzyme activation in Eq. (4.38).

Koffler et al. determined the enzyme activity under various conditions using the curve for no inhibition in Fig. 4.11 to provide the data for the calculation set out in Eq. (4.39).

$$I' = \frac{0.3775 T e^{21 \cdot 61} e^{-6,700/T}}{1 + e^{153.07} e^{-48,000/T}} \tag{4.39}$$

4.2.4. Example 3: Effect of temperature on the rates of mycelial growth, respiration, and penicillin production with *Penicillium chrysogenum*

Calam et al. studied the effect of temperature on the rates of growth, respiration, and penicillin production with *Penicillium chrysogenum*.[1] They cultured the mold in a 2 liter bolthead flask with a medium containing lactose 2%; C.S.L. (corn steep liquor) 2%; and mineral salts.

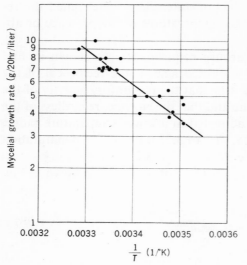

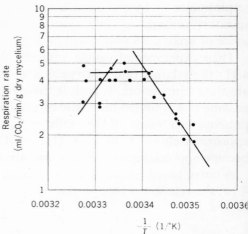

FIG. 4.12. Effect of temperature on the mycelial growth of *Penicillium chrysogenum*;[1] mycelial growth rate is plotted on a semi-logarithmic scale against the reciprocal of the absolute temperature.

FIG. 4.13. Effect of temperature on the respiration rate of *Penicillium chrysogenum*;[1] the respiration rate, measured with the Warburg respirometer, is plotted on a semi-logarithmic scale against the reciprocal of the absolute temperature.

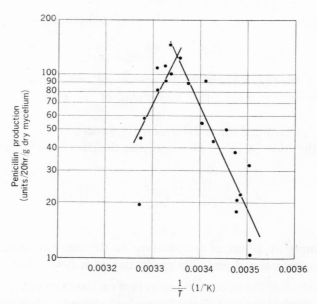

FIG. 4.14. Effect of temperature on the penicillin production rate with *Penicillium chrysogenum*;[1] the production rate is plotted on a semi-logarithmic scale against the reciprocal of the absolute temperature.

The mycelial growth rate, g/20 hr/liter, (see Fig. 4.12), the respiration rate, ml CO_2/min/g dry mycelium, (see Fig. 4.13), and the penicillin production rate, units/20 hr/g dry mycelium, (see Fig. 4.14) were measured at various temperatures. The temperature range studied was from 13 °C to 35 °C.

It is interesting to note from these figures that the effect of temperature on the activity of the various enzymes involved in growth, respiration, and penicillin production is appreciably different. It is also seen from Figs. 4.13 and 4.14 that the enzyme systems are inactivated in the higher temperature range (above 26 °C). If Eq. (4.35) is applied to the assessment of E values,

E for mycelial growth = 8,230 calories/mole   (Fig. 4.12)
E for respiration = 17,800 calories/mole   (Fig. 4.13)
E for penicillin production = 26,800 calories/mole   (Fig. 4.14)

It appears that inactivation of the enzymes participating in the production of mycelium might have occurred at the highest temperature recorded in Fig. 4.12; the optimal temperature for growth was estimated to be around 30 °C. On the other hand, the optimal temperatures for respiration were from 21.7 °C to 28.6 °C, and 24.7 °C was optimal for penicillin production.

The fact that each system of enzymes involved in growth, respiration, and penicillin production was inactivated independently is most interesting, suggesting that the enzymes involved in each sequence are different. Such studies of fermentation kinetics can also be used to investigate other factors; for example, pH, the concentration of nutrients, etc. These studies should prove most helpful in elucidating the kinetic mechanisms of fermentations.

4.3.   Kinetic Patterns of Various Fermentations

As previously mentioned, fermentations have been classified by several researchers. These classifications are listed in Tables 4.2 and 4.3.

The system suggested by Gaden[5] relates the formation of product to substrate utilization. Another way of viewing this classification would be to assess the extent to which energy-producing reactions are coupled to product-forming reactions. This approach has certain advantages for studying continuous fermentation.

The classification proposed by Deindoerfer[2] is based on the course of the fermentation, i.e., consecutive, step-wise, etc. This approach is particularly useful in the study of batch fermentations.

Some examples of the latter classification follow:

Simple reactions. This type of fermentation kinetics involves two subtypes, growth and non-growth reactions. These are shown in Figs. 4.15 and 4.16. Model processes for these reactions are the growth of yeast, and the production of gluconic acid using recycled mycelium.

Simultaneous reactions. Simultaneous reactions are those in which more than one product is produced and the relative rates of production of these products vary

TABLE 4.2

EXAMPLES OF TYPES OF FERMENTATION PROCESSES ACCORDING TO GADEN.[5]

Type	Specific Rate Relationships	Example
I	Product formation directly related to carbohydrate utilization	Ethanol
II	Product formation indirectly related to carbohydrate utilization	Citric acid
III	Product formation apparently not associated with carbohydrate utilization	Penicillin

TABLE 4.3

CLASSIFICATION OF FERMENTATIONS BY TYPE REACTIONS ACCORDING TO DEINDOERFER.[2]

Type	Description
Simple	Nutrients converted to products in a fixed stoichiometry without accumulation of intermediates
Simultaneous	Nutrients converted to products in variable stoichiometric proportion without accumulation of intermediates
Consecutive	Nutrients converted to product with accumulation of an intermediate
Step-wise	Nutrients completely converted to intermediate before conversion to product
	or
	Nutrients selectively converted to product in preferential order

with nutrient concentration. They involve overflow or shunt metabolism. Fig. 4.17 shows some results of relative synthesis of cell protein and cell fat during the growth of *Rhodotorula glutinis*.

Consecutive reactions. Consecutive reactions are those in which an intermediate accumulates to some degree before product is formed. An example is the fermentation of glucose to gluconic acid by an organism lacking in gluconolactonase (see Fig. 4.18). Antibiotic formation in a number of fermentations may fall into this category.

Step-wise reactions. The step-wise reaction is a case of two simple reactions that may be regulated by enzyme induction. Examples of this reaction are shown in Figs. 4.19 and 4.20. In the first case, where two carbohydrate substrates such as hexoses and pentoses are supplied simultaneously, *Escherichia coli* first utilizes completely the hexose sugar before beginning to utilize the pentose sugar. Monod calls this type of growth "diauxie."

Another example is the biooxidation of glucose to 5-ketogluconic acid by *Acetobacter suboxydans*. Here all the sugar is converted to gluconic acid before ketose formation begins. Similar reactions occur in the multi-point but step-wise attack of the steroid nucleus by some microorganisms.

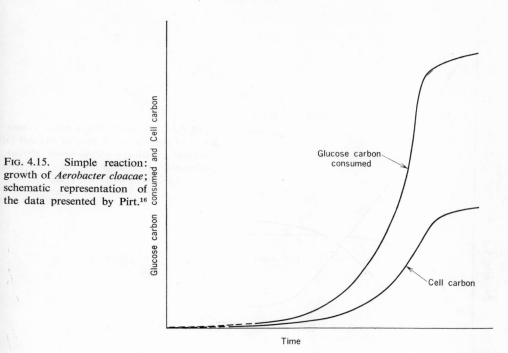

FIG. 4.15. Simple reaction: growth of *Aerobacter cloacae*; schematic representation of the data presented by Pirt.[16]

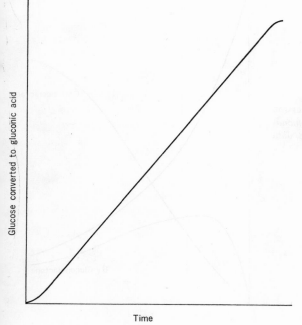

FIG. 4.16. Simple reaction: conversion of glucose to gluconic acid by resuspended *Aspergillus niger* mycelia; schematic representation of the data published by Moyer *et al.*[15]

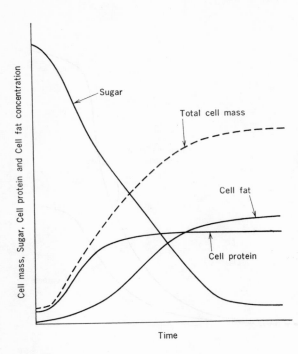

FIG. 4.17. Simultaneous reaction: conversion of sugar into cell protein and cell fat during growth of *Rhodotorula glutinis*; schematic representation of the data presented by Enebo *et al.*[4]

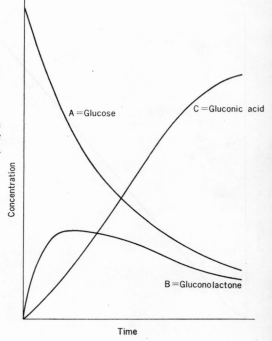

FIG. 4.18. Consecutive reaction: conversion of glucose to gluconic acid by *Pseudomonas ovalis*; schematic representation of the data presented by Reilly and Humphrey.[18]

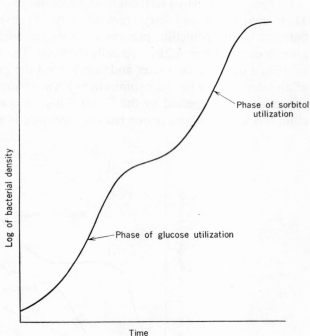

Phase of sorbitol
utilization

Log of bacterial density

Phase of glucose utilization

Time

FIG. 4.19.   Step-wise   reaction:
diauxic growth of *E. coli*; schematic
representation of the data presented
by Monod.[13]

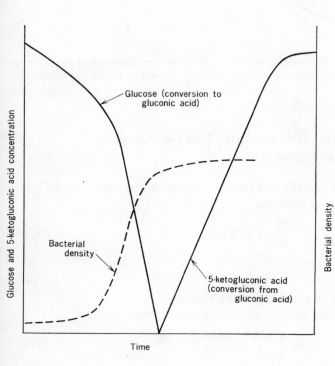

Glucose (conversion to
gluconic acid)

Glucose and 5-ketogluconic acid concentration

Bacterial
density

5-ketogluconic acid
(conversion from
gluconic acid)

Bacterial density

Time

FIG. 4.20.   Step-wise reaction:
diphasic biooxidation of glucose
to 5-ketogluconic acid by *Acetobacter suboxydans*; schematic
representation of the data presented by Stubbs *et al.*[20]

Complex cases. Most fermentation processes involve a combination of reactions. Their complexity can vary tremendously. An examination of the fermentation patterns in the penicillin process suggests just such a number of reactions. The growth curve in Fig. 4.21 is typically diphasic. The penicillin production curve also exhibits a diphasic character and lags behind the growth curve. The accumulation of an intermediate product somewhere between sugar disappearance and penicillin appearance is suggested by the figure. This, as is well known, is the case in penicillin fermentation and is one reason precursor is added during the process.

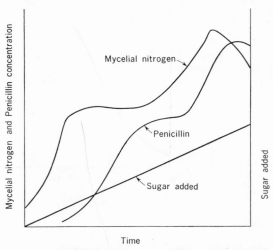

Fɪɢ. 4.21. Penicillin production in synthetic medium with continuous glucose feed (concentrations not to the same scale); schematic representation of the data published by Hosler and Johnson.[8]

4.4. Eχρρεssɪoνs for the Kινετιc Parameter for Unicellular Growth

In the case of unicellular growth, the rate of growth can be expressed by a limiting substrate concentration as follows:

$$\frac{dX}{dt} = f(X, S) \tag{4.40}$$

where
X = mass of cells per unit volume
S = concentration of growth-limiting substrate
Now, the specific growth rate of the cells, μ, can be defined as

$$\mu \equiv \frac{1}{X}\frac{dX}{dt} = \frac{d \ln X}{dt} \tag{4.41}$$

This is the so-called exponential growth equation which says that growth is proportional to the mass of cells present. Note that the specific growth rate is related to the mass-doubling time, t_d, by

$$t_d = 0.693/\mu = \ln 2/\mu \qquad (4.42)$$

Monod, in his study of bacterial growth in a chemostat (continuous culture), where the rate of growth was limited by a single substrate, found that his data generally fitted the curve typified by Fig. 4.22.

FIG. 4.22. Dependency of the specific growth rate on the limiting nutrient concentration (after Monod).[13]

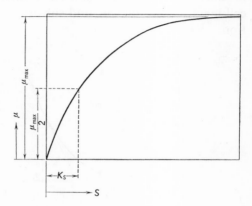

Monod noted that the data behaved in a manner typified by the Michaelis-Menten equation. He therefore suggested the following form:

$$\mu = \mu_{max}\left(\frac{S}{K_s+S}\right) \qquad (4.43)$$

where

μ_{max} = maximum growth rate when the substrate is unlimited
K_s = the substrate concentration at which the specific growth rate observed is one-half the maximum value; saturation constant

Eq. (4.43) leads to the following expression for unicellular growth.

$$\frac{dX}{dt} = \mu_{max}\left(\frac{S}{K_s+S}\right)X \qquad (4.44)$$

Other expressions for the specific growth rate as a function of the substrate concentration have been suggested. One such expression of Moser[14] is:

$$\mu = \frac{\mu_{max}}{(1+\alpha X^{-\gamma})} \qquad (4.45)$$

where

α and γ = constants

None of these other expressions has experienced the wide acceptance of that proposed by Monod. In passing it should be noted that growth, other than the exponential type, has been observed. Linear growth has been reported for filamentous

systems. Also square-law growth (presumably diffusion-controlled growth) has
been reported for mycelial organisms growing in the pellet form.

4.5.   FERMENTATION RATE PATTERNS—GROWTH ASSOCIATED
AND NON-GROWTH ASSOCIATED

Fig. 4.23 shows schematically a typical course of batch fermentation with a
product other than cell mass. The ordinates of each diagram are concentrations of
cell mass, X, product, P, and substrate, S. The abscissae are time, t, of fermentation.

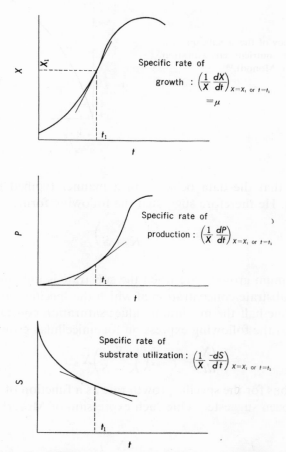

$$\text{Specific rate of growth} : \left(\frac{1}{X}\frac{dX}{dt}\right)_{X=X_1 \text{ or } t=t_1} = \mu$$

$$\text{Specific rate of production} : \left(\frac{1}{X}\frac{dP}{dt}\right)_{X=X_1 \text{ or } t=t_1}$$

$$\text{Specific rate of substrate utilization} : \left(\frac{1}{X}\frac{-dS}{dt}\right)_{X=X_1 \text{ or } t=t_1}$$

FIG. 4.23.   Definitions of specific rates for growth, production, and substrate utilization; where
X=microbial concentration, P = product concentration, S = substrate concentration, t = time.

The specific rates of growth, product formation and substrate consumption at
time $t=t_1$ are defined as shown in Fig. 4.23. It is apparent from Fig. 4.23 that the
specific rate is a function of time, t, during the course of a batch fermentation, and

that the maximum value of specific growth rate, μ_{max}, corresponds to that of the exponential-growth phase. Then,

$$\mu = \mu_{max} = \frac{1}{X}\frac{dX}{dt} = \frac{d \ln X}{dt}$$

Solving the above equation,

$$X = X_0 \exp\{\mu_{max}(t-t_0)\} \qquad (4.46)$$

where

$t_0 =$ time at threshold of logarithmic-growth phase

$X_0 =$ microbial concentration at $t=t_0$

When examples of Gaden's fermentation classifications are plotted in terms of the specific rates as ordinates and the fermentation time as abscissae, patterns typical of those in Fig. 4.24 are obtained. Type 1 shows that product formation is in parallel with microbial growth, i.e., the rate of production is in linear relationship with the growth rate over the course of fermentation. Ethanol fermentation belongs to Type 1. This kind of fermentation is called growth-associated culture. Type 3

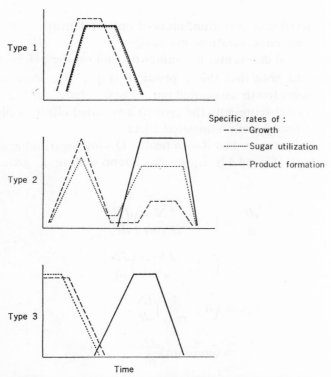

FIG. 4.24.   Fermentation rate patterns; the ordinates are the specific rates of growth, sugar utilization, and product formation; the abscissae are fermentation time. Three typical patterns in industrial fermentations were suggested by Gaden.[6]

suggests that product formation is delayed so that the product begins to appear after the mycelial growth ceases and the substrate is consumed. This type of culture is called non-growth associated. Antibiotics fermentations (streptomycin, penicillin, etc.) and production of some enzymes (for instance, glucoamylase) by fermentation belong to this type of culture. Type 2 is an intermediate between Types 1 and 3; itaconic, lactic, and glutamic acid fermentations belong to this category.

Luedeking et al. studied the kinetics of lactic acid production in a batch fermentation at controlled pH values ranging from 4.5 to 6.0.[12] The rate of lactic acid production was studied with *Lactobacillus delbrueckii* at 45°C in a bench-scale fermentor (capacity, 2 liter). Sodium carbonate was added to neutralize the acid formed in the fermentation medium. The rate of base addition was taken as the rate of acid or product formation.

Luedeking et al. obtained the following empirical relationship between dP/dt (the rate of product formation) and dN/dt (the rate of cell growth measured with optical density):

$$\frac{dP}{dt} = \alpha \frac{dN}{dt} + \beta N \qquad (4.47)$$

where

$N =$ bacterial concentration, units of optical density
$P =$ product concentration, mg acid/ml
$\alpha, \beta =$ empirical constants; the values depend on the pH values

It is interesting to note that this expression—Eq. (4.47)—has both a growth associated and a non-growth associated part. The first term, $\alpha\,dN/dt$, of the right-hand side of Eq. (4.47) represents the growth-associated effect, while the second, βN, represents the non-growth associated effect.

Eq. (4.47) can be rearranged as shown below. During logarithmic growth, where $\mu = \mu_{max} =$ constant, Eq. (4.47) is, in fact, representing a growth-associated fermentation.

$$\frac{dP}{dt} = \left(\alpha + \beta \frac{N}{dN/dt}\right)\frac{dN}{dt}$$

$$= \left(\alpha + \beta \bigg/ \frac{d\ln N}{dt}\right)\frac{dN}{dt}$$

$$= \left(\alpha + \frac{\beta}{\mu_{max}}\right)\frac{dN}{dt}$$

$$= (\text{constant})\frac{dN}{dt} \qquad (4.48)$$

For this reason, confusion often occurs when one talks about the kinetic character of a batch fermentation. Indeed it can change drastically throughout its course.

Nomenclature

c = concentration of enzyme-substrate complex
c_A = concentration of material A
c_B = concentration of material B
c^* = concentration of transient material
d = concentration of enzyme-inhibitor complex
e = concentration of total enzyme
E = enzyme; activation energy defined by the Arrhenius equation
E_f, E_f, E_r = activation energies
$E\text{-}S$ = enzyme-substrate complex
f = concentration of enzyme-substrate-inhibitor complex; function in Eq. (4.40)
ΔG^* = free energy change of activation
ΔG = free energy change
h = Planck's constant, 6.62×10^{-27}, erg sec
ΔH^* = heat of reaction of activation
ΔH = heat of reaction
i = inhibitor concentration
I = inhibitor
I' = enzyme activity
k = Boltzmann constant, 1.37×10^{-16}, erg/°K
k_r = specific rate of reaction
k_{+1} = forward reaction rate constant ($E + S \overset{k_{+1}}{\rightleftharpoons} E\text{-}S$)
k_{-1} = reverse reaction rate constant ($E + S \rightleftharpoons E\text{-}S$)
k_{+2} = reaction rate constant ($E\text{-}S \overset{k_{-1}}{\longrightarrow} E + P$)
K_S = saturation constant
K_s = k_{-1}/k_{+1}, substrate constant (equilibrium constant for $E + S \overset{k_{+1}}{\underset{k_{-1}}{\rightleftharpoons}} E\text{-}S$)
K_s' = equilibrium dissociation constant for $E\text{-}S\text{-}I$ into $E\text{-}S + S$
K_m = Michaelis-Menten constant
K^* = equilibrium constant for $c_A + c_B \rightleftharpoons c^*$
K_i = equilibrium constant for $E\text{-}I$ into $E + I$
K_i' = equilibrium constant of dissociation for $E\text{-}S\text{-}I$ into $E\text{-}S + I$
N = bacterial concentration, units of optical density per ml
P = product or product concentration
R = gas constant, 1.987 calories/°K mole
S = substrate, substrate concentration, or concentration of growth-limiting substrate
S_1, S_2 = substrate concentration
ΔS^* = entropy change of activation
ΔS = entropy change
T = absolute temperature, °K
t = time
t_d = doubling time, hr
t_0 = time at threshold of logarithmic growth
v = rate of product formation
v_i = rate of product formation in the presence of inhibitor
V = maximum reaction rate; all enzymes are saturated with substrate
X = cell mass per unit volume
X_0 = cell mass per unit volume at time, $t = t_0$

Greek letters

α = constant
β = constant
γ = constant
μ = specific growth rate, hr^{-1}
μ_{max} = maximum value of specific growth rate, hr^{-1}

REFERENCES

1. CALAM, C.T., DRIVER, N., and BOWERS, R.H. (1951). "Studies in the production of penicillin, respiration and growth of *Penicillium chrysogenum* in submerged culture, in relation to agitation and oxygen transfer." *J. Appl. Chem.* **1,** 209.

2. DEINDOERFER, F.H. (1960). "Fermentation kinetics and model processes." *Adv. Appl. Microbiol.* (Ed.). UMBREIT, W.W. **2,** 321. Academic, N.Y.

3. DAWES, E.A. (1962). *Quantitative problems in biochemistry* p. 99–154. E.&S. Livingstone, Edinburgh and London.

4. ENEBO, L., ANDERSON, L.G., and LUNDIN, H. (1946). "Microbiological fat synthesis by means of *Rhodotorula* yeast." *Arch. Biochem.* **11,** 383.

5. GADEN, E.L., JR. (1955). "Fermentation kinetics and productivity." *Chem. & Ind.* p. 154. London.

6. GADEN, E.L., JR. (1959). "Fermentation process kinetics." *J. Biochem. Microbiol. Tech. & Eng.* **1,** 413.

7. HINSHELWOOD, C.N. (1952). *The chemical kinetics of the bacterial cell* Oxford.

8. HOSLER, P., and JOHNSON, M.J. (1953). "Penicillin from chemically defined media." *Ind. Eng. Chem.* **45,** 871.

9. KOFFLER, H., JOHNSON, F.H., and WILSON, P.W. (1947). "Combined influence of temperature and urethan on the respiration of *Rhizobium*." *J. Am. Chem. Soc.* **69,** 1113.

10. KOBAYASHI, J., UEYAMA, H., and KAMAUCHI, T. (1963). "Study on the cultural characteristics of yeast cells from a viewpoint of cell age." *J. Ferm. Tech.* **41,** 66.

11. LAIDLER, K.J. (1958). *The chemical kinetics of enzyme action* p. 30–93. Oxford.

12. LUEDEKING, R., and PIRET, E.L. (1959). "A kinetic study of the lactic acid fermentation. Batch process at controlled pH." *J. Biochem. Microbiol. Tech. & Eng.* **1,** 393.

13. MONOD, J. (1949). "The growth of bacterial cultures." *Ann. Review of Microbiol.* **3,** 371.

14. MOSER, H. (1958). "The dynamics of bacterial population maintained in the Chemostat." *Carnegie Inst. Wash. Pub.* No. 614.

15. MOYER, A.J., UMBERGER, E.J., and STUBBS, J.J. (1940). "Fermentation of concentrated solutions of glucose to gluconic acid—Improved process—." *Ind. Eng. Chem.* **32,** 1379.

16. PIRT, S.J. (1957). "The oxygen requirement of growing cultures of an *Aerobacter* species determined by means of the continuous culture technique." *J. gen. Microbiol.* **16,** 59.

17. POWELL, E.O. (1955). "Some features of the generation times of individual bacteria." *Biometrika* **42,** 16.

18. REILLY, P.J., and HUMPHREY, A.E. (1964). "Kinetic studies of gluconic acid fermentations." —presented before the 148th National ACS Meeting, Chicago.

19. SHU, P. (1961). "Mathematical models for the product accumulation in microbiological processes." *J. Biochem. Microbiol. Tech. & Eng.* **3,** 95.

20. STUBBS, J.J., LOCKWOOD, L.B., ROE, E.T., TABENKIN, B., and WARD, G.E. (1940). "Ketogluconic acids from glucose—Bacterial production—." *Ind. Eng. Chem.* **32,** 1626.

21. SIZER, I.W. (1944). "Temperature activation and inactivation of the crystalline catalase-hydrogen peroxide system." *J. Biol. Chem.* **154,** 461.

CHAPTER 5

CONTINUOUS FERMENTATION

Continuous fermentation was initiated about 40 years ago when fodder yeast was produced by a continuous process. Since then, continuous culture of microorganisms has been carried out by a large number of workers. Especially during the past decade, considerable attention has been focused on the continuous cultivation of microbes. Various international symposia have been devoted specifically to the topic of continuous fermentation.[9, 17, 18, 20]

FIG. 5.1.   Continuous fermentors in series; working volume of each vessel = 25 liter. (*Courtesy*   Dr. S. Shichiji, *Fermentation Research Institute, Chiba.*)

So far, most publications on continuous culture have been related to the physiological behavior of microorganisms. Specific devices—the "Chemostat," "Turbidostat," "Bactogen," etc., have been utilized for continuous culture.[3, 4, 8] Continuous culture has been favored for physiological studies primarily because environmental conditions can be kept constant, in sharp contrast with batch cultivation, where microorganisms are subject to continual change.

Tables 5.1 and 5.2 list some of the organisms and products which have been studied with continuous systems. Most of these systems have been studied in laboratories rather than on a commercial scale. Exceptions are *Chlorella*, yeast, and activated sludge; the last contains a variety of microorganisms extending from protozoa to bacteria. The activated-sludge process is for the biological treatment of domestic sewage and industrial wastes.

TABLE 5.1

REPRESENTATIVE GENERA OF ORGANISMS GROWN IN CONTINUOUS CULTURE.[14]

Organisms	Genera
Actinomycetes	*Streptomyces*
Algae	*Chlorella*
	Euglena
	Scenedesmus
Bacteria	*Aerobacter*
	Azotobacter
	Bacillus
	Brucella
	Clostridium
	Salmonella
Fungi	*Ophiostoma*
	Penicillium
Protozoa	*Tetrahymena*
Yeast	*Saccharomyces*
	Torula
Mammalian Cells	Embryo rabbit kidney

TABLE 5.2

REPRESENTATIVE CHEMICALS PRODUCED BY CONTINUOUS FERMENTATION.[14]

Growth-associated	Non-growth associated
Acetic acid	Acetone
Butanediol	Butanol
Ethanol	Glycogen
Gluconic acid	Subtilin
Hydrogen sulfide	Chloramphenicol
Lactic acid	Penicillin
	Streptomycin
	Vitamin B_{12}

Although many studies of yeast, bacteria, and fungi in continuous fermentation in laboratories have been published, full-scale production in continuous fermentation systems has been surprisingly scarce.[2, 17, 21, 22] Exceptions are as follows: continuous beer production in Germany, Canada, Australia, and New Zealand; continuous fodder yeast production from sulfite paper-mill waste; continuous baker's-yeast culture from molasses in England; and the activated-sludge process to purify sewage and industrial wastes.

This lack of large-scale continuous processes may be ascribed to the following difficulties: (a) a possibility that the desired microbial species will undergo deleterious mutations, (b) technical difficulties of running aseptically for a long period of time, and (c) lack of knowledge on the dynamic aspects of microbial behavior.

As will be shown later, the productivity of continuous fermentation is usually higher than that for batch culture, so even a semi-continuous fermentation, which avoids a high incidence of microbial mutation, may be advantageous. Technical difficulty of aseptic control may also be avoided to some extent in a semi-continuous operation. References to this point will be made later in this chapter.

Fig. 5.2 exemplifies the dynamic response of bacteria in continuous culture. By changing the value of pH sinusoidally, the changes in the concentrations of bacterial cells, X, and of glucose, Z, were studied by Fuld et al.[7] using *Lactobacillus delbrueckii*. The figure also shows that the bacterial concentration changed in direct response to the sinusoidal change of the pH values of the incoming broth, but that the glucose concentration of the medium was unchanged. This sort of study is important to future development of practical continuous fermentations.

This chapter will be devoted primarily to a consideration of continuous fermentations from an engineering viewpoint. The discussions, moreover, will be

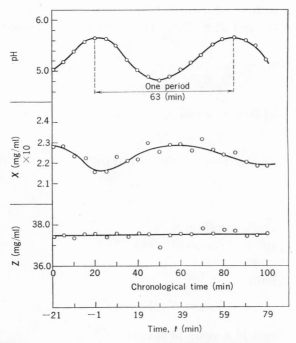

FIG. 5.2. Response of different variables with time (*Lactobacillus delbrueckii*).[7] The ordinate represents pH, cell concentration, X mg/ml, and glucose concentration, Z mg/ml, in the broth, while the abscissa is time, t min.

restricted to the basic principles underlying the theory of the continuous stirred fermentor, without considering the theory of variations such as tubular or cylindrical types of fermentors. However, the well-defined character of continuous fermentation is of considerable help in gaining an understanding of the physiological and kinetic activities of microbes.

The nomenclature used in this chapter will follow as closely as possible the recommendations made by a committee organized at the Symposium on Continuous Fermentation held in Czechoslovakia in 1962.[6]

5.1. STEADY-STATE CONTINUOUS FERMENTATION THEORY

5.1.1. Yield concepts

Most continuous fermentation studies are performed using a growth-limiting substrate to control the activity of the microbe of interest. A limiting substrate is that material which, when subject to a change of concentration, affects the growth, substrate consumption, and product formation of the cultured microorganisms. A mathematical model proposed by Monod regarding the effect of a limiting substrate concentration, S, on the specific growth rate of the microbe was discussed previously in Chapter 4; it has been demonstrated that most experimental data follow Eq. (4.43) except the abnormal examples cited by Spicer.[18]

For ease of discussions which will follow in the next section, the concepts of "yield" will be introduced here. Three kinds of yield are defined by the following three equations.

Yield of growth,

$$Y_{X/S} = -\Delta X/\Delta S \tag{5.1}$$

Yield of product based on cell mass,

$$Y_{P/X} = \Delta P/\Delta X \tag{5.2}$$

Yield of product based on limiting substrate,

$$Y_{P/S} = -\Delta P/\Delta S \tag{5.3}$$

where

X = cell mass concentration
S = limiting substrate concentration
P = product concentration

From the above definitions,

$$Y_{P/S} = Y_{X/S} Y_{P/X} \tag{5.4}$$

5.1.2. Mass balance in a series of vessels

To provide a general model, a series of equi-volume vessels, n in total number, will be considered. Denoting in Fig. 5.3 the rate of medium flow through the series of vessels as F liter/hr, and the volume of each vessel as V liter, the mass balance equations regarding X, P, and S can be expressed respectively as follows:

$$X: \quad \left| V\frac{dX_n}{dt} = FX_{n-1} - FX_n + V\left(\frac{dX_n}{dt}\right)_{\substack{\text{Growth in} \\ n\text{th vessel}}} \to \mu_n X_n - K_0 X_n \right. \quad (5.5)$$

$$= FX_{n-1} - FX_n + V\mu_n X_n$$

$$\frac{dX_n}{dt} = D(X_{n-1} - X_n) + \mu_n X_n \quad (5.6)$$

where

$D = F/V =$ dilution rate, hr^{-1}
$\quad = 1/(V/F) = 1/\theta$
$\quad =$ reciprocal of mean holding time (or retention time) of flowing medium in each vessel

subscripts : n, $(n-1) = n$th, $(n-1)$th vessels, respectively

Similarly,

$$P: \quad \frac{dP_n}{dt} = \frac{F}{V}(P_{n-1} - P_n) + \left(\frac{dP_n}{dt}\right)_{\substack{\text{Production in} \\ n\text{th vessel}}} \quad (5.7)$$

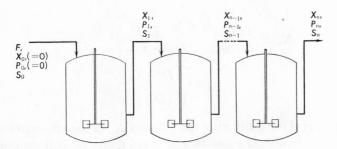

FIG. 5.3. n vessels in series; $F =$ flow rate of medium; $X =$ cell mass concentration; $P =$ product concentration; $S =$ limiting substrate concentration; subscripts, 1, 2, $\cdots$, n are for the 1st, 2nd, $\cdots$, nth vessels, whereas the subscript, 0, is for the incoming medium. If a fresh medium is charged into the 1st vessel, $X_0 = 0$ and $P_0 = 0$.

Combining Eq. (5.2) and the last term of the right-hand side of Eq. (5.7), followed by the substitution of specific growth rate, μ_n, for $(1/X_n)(dX_n/dt)$ in the nth vessel,

$$\frac{dP_n}{dt} = D(P_{n-1} - P_n) + Y_{P/X}\mu_n X_n \quad (5.8)$$

For

$$S: \quad \frac{dS_n}{dt} = \frac{F}{V}(S_{n-1} - S_n) + \left(\frac{dS_n}{dt}\right)_{\substack{\text{Consumption in} \\ n\text{th vessel}}} \quad (5.9)$$

Rearranging the last term of the right-hand side of Eq. (5.9) and using Equations (5.2) and (5.3), Eq. (5.9) is modified as follows:

$$\frac{dS_n}{dt} = D(S_{n-1}-S_n) - \frac{Y_{P/X}}{Y_{P/S}}\mu_n X_n$$

$$= D(S_{n-1}-S_n) - \frac{1}{Y_{X/S}}\mu_n X_n \qquad (5.10)$$

It is assumed that the medium flowing from the $(n-1)$th vessel into the nth vessel is mixed instantaneously and completely with the contents of the nth vessel; this is a necessary assumption for the derivation of Equations (5.5) to (5.10). Values of $Y_{X/S}$, $Y_{P/X}$, and $Y_{P/S}$ in these equations are all assumed to be constant, regardless of the number of vessels under consideration. Discussions of these assumptions will appear later.

At steady-state condition, the left-hand side of all equations from (5.5) to (5.10) is zero. Then, from Eq. (5.6),

$$X_n = \frac{DX_{n-1}}{D-\mu_n} \qquad (n\neq1) \qquad (5.11)$$

Accordingly,

$$X_{n-1} = \frac{DX_{n-2}}{D-\mu_{n-1}}$$

$$\vdots \qquad \vdots$$

$$X_n = \frac{DX_{n-1}}{D-\mu_n} = \frac{D^2 X_{n-2}}{(D-\mu_n)(D-\mu_{n-1})} = \cdots$$

$$\cdots = \frac{D^{n-1}X_1}{\prod_{i'=2}^{n}(D-\mu_{i'})} \qquad (5.12)$$

Eq. (5.12) is useful for estimating the value of X_n in the nth vessel or, conversely, the value of μ_n in steady state can be estimated from the cell concentrations, X_n, X_{n-1}, etc. For single vessels $(n=1)$, the value of X_0 in the right-hand side of Eq. (5.6) or (5.5) is zero. Then,

$$\mu_1 = D = \mu_{\max}\frac{S_1}{K_s+S_1} \qquad \text{(see Eq. (4.43))} \qquad (5.13)$$

Note that since $\frac{S_1}{K_s+S_1}<1$, the maximum growth rate attainable in the first fermentor is always less than the maximum growth rate theoretically possible, i.e., $D<\mu_{\max}$. This is not true, however, when the fermentor is not perfectly mixed, when there are concentration effects in the exit line, or when there is recycling.

The steady-state equation for P is given by:

$$P_n = \frac{DP_{n-1}+Y_{P/X}\mu_n X_n}{D} \qquad (5.14)$$

Since the value of P_0 is zero in a single fermentor or in the first of a series of continuous fermentors, then

$$P_1 = \frac{Y_{P/X}\mu_1 X_1}{D} = Y_{P/X} X_1 \qquad (5.15)$$

Lastly, the steady state for S is given by:

$$S_n = S_{n-1} - \frac{1}{D}\frac{Y_{P/X}}{Y_{P/S}}\mu_n X_n$$

$$= S_{n-1} - \frac{1}{D}\frac{1}{Y_{X/S}}\mu_n X_n \qquad (5.16)$$

For $n=1$,

$$S_1 = S_0 - \frac{\frac{Y_{P/X}}{Y_{P/S}}}{D}\mu_1 X_1$$

$$= S_0 - \frac{Y_{P/X}}{Y_{P/S}} X_1$$

$$= S_0 - \frac{1}{Y_{X/S}} X_1 \qquad (5.17)$$

An interesting consideration is the case of single vessels with re-use or recycle of some of the microbial mass. Letting $r=$ fraction of the mass recycled, then for a single stage continuous culture,

$$\frac{dX_1}{dt} = D_1(rX_1 - X_1) + \mu_1 X_1 \qquad (5.18)$$

In steady state for X_1,

$$D_1 = \mu_1\frac{1}{1-r} = \mu_{max}\frac{S_1}{K_s + S_1}\frac{1}{1-r} \qquad (5.19)$$

It should be obvious that in this situation it is possible to have conditions such that $D_1 > \mu_{max}$. A similar analysis can be made for conditions of non-perfect mixing or of concentration effects in the effluent stream.

5.1.3. Design criteria

The single vessel will be considered first. Replacing μ and S in Eq. (4.43) in Chapter 4 with μ_1 and S_1 respectively,

$$S_1 = \frac{\mu_1 K_s}{\mu_{max} - \mu_1} \qquad (5.20)$$

Substituting $D = \mu_1$ into Eq. (5.20),

$$S_1 = \frac{DK_s}{\mu_{max} - D}$$

$$S_1 = \frac{K_S}{\dfrac{\mu_{max}}{D} - 1} \qquad (5.21)$$

For the special case where $D \ll \mu_{max}$, Eq. (5.21) can be reduced to:

$$S_1 = \frac{DK_S}{\mu_{max}} \qquad (5.22)$$

From Eq. (5.17),

$$X_1 = Y_{X/S}(S_0 - S_1) \qquad (5.23)$$

It is noted from Equations (5.21) and (5.22) that the value of S_1, the concentration of a limiting substrate in the culture medium in the single vessel, starts from zero and increases in proportion to the increase of D as long as $D \ll \mu_{max}$ (see Eq. (5.22)). As the value of D approaches that of μ_{max}, S_1 increases sharply (see Eq. (5.21)). Although Eq. (5.21) indicates that the value of S_1 becomes infinite when $D = \mu_{max}$, such a situation cannot be realized in practice since $S_1 \leq S_0$.

The cell concentration, X_1, from the vessel is approximately $Y_{X/S} S_0$ at low values of D. However, as D approaches μ_{max} where $S_1 \rightarrow S_0$, the value of X_1 approaches zero. This situation is referred to as "wash out" and occurs because the growth rate can no longer keep up with the dilution rate. These various conditions are depicted in Fig. 5.4.

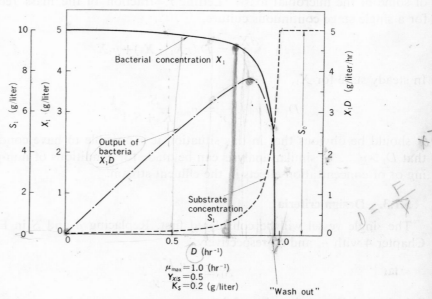

FIG. 5.4. S_1 vs. D and X_1 vs. D (calculated).[9, 10] The abscissa represents dilution rate, D, while the ordinates of the figure are limiting substrate concentration, S_1, cell concentration, X_1, and the product of $X_1 D$. These curves were calculated using the values of $\mu_{max} = 1.0$ hr^{-1}, $Y_{X/S} = 0.5$, $S_0 = 10$ g/liter, and $K_S = 0.2$ g/liter.

Curves in Fig. 5.4 were prepared from Equations (5.21), (5.22), and (5.23), into which the following values were substituted:

$$\mu_{max} = 1.0 \text{ hr}^{-1}$$
$$Y_{X/S} = 0.5$$
$$S_0 = 10 \text{ g/liter}$$
$$K_s = 0.2 \text{ g/liter}$$

By and large, it is difficult to maintain the steady state near conditions of "wash out," since a slight change of D will result in a large variation of either S_1 or X_1. The curve of bacterial output in the figure was obtained from a curve for $X_1F/V = X_1D$, namely, from Equations (5.23) and (5.21),

$$X_1 D = DY_{X/S}\left(S_0 - \frac{DK_s}{\mu_{max} - D}\right) \tag{5.24}$$

To find the particular value of D at which the value of X_1D becomes maximum,

$$\frac{d(X_1 D)}{dD} = 0 \tag{5.25}$$

Solving Eq. (5.25) for D with Eq. (5.24),

$$D = D_m = \mu_{max}\left(1 - \sqrt{\frac{K_s}{K_s + S_0}}\right) \tag{5.26}$$

Since $K_s \ll S_0$ in most fermentations, it is noted from Eq. (5.26) that the maximum output (productivity), $(XD)_{max} = (X_1F/V)_{max} =$ (mass of cells per unit volume of broth per unit time)$_{max}$, is realized near the "wash out" condition (see Fig. 5.4).

Similarly, from Equations (5.15), (5.21), and (5.23),

$$P_1 D = Y_{P/X}Y_{X/S}D\left(S_0 - \frac{DK_s}{\mu_{max} - D}\right) \tag{5.27}$$

Substituting Eq. (5.4) into Eq. (5.27),

$$P_1 D = DY_{P/S}\left(S_0 - \frac{DK_s}{\mu_{max} - D}\right) \tag{5.28}$$

Eq. (5.28) is similar to Eq. (5.24). The maximum productivity, $(P_1D)_{max} =$ (mass of product per unit volume of broth per unit time)$_{max}$, is then expected to be at the value of $D = D_m$ expressed by Eq. (5.26). Substituting Eq. (5.26) into Eq. (5.28), the concentration of product, P_{1m}, at the maximum productivity is given by:

$$P_{1m} = Y_{P/S}\{S_0 + K_s - \sqrt{K_s(S_0 + K_s)}\} \tag{5.29}$$

Similarly, the cell concentration, X_{1m}, at the maximum output will be:

$$X_{1m} = Y_{X/S}\{S_0 + K_s - \sqrt{K_s(S_0 + K_s)}\} \tag{5.30}$$

All of the above equations from (5.5) to (5.30) are useful in the design of continuous fermentations. Fig. 5.4 is useful in determining the values of D which are most economical for a specific continuous fermentation.

It should be remembered that the above equations present design criteria of continuous fermentations which are based on constant values of $Y_{X/S}$, $Y_{P/X}$, and $Y_{P/S}$ irrespective of the values of D or μ.

The material balance (Eq. (5.5)) and the experimental data (dX/dt vs. X) obtainable from batch fermentation provide another approach to the design of continuous fermentation. Readers should be cognizant that, in this case, batch data may not be reliable, since they are obtained under continuously varying conditions. From Eq. (5.5) for steady state, considering that $X_0=0$,

$$\frac{dX_1}{dt} = 0 = \left(\frac{dX_1}{dt}\right)_{Growth} - \frac{F}{V}X_1$$

from which

$$X_1 = \frac{\left(\frac{dX_1}{dt}\right)_{Growth}}{F/V} \qquad (5.31)$$

Likewise,

$$\frac{dX_2}{dt} = 0 = \left(\frac{dX_2}{dt}\right)_{Growth} - \frac{F}{V}(X_2-X_1)$$

$$X_2 - X_1 = \frac{\left(\frac{dX_2}{dt}\right)_{Growth}}{F/V} \qquad (5.32)$$

$$X_n - X_{n-1} = \frac{\left(\frac{dX_n}{dt}\right)_{Growth}}{F/V} \qquad (5.33)$$

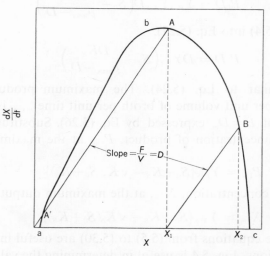

FIG. 5.5.   Graphical solution of design equation in continuous fermentation;[13] cell growth rate, dX/dt, is plotted against cell concentration, X, both of which are obtained from batch experiment.

Typical batch data in terms of dX/dt vs. X are represented by Curve abc in Fig. 5.5. The value of X_1 for the first continuous fermentor can be graphically determined from an intersection at A, of Curve abc with a straight line whose slope is F/V, as shown by Eq. (5.31). By repeating such procedures, the values of X_2, X_3,—will be determined successively as indicated by Equations (5.32) and (5.33) and as shown in the figure.[5, 13, 21] The intersection labeled A' in the figure is not the steady-state value of (dX/dt); it is unstable since it occurs in the lag phase of growth before cell division begins.

If a fermentation is considered in which a product other than cell mass is produced, the values of P_1, P_2,—in each vessel in the series can be obtained graphically following the same procedure as that in Fig. 5.5; i.e., (dP/dt) is plotted against P using data from batch experiments (refer to Eq. (5.7) and Equations (5.31) to (5.33)).

It must be emphasized that the design procedure mentioned above is acceptable only if the microbial characteristics expressed by $(dX/dt$ vs. $X)$ or $(dP/dt$ vs. $P)$ in batch runs represent those in continuous operation. Many questions relating to this controversial procedure are left open for discussion and further experimentation. However, graphical estimations of X_1, X_2,... or P_1, P_2,... from batch fermentation data are not totally worthless; they can be a valuable guide for the design and operation of a continuous-fermentation plant. For the rational design of a large-scale plant, however, there is no substitute for data obtained from continuous-fermentation experiments in pilot-plant equipment.

5.2.   Unsteady-state Continuous Fermentation Theory

5.2.1.   Single vessels

(a)   Cell concentration

From Eq. (5.5),

$$V\left(\frac{dX_1}{dt}\right) = -FX_1 + V\left(\frac{dX_1}{dt}\right)_{\text{Growth}}$$

$$= -FX_1 + VX_1\mu_1$$

$$\frac{dX_1}{dt} = X_1\left(\mu_1 - \frac{F}{V}\right)$$

$$X_1 = X_{1i}e^{(\mu_1 - F/V)t} = X_{1i}e^{(\mu_1 - D)t} \qquad (5.34)$$

where

$\qquad X_1 = X_{1i}$ at $t = 0$ and μ_1 is independent of t.

Eq. (5.34) indicates that the value of μ_1, the assessment of which is often difficult in batch culture, can be determined by measuring the variation of X_1 with time in unsteady-state continuous culture, provided that at $t=0$, $F/V \neq \mu_1$. At the same time, it is implied in Eq. (5.34) that the value of X_1 becomes instantaneously equal to X_{1i} if the value of F/V (or D) is suddenly adjusted exactly equal to μ_1. No time lag is taken into account. Recent experiments indicate that there is indeed a lag.[11]

(b) Product

From Eq. (5.8),

$$\frac{dP_1}{dt} = -DP_1 + Y_{P/X}X_1\mu_1 \qquad (5.35)$$

Substituting Eq. (5.34) into Eq. (5.35),

$$\frac{dP_1}{dt} + DP_1 = Y_{P/X}\mu_1 X_{1i}e^{(\mu_1 - D)t}$$

Solving for P_1,

$$P_1 = P_{1i}e^{-Dt} + Y_{P/X}X_{1i}e^{-Dt}(e^{\mu_1 t} - 1) \qquad (5.36)$$

where

$$P_1 = P_{1i} \qquad \text{at } t = 0$$

Rearranging Eq. (5.36),

$$P_1 = (P_{1i} - Y_{P/X}X_{1i})e^{-Dt} + Y_{P/X}X_{1i}e^{(\mu_1 - D)t} \qquad (5.37)$$

Even if the condition of $\mu_1 = D$ is satisfied at $t=0$, Eq. (5.37) shows that a certain time lag exists before the value of P_1 becomes stabilized. The value of P_1 becomes $Y_{P/X}X_{1i}$ at $t=$ infinity. Letting the term, $Y_{P/X}X_{1i} = P_{1\infty}$ and rearranging Eq. (5.37) with the condition of $\mu_1 = D$ and $P_{1\infty} = Y_{P/X}X_{1i}$,

$$1 - \frac{P_1}{P_{1\infty}} = \left(1 - \frac{P_{1i}}{P_{1\infty}}\right)e^{-Dt}$$

$$= \left(1 - \frac{P_{1i}}{P_{1\infty}}\right)e^{-t/\theta} \qquad (5.38)$$

However, if $P_{1i} = Y_{P/X}X_{1i}$ is realized, Eq. (5.37) indicates that the value of P_1 must be equal instantaneously to $Y_{P/X}X_{1i}$ when $\mu_1 = D$. This condition implies that a time lag does not exist when a growth-associated fermentation is carried out continuously in single vessels with the conditions of $\mu_1 = F/V = D$ and, in addition, $P_{1i} = Y_{P/X}X_{1i}$.

(c) Substrate

From Eq. (5.10),

$$\frac{dS_1}{dt} = D(S_0 - S_1) - \frac{1}{Y_{X/S}}\mu_1 X_1 \qquad (5.39)$$

From Equations (5.39) and (5.34),

$$\frac{dS_1}{dt} + DS_1 = -\frac{1}{Y_{X/S}}\mu_1 X_{1i}e^{(\mu_1 - D)t} + DS_0$$

Solving for S_1,

$$S_1 = S_0(1 - e^{-Dt}) + \left(S_{1i} + \frac{1}{Y_{X/S}}X_{1i}\right)e^{-Dt} - \frac{1}{Y_{X/S}}X_{1i}e^{(\mu_1 - D)t} \qquad (5.40)$$

where

$$S_1 = S_{1i} \quad \text{at } t = 0$$

Setting

$$S_0 - \frac{1}{Y_{X/S}} X_{1i} = S_{1\infty}$$

and equating μ_1 to D,

$$1 - \frac{S_1}{S_{1\infty}} = \left(1 - \frac{S_{1i}}{S_{1\infty}}\right) e^{-Dt}$$

$$= \left(1 - \frac{S_{1i}}{S_{1\infty}}\right) e^{-t/\theta} \tag{5.41}$$

Eq. (5.41) is similar to Eq. (5.38). It is apparent from Eq. (5.40) that a certain time is required before the value of S_1 reaches a constant value after the start of continuous operation with $\mu_1 = D$ at $t=0$ (see Eq. (5.41)). However, if $S_0 = S_{1i} + \frac{1}{Y_{X/S}} X_{1i}$ is satisfied when a continuous fermentation is carried out with $\mu_1 = D$ at $t=0$, the value of S_1 becomes $S_0 - \frac{1}{Y_{X/S}} X_{1i}$ instantaneously as with the case of P_1 and X_1.

5.2.2. Multi-stage vessels

Suppose that a continuous fermentation is to be conducted in steady state with equi-volume vessels in series, the flow rate being F_0. Suppose also that the flow rate to the nth vessel is abruptly changed from F_0 to $F=(F_0+F')$, while the cell concentration, X_{n-1}, which flows from the $(n-1)$th into the nth vessel is kept unchanged. The variation of X_n in the nth vessel with time can then be derived as shown below.

Setting

$$\alpha_n = \frac{V\mu_n}{F_0}, \qquad \gamma = \frac{X_n}{X_{n-1}},$$

$$\lambda = \frac{tF_0}{V} \quad \text{and} \quad k = \frac{F'}{F_0}$$

and substituting into Eq. (5.5), there is obtained:

$$\frac{d\gamma}{d\lambda} + \gamma(1+k-\alpha_n) = 1+k \tag{5.42}$$

Solving for γ,

$$\gamma = \frac{1+k}{1+k-\alpha_n} + \left(\gamma_i - \frac{1+k}{1+k-\alpha_n}\right) e^{-(1+k-\alpha_n)\lambda} \tag{5.43}$$

where

$$\gamma = \gamma_i \quad \text{at } \lambda=0 \ (t=0)$$

Defining,

$$\gamma_\infty = \frac{1+k}{1+k-\alpha_n}$$

and rearranging Eq. (5.43),

$$1 - \frac{\gamma}{\gamma_\infty} = \left(1 - \frac{\gamma_i}{\gamma_\infty}\right)e^{-\{(F/V)-\mu_n\}t}$$

$$= \left(1 - \frac{\gamma_i}{\gamma_\infty}\right)e^{-t/\theta'} \qquad (5.44)$$

provided that

$$\frac{F}{V} - \mu_n = \frac{1}{\theta'} \qquad (5.45)$$

5.2.3. Mean cumulative age concept in relation to microbial activities[1]

Synchronous growth studies have shown that between division cycles the enzyme content, and hence the metabolic activities of microbial cells, vary. For this reason it may prove fruitful to describe microbial populations in terms of their cell-age distribution.

Mean cumulative age, $\overline{A}$, of an aggregate of cells can be defined by an average of total cell ages assuming that the age of each cell is zero at the time of its birth and the age becomes larger in proportion to the time elapsed after the birth. Suppose that cells of X concentration have $\overline{A}$ mean cumulative age at a particular time, $t = t$ in a batch fermentation. From the above definition of $\overline{A}$, the change of $\Delta(X\overline{A})$ with time, Δt, will be:

$$\Delta(X\overline{A}) = X\Delta t + \Delta X \Delta t' \qquad (5.46)$$

where

$\quad \Delta X = $ increase of cell mass during Δt

provided:

$$0 \angle \Delta t' \angle \Delta t$$

Therefore,

$$\lim_{\Delta \to 0} \Delta(X\overline{A}) = \lim_{\Delta t \to 0} X\Delta t + \lim_{\Delta t \to 0} \Delta X \Delta t'$$

Neglecting the second term of the right-hand side of the above equation, which approaches zero,

$$d(X\overline{A}) = X dt \qquad (5.47)$$

Denoting the initial conditions as $X = X_i$ and $\overline{A} = \overline{A}_i$ at $t = 0$, then,

$$\overline{A} = \frac{X_i \overline{A}_i + \int_0^t X dt}{X} \qquad (5.48)$$

For n equi-volume vessels in a series in continuous fermentation, the relation of $\overline{A}$ with time can be obtained as follows:

$$X_n \Delta \overline{A}_n = X_{n-1} \overline{A}_{n-1} \frac{F}{V} \Delta t - X_n \overline{A}_n \frac{F}{V} \Delta t + X_n \Delta t$$

$$\Delta \overline{A}_n = \Delta t + \frac{X_{n-1}}{X_n} \overline{A}_{n-1} \frac{F}{V} \Delta t - \overline{A}_n \frac{F}{V} \Delta t$$

$$\frac{d\overline{A}_n}{dt} = 1 + \frac{X_{n-1}}{X_n} \overline{A}_{n-1} \frac{F}{V} - \overline{A}_n \frac{F}{V}$$

Substituting Eq. (5.11) into the second term of the right-hand side of the above equation,

$$\frac{d\overline{A}_n}{dt} = 1 + \left(\frac{1}{\theta} - \mu_n\right) \overline{A}_{n-1} - \frac{1}{\theta} \overline{A}_n \qquad (5.49)$$

For single vessels, it is assumed that $\overline{A}_0 = 0$. Then,

$$\frac{d\overline{A}_1}{dt} + \frac{1}{\theta} \overline{A}_1 = 1 \qquad (5.50)$$

Solving for $\overline{A}_1$,

$$\overline{A}_1 = \overline{A}_{1i} e^{-t/\theta} + \theta(1 - e^{-t/\theta}) \qquad (5.51)$$

where

$$\overline{A}_1 = \overline{A}_{1i} \quad \text{at } t = 0$$

Substituting $\overline{A}_{1\infty}$ at $t = \infty$ into Eq. (5.51),

$$1 - \frac{\overline{A}_1}{\overline{A}_{1\infty}} = \left(1 - \frac{\overline{A}_{1i}}{\overline{A}_{1\infty}}\right) e^{-t/\theta} \qquad (5.52)$$

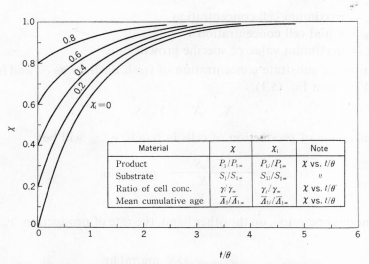

Material	χ	χ_i	Note
Product	$P_1/P_{1\infty}$	$P_{1i}/P_{1\infty}$	χ vs. t/θ
Substrate	$S_1/S_{1\infty}$	$S_{1i}/S_{1\infty}$	"
Ratio of cell conc.	γ/γ_∞	γ_i/γ_∞	χ vs. t/θ'
Mean cumulative age	$\overline{A}_1/\overline{A}_{1\infty}$	$\overline{A}_{1i}/\overline{A}_{1\infty}$	χ vs. t/θ

FIG. 5.6. χ vs. t/θ; χ represented by the ordinate has several meanings as shown in the figure, while the abscissa represents the number of cycles of flowing medium.

Eq. (5.52) implies that the value of $\overline{A}_1$ would be stabilized after a certain period of time when the continuous feeding is started at $t=0$ so that the value of X_1 remains unchanged and $D=\mu_1$. It is interesting to note that Equations (5.38), (5.41), (5.44), and (5.52) are similar. All of these equations, then, have similar solutions represented by Fig. 5.6. This figure indicates how much time and what number of cycles are needed before the respective value of $P_1/P_{1\infty}$, $S_1/S_{1\infty}$, γ/γ_∞, or $\overline{A}_1/\overline{A}_{1\infty}$ levels off.

This analogy between P, S, γ, and $\overline{A}$ leads to a surmise that the mean cumulative age will be of help in correlating the microbial activities in the design and operation of continuous fermentation, especially for multi-cellular systems.

5.3.   COMPARISONS BETWEEN BATCH AND CONTINUOUS FERMENTATIONS

The upper graph of Fig. 5.7 illustrates schematically an operating cycle for batch fermentation. For simplicity, the curve is divided into four periods—logarithmic growth, harvest of cells, preparation for another batch run, and the lag following inoculation. These periods are designated as t_m, t_0, t_1, and t_2 respectively (see Fig. 5.7). The total period of time, t_c, required for one cycle of the batch fermentation is:

$$t_c = t_m + t_0 + t_1 + t_2$$
$$= t_m + t_l$$
$$= \frac{1}{\mu_{\max}} \ln \frac{X_m}{X_i} + t_l \tag{5.53}$$

where
$$t_l = t_0 + t_1 + t_2$$
$$X_m = \text{maximum cell concentration}$$
$$X_i = \text{initial cell concentration}$$
$$\mu_{\max} = \text{maximum value of specific growth rate}$$

Designating the substrate concentration of fresh medium as S_0 and introducing the yield, $Y_{X/S}$ from Eq. (5.1),

$$X_m - X_i = Y_{X/S} S_0 \tag{5.54}$$

Consequently, rate of production of cells in batch, r_{batch}, will be:

$$r_{\text{batch}} = \frac{Y_{X/S} S_0}{\dfrac{1}{\mu_{\max}} \ln \dfrac{X_m}{X_i} + t_l} \quad \text{mg/ml hr} \tag{5.55}$$

In continuous operation, on the other hand, the rate of production, $r_{\text{cont.}}$, is given by:

$$r_{\text{cont.}} = DX \quad \text{mg/ml hr} \tag{5.56}$$
$$\text{or} \quad (r_{\text{cont.}})_{\max} = D_m X_{1m}$$

(a)

(b)

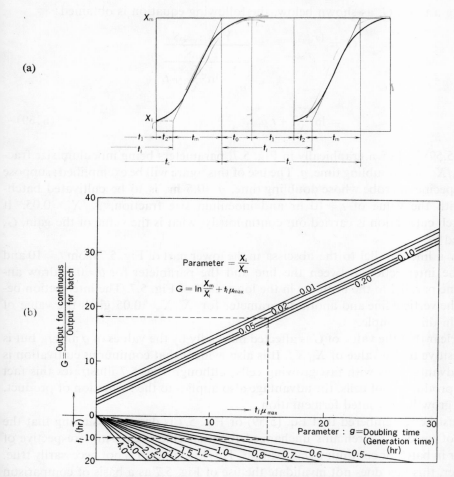

FIG. 5.7.   Comparison between batch and continuous fermentations; the upper graph of the figure shows schematically the cycle of a batch fermentation expressed by the cell concentration, X, and the time, t, of fermentation. The lower graph represents how much gain, G, is obtained by the continuous fermentation compared with the batch. For symbols and use of the figure, see the text.

From Equations (5.26) and (5.30), $(r_{\text{cont.}})_{\text{max}}$ is given by:

$$(r_{\text{cont.}})_{\text{max}} = D_m X_{1m}$$

$$= \left\{ \mu_{\text{max}} \left(1 - \sqrt{\frac{K_S}{K_S + S_0}} \right) \right\} Y_{X/S} \left\{ S_0 + K_S - \sqrt{K_S(S_0 + K_S)} \right\}$$

$$= Y_{X/S} \mu_{\text{max}} S_0 \left\{ \sqrt{\frac{K_S + S_0}{S_0}} - \sqrt{\frac{K_S}{S_0}} \right\}^2 \qquad (5.57)$$

Assuming that $K_S \ll S_0$, Eq. (5.57) reduces to:

$$(r_{\text{cont.}})_{\text{max}} \doteqdot Y_{X/S} \mu_{\text{max}} S_0 \qquad (5.58)$$

Defining a term, G, as shown below, the following equation is obtained:

$$G = \frac{(r_{\text{cont.}})_{\max}}{r_{\text{batch}}} = \frac{Y_{X/S}\mu_{\max}S_0}{\dfrac{Y_{X/S}S_0}{\dfrac{1}{\mu_{\max}}\ln\dfrac{X_m}{X_i}+t_l}}$$

$$= \ln\frac{X_m}{X_i}+t_l\mu_{\max} \qquad (5.59)$$

Eq. (5.59) is shown graphically in Fig. 5.7, parameters being inoculum size fraction, X_i/X_m, and doubling time, g. The use of this figure will be exemplified; suppose that a specific microbe whose doubling time, $g=0.5$ hr, is to be cultivated batchwise with the value of $t_l=10$ hr and inoculum size fraction, $X_i/X_m=0.05$. If this batch cultivation is carried out continuously, what is the value of the gain, G, obtained?

Draw a line parallel to the abscissa in the lower part of Fig. 5.7 from $t_l=10$ and from the intersection between the line and the parameter for $g=0.5$, draw another line parallel to the ordinate in the lower half of Fig. 5.7. The intersection between the vertical line and another parameter for $X_i/X_m=0.05$ gives the value of $G=18$ in this example.

It is clear that the value of G is affected markedly by the values of g and t_l, but is less sensitive to the value of X_i/X_m. It is also evident that continuous cultivation is more advantageous with fast-growing cells; although Fig. 5.7 illustrates this fact for the production of cells, the advantage also applies to the formation of product, P, in a growth-associated fermentation.

It must be remembered that Eq. (5.59) or Fig. 5.7 is derived assuming that the values of yield, $Y_{X/S}$, remains unchanged for a specific organism, irrespective of whether in batch or continuous cultivation. This assumption is not necessarily true. However, this fact does not invalidate the use of Fig. 5.7 as a basis of comparison between batch and continuous fermentations.

5.4.   EXAMPLES OF CONTINUOUS FERMENTATION

5.4.1.   Yeast

Fig. 5.8 is an example of baker's-yeast production in continuous culture, as conducted by Humphrey with a 5-liter jar type fermentor.[11] The ordinate of Fig. 5.8 is the value of yield, $Y_{X/S}$, while the abscissa represents the dilution rate, D (or specific growth rate, μ). The various data points on which the curve is based were obtained by maintaining the continuous fermentation in steady state for a couple of days.

It is seen from Fig. 5.8 that the value of $Y_{X/S}$ is not constant even over a narrow range of D. The reasons for variation in $Y_{X/S}$ were considered by Humphrey to be due to inefficient endogenous respiration at the low-dilution rates where substrate concentration is low, and to the difficulties in maintaining a true steady state near

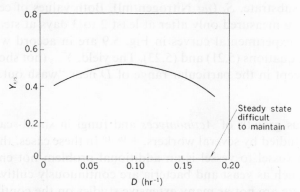

FIG. 5.8.   Continuous yeast fermentation;[11] yield, $Y_{X/S}$, is plotted against dilution rate, D.

"wash out" at high-dilution rates. An interesting observation was that after several days of continuous operation at the relatively high-dilution rates, mycelial forms of the yeast begin to appear. These were not contaminants because when transferred to shaken flasks with poorer aeration, the ellipsoidal or normal forms reappeared. This mycelical yeast form, although having a very high respiratory activity, would not make good baker's yeast because of its grainy character.

5.4.2.   Bacteria

Fig. 5.9 is an example of continuous steady-state culture of the bacterium *Aerobacter aerogenes*. This example applied to the conditions where NH_3 was the

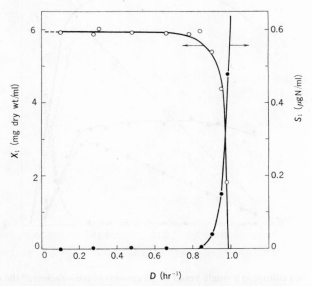

FIG. 5.9.   Continuous culture of *Aerobacter aerogenes*;[9] cell concentration, X_1, and limiting substrate concentration, S_1, in single vessels are plotted against dilution rate, D.

growth-limiting substrate, S_1 (μg Nitrogen/ml). Both values of cell mass, X_1, and
substrate, S_1, were measured only after at least 2 to 3 days at steady state at each
value of D. The experimental curves in Fig. 5.9 are in accord with those shapes
predicted from Equations (5.21) and (5.23). The yield, $Y_{X/S}$ (not shown in the figure)
was constant except in the particular range of D near "wash out."

5.4.3. Fungi

The continuous growth of *Actinomyces* and fungi in small-scale fermentors in
series has been studied by several workers. [2, 16, 19] In these cases, the transportation
of mycelia from vessel to vessel is an additional problem not encountered when
other microbes such as yeast and bacteria are continuously cultivated. Because of
this problem, there are not as many extensive studies on the continuous culture of
fungi as there are on yeast and bacteria.

Sikyta *et al.*[15] studied the continuous culture of *Streptomyces aureofaciens* with a

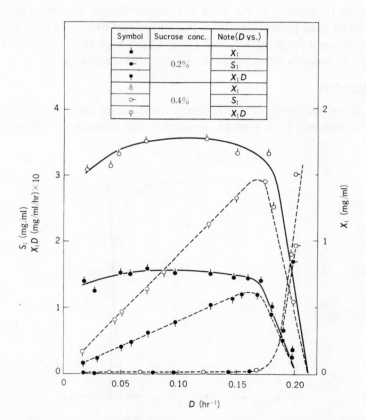

Symbol	Sucrose conc.	Note(D vs.)
●		X_1
●-	0.2%	S_1
♀		$X_1 D$
○		X_1
○-	0.4%	S_1
♀		$X_1 D$

FIG. 5.10.   Continuous culture in a single vessel of *Streptomyces aureofaciens*;[15] the ordinate represents
limiting substrate concentration (sucrose), S_1, cell concentration, X_1, and productivity of cells, $X_1 D$,
while the abscissa is dilution rate, D.

10-liter fermentor using synthetic medium. Sucrose was selected as the limiting substrate. Two levels of sucrose concentration were studied. Steady states at each dilution rate were maintained for 1 to 3 days before the values of S_1 and X_1 were measured. Fig. 5.10 is an example of the results obtained with *Streptomyces aureofaciens*. Again, these results are similar to those predicted by Equations (5.21) and (5.23). In these experiments the value of $Y_{X/S}$ was found not to be constant, as was the case with the continuous culture of yeast in Fig. 5.8. The maximum outputs of mycelia for both levels of sucrose concentration in the feed were observed to occur near "wash out." This experimental fact is in agreement with Eq. (5.26).

5.5. PRACTICAL PROBLEMS WITH CONTINUOUS OPERATION

There are certain practical problems inherently associated with continuous operation. These often detract from the utility of continuous fermentations.

5.5.1. Lack of homogeneity in the continuous-fermentor vessel

The cause of poorer yields at low-dilution rates, as shown in Figs. 5.8 and 5.11, is believed to be endogenous respiration of the organisms. This may be accentuated by a lack of homogeneity in the fermentor.

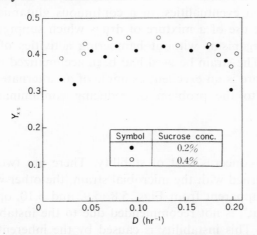

Symbol	Sucrose conc.
●	0.2%
○	0.4%

FIG. 5.11. $Y_{X/S}$ vs. D (*Streptomyces aureofaciens*); yield, $Y_{X/S}$ is plotted against dilution rate, D; data points were calculated from those in Fig. 5.10.[15]

The problem of insuring homogeneity of nutrients throughout a fermentor becomes more serious at low-dilution rates where the limiting substrate concentration is low, especially in the case of thick and viscous media and for large-scale equipment. In order to minimize the problem, good mixing of the broth, either with mechanical agitation or with high aeration, becomes significant. Research projects on the mixing of highly viscous or non-Newtonian fluids are lacking at present, but are necessary if this problem is to be understood and solved in large-scale continuous fermentations.

Convenient and reliable techniques are needed for measuring the dissolved oxygen concentration in fermentation broth and for following changes in viscosity with time. These would allow the aeration to be varied to control the dissolved oxygen at a selected concentration, and in addition, the broth could be diluted to provide a constant viscosity. These measures would assist in maintaining homogeneous conditions during continuous operation. Measurement and control in fermentations will be discussed in Chapter 10.

5.5.2. Maintenance of sterility

A second problem is that of maintaining a continuous fermentation under aseptic conditions for long periods of time. The maintenance of such conditions places a serious burden on the operations of sterilizing media and air. Hence, in continuous fermentation, these systems must be designed and operated with extreme care.

However, even with the most appropriately designed fibrous air filter there exists a finite chance of contaminating microbes eventually passing through the filter into the fermentation medium. Also in the medium sterilization, even if the operation is performed with the utmost care, the probability of undesirable microbes being charged into the broth cannot be reduced absolutely to zero.

To cope with such eventualities, in a continuous glutamic acid fermentation Ueda advocated the use of a mixture of drugs which suppressed the growth of undesirable microorganisms without hampering activities of the glutamic acid producing strain.[22] The strain he used had been acclimatized to the drug mixture. This sort of procedure is an excellent example of an alternate, and perhaps more practical, solution to the problem of reducing contamination in continuous fermentations.

5.5.3. Stability

A third problem concerns that of stability. There are two kinds of stability involved; one concerned with the microbial strain, the other with the mechanical operation. As was apparent from Figs. 5.8, 5.9, and 5.10, operation at dilution rates near "wash out" is not recommended due to the instability experienced in practical operation. This instability is caused by the inherent variations of feed devices and the sensitivity of the cell mass, X, and of the substrate concentration, S, near "wash out" to slight changes in dilution rate, D. Although the constancy of the feeding device is of prime importance in the case of small-scale laboratory experiments, the problem in large fermentors will not be so serious.

In long continuous fermentations the microbes are inevitably subject to mutations. When the mutant form has a selective advantage over the desired strain, the mutant will overrun the fermentation. Knowledge of ways to suppress undesirable mutations or of maintaining the desired strain in continuous fermentations is needed. One technique is that of semi-continuous fermentation in which the first vessel of the series is periodically re-seeded. In passing it should be noted that continuous culture is an excellent tool for studying mutations of microbial populations.

5.6.   AN EXAMPLE OF A DESIGN CALCULATION

Batch data on growth of *Lactobacillus delbrueckii* with a medium containing glucose 5%, yeast extract 3%, and mineral salts at 45°C and pH=6.0 are given in Table 5.3 (two columns from left in the table).[12] For this example, the organism is to be transferred to grow continuously in two vessels in series each with a working volume=100 liter. It is desired to adjust the cell concentration in terms of optical density so that the effluent from the second vessel will have a concentration, $N_2=8$ U.O.D./ml. The necessary flow rate, F, and the values of N_1 and N_2 in each vessel are to be determined.

TABLE   5.3

BATCH DATA ON GROWTH OF *Lactobacillus delbrueckii*.[12]

t (hr)	$N\left(\dfrac{\text{U.O.D.}}{\text{ml}}\right)$	$\dfrac{dN}{dt}\left(\dfrac{\text{U.O.D.}}{\text{ml hr}}\right)$	t (hr)	$N\left(\dfrac{\text{U.O.D.}}{\text{ml}}\right)$	$\dfrac{dN}{dt}\left(\dfrac{\text{U.O.D.}}{\text{ml hr}}\right)$
1.00	0.12	0.04	7.50	2.21	1.06
1.50	0.14	0.05	8.00	2.79	1.33
2.00	0.17	0.06	8.50	3.46	1.63
2.50	0.22	0.09	9.00	4.31	1.99
3.00	0.28	0.13	9.50	5.35	2.09
3.50	0.35	0.16	10.00	6.30	1.70
4.00	0.45	0.21	10.50	7.00	1.30
4.50	0.57	0.27	11.00	7.60	1.06
5.00	0.72	0.35	11.50	8.14	0.89
5.50	0.91	0.44	12.00	8.51	0.74
6.00	1.15	0.55	12.50	8.84	0.62
6.50	1.39	0.67	13.00	9.13	0.54
7.00	1.76	0.85	13.50	9.40	0.44

Solution

From the batch data (t vs. N in Table 5.3), each value of dN/dt is calculated and plotted against N as shown in Fig. 5.12.

Utilizing the graphical method to determine the cell concentration in each vessel, as was shown in Fig. 5.5, the value of F required for the desired condition of $N_2=$ 8 U.O.D./ml can be determined by a trial and error method (see Fig. 5.12). The answers to this problem are:

$$F/V = 0.40 \text{ hr}^{-1}$$
$$F = 0.40 \times 100 = 40 \text{ liter/hr}$$
$$N_1 = 5.35 \text{ U.O.D./ml}$$
$$N_2 = 7.95 \text{ U.O.D./ml}$$

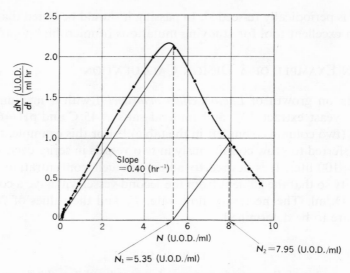

FIG. 5.12.   Plot of dN/dt against N from the data given in Table 5.3.

NOMENCLATURE

D = dilution rate, hr^{-1}

D_m = dilution rate at which either X_1D or P_1D becomes maximum

F = flow rate of medium, liter/hr

F_0 = flow rate of medium, liter/hr

F' = flow rate of medium, liter/hr

G = gain, productivity ratio of continuous to batch fermentation

g = generation time (doubling time)=$0.693/\mu$, hr

K_S = saturation constant, g/liter

k = F'/F_0

N = concentration of microorganisms, l/ml or U.O.D./ml

P = product concentration, mg/ml

P_i = product concentration at $t=0$, mg/ml

P_∞ = product concentration at $t=$infinity, mg/ml

r_{batch} = cell productivity in batch, mg/ml hr

$r_{cont.}$ = cell productivity in continuous run, mg/ml hr

r = fraction of mass recycled

S = limiting substrate concentration, mg/ml

S_0 = limiting substrate concentration in fresh medium, mg/ml

S_i = limiting substrate concentration at $t=0$, mg/ml

S_∞ = limiting substrate concentration at $t=$infinity

t = time, hr

t_m = time for exponential growth in batch, hr

t_1 = time of preparation for another batch run, hr

t_2 = lag time, hr

t_0 = time required for harvest in batch, hr

$t_l = t_0 + t_1 + t_2$, hr

$t_c = t_0 + t_1 + t_2 + t_m$, hr

$\Delta t \geq \Delta t' \geq 0$, hr

V = volume of broth, liter

X = cell mass concentration, mg/ml

X_m = maximum cell mass concentration, mg/ml

X_i = cell mass concentration at $t = 0$, mg/ml

X_0 = cell mass concentration in fresh medium ($X_0 = 0$)

$Y_{X/S} = -\Delta X / \Delta S$, yield

$Y_{P/X} = \Delta P / \Delta X$, yield

$Y_{P/S} = -\Delta P / \Delta S$, yield

Z = substrate concentration, mg/ml

subscripts, unless otherwise noted:

1, 2, $\cdots$, $(n-1)$, n = 1st, 2nd, $\cdots$ $(n-1)$th, and nth vessels

i = initial value

∞ = value at time = infinity

0 = value regarding fresh medium

m; max = maximum value

Greek letters

$\alpha_n = \dfrac{V\mu_n}{F_0}$, Eq. (5.42)

$\gamma = X_n / X_{n-1}$

θ = nominal (mean) holding time of flowing medium = V/F, hr

$\dfrac{1}{\theta'} = \dfrac{F}{V} - \mu_n$

$\lambda = \dfrac{tF_0}{V}$, Eq. (5.42)

$\bar{\Lambda}$ = mean cumulative age of microbes, hr

μ = specific growth rate, hr^{-1}

$\mu_{\max}$ = maximum value of specific growth rate, hr^{-1}

$\chi = \dfrac{P_1}{P_{1\infty}}, \ \dfrac{S_1}{S_{1\infty}}, \ \dfrac{\gamma}{\gamma_\infty}, \ $ or $\ \dfrac{\bar{\Lambda}_1}{\bar{\Lambda}_{1\infty}}$

$\chi_i = \dfrac{P_{1i}}{P_{1\infty}}, \ \dfrac{S_{1i}}{S_{1\infty}}, \ \dfrac{\gamma_i}{\gamma_\infty}, \ $ or $\ \dfrac{\bar{\Lambda}_{1i}}{\bar{\Lambda}_{1\infty}}$

REFERENCES

1. AIBA, S., and HARA, M. (1963). "Some analyses on continuous culture." *Proc. 5th Symposium, Inst. Appl. Microbiol. Univ. of Tokyo*, 198.

2. BARTLETT, M.C., and GERHARDT, P. (1959). "Continuous antibiotic fermentation—Design of a 20 liter, single-stage pilot plant and trials with two contrasting processes." *J. Biochem. Microbiol. Tech. & Eng.* **1**, 359.

3. BORZANI, W., FALCOME, M., and VARIO, M.L.R. (1960). "Kinetics of the continuous alcoholic fermentation of blackstrap molasses." *Appl. Microbiol.* **8**, 136.

4. CONTOIS, D.E. (1959). "Kinetics of bacterial growth: Relationship between population density and specific growth rate of continuous cultures." *J. gen. Microbiol.* **21**, 40.

5. DEINDOERFER, F.H., and HUMPHREY, A.E. (1959). "A logical approach to—Design of multistage systems for simple fermentation processes." *Ind. Eng. Chem.* **51**, 809.

6. FENCL, Z. (1963). "A uniform system of basic symbols for continuous cultivation of microorganisms." *Folia Microbiol.* **8**, 192.

7. FULD, G.J., MATELES, R.I., and KUSMIEREK, B.W. (1961). "A method for the study of the dynamics of continuous fermentation." p. 54, *S.C.I. Monograph No. 12* (Soc. of Chem Industry), London.

8. GOLLE, H.A. (1953). "Theoretical considerations of a continuous culture system." *Agr. Food Chem.* **1**, 789.

9. HERBERT, D. (1961). "A theoretical analysis of continuous culture systems." p. 21, *S.C.I. Monograph No.12* (Soc. of Chem. Industry), London.

10. HERBERT, D., ELSWORTH, R., and TELLING, R.C. (1956). "The continuous culture of bacteria; a theoretical and experimental study." *J. gen. Microbiol.* **14**, 601.

11. HUMPHREY, A.E. (1963). "Some observations of continuous fermentation." *Proc. 5th Symposium, Inst. Appl. Microbiol. Univ. of Tokyo*, 215.

12. LUEDEKING, R., and PIRET, E.L. (1959). "A kinetic study of the lactic acid fermentation Batch process at controlled pH." *J. Biochem. Microbiol. Tech. & Eng.* **1**, 393.

13. LUEDEKING, R., and PIRET, E.L. (1959). "Transient and steady states in continuous fermentation. Theory and experiment." *ibid.* **1**, 431.

14. MAXON, W.D. (1960). "Continuous fermentation." *Advances in Applied Microbiology* (Ed.). UMBREIT, W.W. **2**, 335. Academic, N.Y.

15. SIKYTA, B., SLEZAK, J., and HEROLD, M. (1961). "Growth of *Streptomyces aureofaciens* in continuous culture." *Appl. Microbiol.* **9**, 233.

16. SIKYTA, B., DOSKOCIL, J., and KASPAVORA, J. (1959). "Continuous streptomycin fermentation." *J. Biochem. Microbiol. Tech. & Eng.* **1**, 379.

17. SHICHIJI, S. (1963). "Continuous alcohol fermentation with re-use process." *Proc. 5th Symposium, Inst. Appl. Microbiol. Univ. of Tokyo*, 279.

18. SPICER, C.C. (1955). "The theory of bacterial constant growth apparatus." *Biometric* **11**, 225.

19. TERUI, G., KONNO, N., and OKAZAKI, M. (1963). "Studies on continuous culture for enzyme production through preferential synthesis." *Proc. 5th Symposium, Inst. Appl. Microbiol. Univ. of Tokyo*, 259.

20. TERUI, G. (1963). "Some problems of continuous culture." *Proc. 5th Symposium, Inst. Appl. Microbiol. Univ. of Tokyo*, 159.

21. UEDA, K. (1956). "Studies on continuous fermentation. Part 6. Fermentation cycle in multi-stage system." *J. Agr. Chem. Soc.* **30**, 335.

22. UEDA, K., TAKAHASHI, H., and OGUMA, T. (1963). "Production of glutamic acid by continuous multi-stage fermentation." *Proc. 5th Symposium, Inst. Appl. Microbiol. Univ. of Tokyo*, 232.

CHAPTER 6

AERATION AND AGITATION

The purposes of aeration and agitation in fermentors are, first, to supply micro-organisms with oxygen, and secondly, to mix fermentation broths in such a way that a uniformity of suspension of microbes can be achieved and the mass-transfer rate of the metabolic product can be accelerated. Many fermentors are equipped with impellers for the mechanical agitation of broths to disintegrate air bubbles and to intensify the turbulence of the liquid, but fermentors without mechanical agitators are also used as in the case of yeast fermentors (see Fig. 6.1).

Capacity = 100 m³
Pipe diameter:
  main,
    (see center, vertical), 8″
  medium,
    (see center, horizontal), 2″
  manifold, 1½″
Sparger hole diameter = 2 mm

Fig. 6.1.   Interior view of a yeast fermentor; note the manifold for diffusing air bubbles.
(*Courtesy   Sankyo Co., Tanashi, Tokyo.*)

The discussions which follow in this chapter are concerned both with bubble aeration and with mechanical agitation. In 1944, Cooper *et al.*[7] published an experimental procedure for measuring the oxygen-absorption coefficient in a bubble aerator using the sulfite-oxidation method. Many works on this subject of oxygen transfer in bubble aeration have appeared since then. The rational design of an aerator for Newtonian liquids has been made possible, but much work on oxygen transfer to non-Newtonian liquids in aerators remains to be done before a rationale can be established for dealing with concentrated mycelial broths, which usually exhibit non-Newtonian behavior. Hence most of this chapter will be confined to Newtonian liquids.

After reviewing briefly the mass-transfer theories now current, some significant experimental data regarding bubble motion in liquids and, in addition, several important concepts associated with liquid agitation by impellers will be discussed.

133

The correlation between the oxygen-transfer coefficient and operating variables will then be elaborated. Neither the experimental procedure for determining the oxygen-transfer coefficient in fermentors nor the mixing-time concept will be treated here; the former, which is important in fermentation practice, will be described in Chapter 10, while the latter concept will be discussed in the next chapter.

6.1. MASS-TRANSFER THEORIES

6.1.1. Two-film theory

The following three assumptions are involved in Fig. 6.2: (1) laminar flow of fluids along the gas-liquid interphase; (2) concentration profiles independent of time (i.e., in a steady state); and (3) instantaneous establishment of equilibrium between p_i and C_i when gas is brought into contact with liquid.

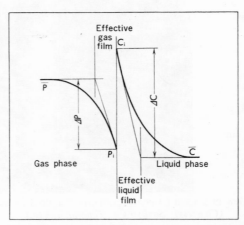

FIG. 6.2. Concentration profiles across a gas-liquid interphase. The partial pressure of the gas component (oxygen) in the gas phase in bulk and at the interphase are $\bar{p}$ and p_i, the driving force being expressed by $\varDelta p$. Dissolved gas (oxygen) concentrations at the interphase and in the liquid phase in bulk are C_i and $\bar{C}$ respectively, the driving force in this phase being shown as $\varDelta C$. The value of p_i is in equilibrium with that of C_i. Two effective films (gas and liquid) are assumed for both sides of the interphase. The concentrations (C and p) within the effective films change linearly with distance from the interphase.

The unidirectional rate of mass transfer, N_A, for the gas component A (oxygen) across the unit area in steady state is expressed by:

mass-transfer rate $= N_A =$ driving force/resistance

$$= \frac{\varDelta P}{\dfrac{1}{k_g}} = \frac{\varDelta C}{\dfrac{1}{k_L}} \qquad (6.1)$$

where

k_L, k_g = mass-transfer coefficients of liquid and gas films respectively

Assuming a linear relation between C_i and p_i,

$$C_i = Hp_i + H'_0 \tag{6.2}$$

Introducing the terms C^* and p^*,

$$\left. \begin{aligned} H(\bar{p} - p_i) &= C^* - C_i \\ H(p_i - p^*) &= C_i - \bar{C} \end{aligned} \right\} \tag{6.3}$$

where

C^*, p^* = hypothetical values which are in equilibrium with $\bar{p}$ in gas phase in bulk and $\bar{C}$ in liquid phase in bulk respectively

Eq. (6.1) will be rearranged to give,

$$N_A = \frac{\bar{p} - p_i}{\dfrac{1}{k_g}} = \frac{C_i - \bar{C}}{\dfrac{1}{k_L}} = \frac{p_i - p^*}{\dfrac{1}{Hk_L}} = \frac{C^* - C_i}{\dfrac{H}{k_g}}$$

$$= \frac{\bar{p} - p^*}{\dfrac{1}{k_g} + \dfrac{1}{Hk_L}} = \frac{C^* - \bar{C}}{\dfrac{1}{k_L} + \dfrac{H}{k_g}} \tag{6.4}$$

$$N_A = K_G(\bar{p} - p^*) = K_L(C^* - \bar{C}) \tag{6.5}$$

where

K_G = over-all coefficient of mass transfer based on gas film

K_L = over-all coefficient of mass transfer based on liquid film

Lewis and Whitman first attempted to express the concentration gradient across a gas-liquid interphase in consistent unit based on either the partial pressure, p, in gas or the dissolved concentration, C, in liquid, and introduced the over-all coefficient K_G or K_L. As apparent from Fig. 6.2, the model by Lewis and Whitman is composed of two films of gas and liquid. The steady rate of mass-transfer is given by Eq. (6.4) or Eq. (6.5). The model and the rate equations derived from it, as shown in Equations (6.4) and (6.5), are called the two-film theory.[15] Although the theory abounds with factors which have simplified extremely the true picture of a gas-liquid interphase, Equations (6.3) to (6.5) are still used in the design and operation of aerators.

Experiments have shown that liquid-film resistance is controlling for oxygen transfer in bubble aeration.[1]

6.1.2. Penetration theory

The penetration theory originates from the premise that the concentration profiles in Fig. 6.2 are dependent on time after gas is brought into contact with liquid. Now, the rate of change, $\partial C/\partial \theta$, for dissolved-gas concentration in liquid with time will be considered along a one-dimensional basis, x, as shown by the following equation (Fick's second law of diffusion):

$$\frac{\partial C}{\partial \theta} = D\frac{\partial^2 C}{\partial x^2} \qquad (6.6)$$

where
θ = time
D = molecular diffusivity of gas component in liquid

Initial and boundary conditions are:

$$\left. \begin{array}{lll} \theta = 0, & x > 0, & C = \bar{C} \\ \theta > 0, & x = 0, & C = C_i \\ \theta > 0, & x = \infty, & C = \bar{C} \end{array} \right\} \qquad (6.7)$$

Solving Eq. (6.6) with the above conditions,

$$C = \bar{C} + \frac{C_i - \bar{C}}{\sqrt{\pi D\theta}} \int\limits_{x}^{\infty} \exp\left(-\frac{X^2}{4D\theta}\right)dX \qquad (6.8)$$

Therefore,

$$\frac{\partial C}{\partial x}\bigg|_{x=0} = -\frac{C_i - \bar{C}}{\sqrt{\pi D\theta}}$$

Introducing mass flux, $f(\theta)$, at the gas-liquid interphase (Fick's first law of diffusion),

$$f(\theta) = -D\left(\frac{\partial C}{\partial x}\right)_{x=0} = (C_i - \bar{C})\sqrt{\frac{D}{\pi\theta}}$$

The amount of gas, F, absorbed during the time, θ,

$$F = \int\limits_{0}^{\theta} f(\theta)d\theta = \int\limits_{0}^{\theta} (C_i - \bar{C})\sqrt{\frac{D}{\pi\theta}}\, d\theta$$

$$= 2(C_i - \bar{C})\sqrt{\frac{D\theta}{\pi}} \qquad (6.9)$$

Eq. (6.9) represents the penetration theory presented by Higbie.[14] The mean rate of mass transfer, N_A', during θ per unit interfacial area is:

$$N_A' = \frac{F}{\theta} = 2\sqrt{\frac{D}{\pi\theta}}(C_i - \bar{C}) = 2\sqrt{\frac{D}{\pi\theta}}\varDelta C \qquad (6.10)$$

Therefore, the term k_L in Eq. (6.1) corresponds to that of $2\sqrt{\dfrac{D}{\pi\theta}}$ in Eq. (6.10).

$$k_L \sim 2\sqrt{\frac{D}{\pi\theta}} \qquad (6.11)$$

The physical meaning of k_L in Eq. (6.1) can then be elaborated by Eq. (6.11), which shows that the value of k_L is much larger during unsteady state after single bubbles are generated than it is during steady state. Higbie defined the value of θ thus:

$$\theta = d_B/v_B \qquad (6.12)$$

where
d_B = bubble diameter

v_B = ascending velocity of bubble through liquid

According to Higbie's definition, the value of θ in Equations (6.11) and (6.12) is the period of time needed for single bubbles to travel through liquid a distance equal to the diameter of bubbles.

6.1.3. Surface-renewal theory

The surface-renewal rate, s, was introduced by Danckwerts,[9] in addition to the unsteady-state molecular-diffusion model described in the preceding section. Defining $se^{-s\theta} d\theta$ as the area of surface elements whose ages are between θ and $\theta + d\theta$, the mass flux, $f(\theta)$, at the liquid-gas interphase mentioned previously is multiplied by $se^{-s\theta} d\theta$ to obtain the rate of mass transfer into/from these turbulent elements. The mean rate of mass transfer, N_A'' per unit interfacial area, is then calculated from:

$$f(\theta)se^{-s\theta}d\theta = (C_i - \overline{C})se^{-s\theta}\sqrt{\frac{D}{\pi\theta}}\,d\theta$$

$$N_A'' = (C_i - \overline{C})\sqrt{\frac{D}{\pi}} \int_0^\infty \frac{se^{-s\theta}}{\sqrt{\theta}}\,d\theta = (C_i - \overline{C})\sqrt{Ds} \qquad (6.13)$$

From Equations (6.13), (6.10), and (6.11),

$$k_L \sim \sqrt{Ds} \qquad (6.14)$$

Eq. (6.14) indicates that the value of k_L changes in proportion to $s^{1/2}$; the increase/decrease of the value of s implies the increase/decrease of turbulent motion of bubbles. This analysis, as mentioned above, is called the surface-renewal theory.[9]

Mochavola et al.[20] also presented the following relation:

$$k_L \sim \sqrt{\frac{D}{\Delta\tau}} \qquad (6.15)$$

where

$\Delta\tau$ = replacement period of liquid film surrounding single bubbles

They suggested the use of eddy diffusivity of dissolved gas in liquid in preference to the molecular diffusivity, D, in Eq. (6.15).

To recapitulate, Equations (6.5), (6.10), (6.13), and (6.15), which have been derived from the respective theories, are useful for solving various problems on mass transfer of aeration in fermentors.

6.2. BUBBLE AERATION AND MECHANICAL AGITATION

6.2.1. Bubble aeration

6.2.1.1. *Single bubbles*

The size of single bubbles emerging from an orifice at low frequencies is shown by:

$$\frac{\pi}{6} d_B^3 \Delta \rho g = \pi d \sigma \tag{6.16}$$

where

d_B = bubble diameter
d = orifice diameter
$\Delta \rho$ = density difference between gas (air) and liquid
g = acceleration due to gravity
σ = surface tension of liquid

The left-hand side of Eq. (6.16) represents the force of buoyancy of bubbles, while the force retaining bubbles at the orifice is shown by the right-hand side of the equation. Van Klevelen et al. showed experimentally with an air-water system that Eq. (6.16) held nearly true for Q ranging from 0.02 to 0.5 cm³/sec.[29] So far, the size, d_B, of bubbles is proportional to the cube root of the orifice diameter, $d^{1/3}$ and independent of the gas-flow rate, Q. However, the above fact regarding the size, d_B, does not hold true when the value of Q exceeds the above range. In aeration practices in the fermentation industry, the following equation, which is purely empirical in nature, is applied in estimating the value of d_B:

$$d_B \propto Q^{n'}, \qquad n' = 0.2 \sim 1.0 \quad [12] \tag{6.17}$$

All the experimental data reported by the many workers who have studied the relation between bubble diameter, d_B, and terminal ascending velocity, v_B, in water are summarized in Fig. 6.3.[29] Various symbols in the figure correspond to the data obtained by the many workers whose names and references to their original papers are omitted. A characteristic type of curve is drawn through the data points in Fig. 6.3. It was urged by van Klevelen et al.[29] that the value of v_B was approximately proportional to $d_B^{1\sim2}$ when $d_B \leq 1.5$ mm. The bubbles were nearly spherical in shape in this region. As the value of d_B increased from 1.5 to 6 mm, the shape of the bubbles began to deform appreciably, eventually mushrooming when the value of d_B exceeded 6 mm.

Peebles et al.[24] conducted an extensive experiment in which the relation between d_B and v_B was studied with air and 22 different kinds of liquid. The viscosities and surface tensions of the liquids used were from 0.233 to 59 c.p. and from 71.2 to 15.9 dynes/cm respectively. Their experimental data were correlated in terms of the drag coefficient vs. the modified Reynolds number of bubbles. From the correlation (not shown) they found some differences in the motion of the air bubbles depending upon the liquid used.

It seems worthy to remark here that experimental data on the motion of air bubbles in liquid other than in water, especially in non-Newtonian liquids, are needed for future exploitation of aeration equipment

Air bubbles used in the fermentation industry range from about 1.5 to 10 mm in diameter. The values of v_B may then range from 20 to 30 cm/sec in the case of single bubbles in dilute fermentation media whose characteristics are nearly similar to those of water (see Fig. 6.3)

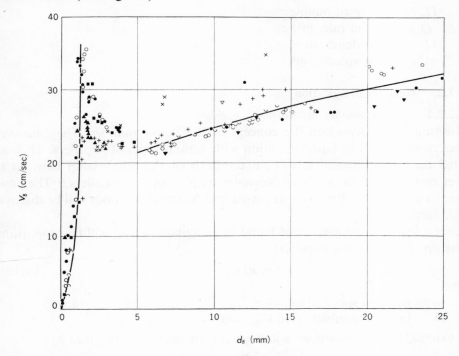

FIG. 6.3.   Ascending terminal velocity of single bubbles in water; the ordinate is the ascending terminal velocity, v_B, of single bubbles, while the abscissa represents bubble diameter, d_B. Various symbols used in the figure indicate respective sources of original data.[29]

6.2.1.2.   Swarms of bubbles

In actual practice, single bubbles are rarely encountered in aerations in the fermentation industry; hence it is necessary to deal with swarms of bubbles. If there is no coalescence of bubbles in aeration and if no appreciable distribution is seen in bubble diameter, the values of v_B for single bubbles approximate those for a swarm of bubbles. Aeration in the fermentation industry is sometimes accompanied by mechanical agitation, and the physical properties of fermentation broths change markedly with the progress of a fermentation, especially for mycelial cultivation. The motion of bubbles is affected by the turbulence caused by impellers; bubbles deform and change in diameter considerably during the course of fermentation. The estimation of v_B with Fig. 6.3 for a swarm of bubbles seems to become unacceptable under the above-mentioned circumstances.

Hence it is proposed to approximate the values of v_B with the following equation for a swarm of bubbles in the fermentation process:

$$v_B = \frac{QH_L}{H_0 V} \qquad (6.18)$$

where

v_B = ascending velocity of bubbles in a swarm, m/sec
H_0 = hold-up of bubbles
Q = aeration rate, m³/sec
H_L = liquid depth, m
V = liquid volume, m³

6.2.2.   Mechanical agitation

6.2.2.1.   *Power number vs. Reynolds number*

Rushton *et al.* developed the concept of the Power number. They measured power requirements of liquid agitation with various types of impellers. They correlated their experimental results on the basis of the relationship between the Power number and the modified Reynolds number of the impellers.[27] The power characteristics of impellers with ungassed and Newtonian liquids will be discussed in this section.

A representative velocity, v, of liquid in an agitated vessel will be proportional to the tip velocity of the impeller:

$$v \propto nD_i \qquad (6.19)$$

where

n = rotation speed of impeller
D_i = impeller diameter (see Fig. 6.4)

The external force imposed on a unit volume of liquid will be given by:

$$\frac{Pg_c}{nD_i}\frac{1}{D_i^3}$$

where

P = power requirements of agitation
g_c = conversion factor

On the other hand, the inertial force of a unit volume of liquid in the vessel will be:

$$\frac{\rho n D_i}{\frac{1}{n}} = \rho n^2 D_i$$

In addition, the viscous force of the liquid will be:

$$\mu \frac{D_i^2}{D_i^3}\frac{nD_i}{D_i} = \mu \frac{n}{D_i}$$

provided: μ = liquid viscosity

The ratio of external to inertial forces of liquid is defined as the Power number.

$$\frac{\text{External force}}{\text{Inertial force}} = \frac{\dfrac{Pg_c}{nD_i}\dfrac{1}{D_i^3}}{\rho n^2 D_i} = \frac{Pg_c}{n^3 D_i^5 \rho} = N_P$$

$$= \text{Power number (Dimensionless)} \qquad (6.20)$$

Liquid motions in agitated vessels are depicted by the ratio of inertial to viscous forces of liquids; namely, by the modified Reynolds number of the impellers.

$$\frac{\text{Inertial force}}{\text{Viscous force}} = \frac{\rho n^2 D_i}{\dfrac{\mu n}{D_i}} = \frac{n D_i^2 \rho}{\mu} = N_{\text{Re}}$$

= modified Reynolds number (Dimensionless) (6.21)

The power characteristics of liquid agitation with various types of impellers have been established by Rushton *et al.*[27] as shown in Fig. 6.4. In the figure, N_P is plotted against N_{Re}. The experimental determination of the values of P by varying the values of n, D_i, ρ, and μ with each type of impeller in a series of geometrically similar systems will yield the plot in Fig. 6.4 in which the data points are omitted. The types of impellers shown in Fig. 6.4 are most commonly used in industry. If the geometrical ratios of each system deviate from those which are indicated in the figure, each curve in Fig. 6.4 is shifted from case to case, though the general shape of each curve remains unchanged. If more detailed information is needed, the original study[27] may be consulted.

It is significant that the geometrical ratios described in Fig. 6.4 are regarded as standard, especially in the case of the flat-blade turbine. It is also important that the values of N_P at higher values of N_{Re} (i.e., in the turbulent region) become con-

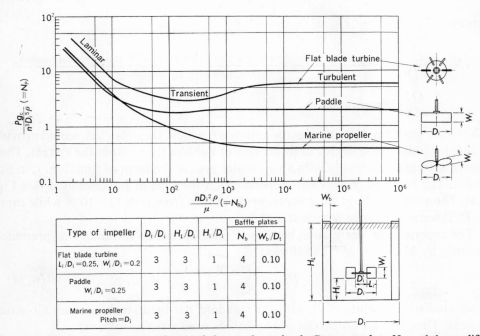

FIG. 6.4. N_P vs. N_{Re}; the power characteristics are shown by the Power number, N_P, and the modified Reynolds number, N_{Re}, of impellers. For more detailed information on each dimensionless term, see the text. The lower part of the figure shows the geometrical ratios of representative types of impellers: turbine, paddle, and marine propeller.

stant irrespective of the type of impeller and that the value of N_P for the flat-blade turbine in this region is:

$$N_P \doteqdot 6 \tag{6.22}$$

6.2.2.2. *Decrease of power requirements in aeration*

Power requirements of impellers for liquid agitation in a gassed system decrease considerably compared with those of an ungassed system. The gassed system is the usual case in the fermentation industry. The power decrease is principally due to the fact that values of liquid density, around the impeller in particular, will decrease apparently because of the existence of bubbles. Therefore, even in a gassed system, power requirements for agitation will be affected only to a slight extent if the bubbles ascending through the liquid in an agitated vessel do not meet effectively with the impeller.

The degree of power decrease in a gassed as compared with an ungassed system, P_g/P, extends from 0.3 to 1.0 (unaffected), depending on the type of impeller and the rate of aeration.[23] As is apparent from the above, the term P_g/P will be correlated with a criterion which represents the degree of dispersion of bubbles around the impeller and in the vessel. Ohyama *et al.* presented the following formula:[23]

$$\frac{P_g}{P} = f(N_a) \tag{6.23}$$

where

$$N_a = \frac{\dfrac{Q}{D_i^2}}{nD_i} = \frac{\text{Apparent velocity of gas (air) through sectional area of vessel}}{\text{Tip velocity of impeller}}$$

$$= \frac{Q}{nD_i^3} \text{ (Dimensionless)}$$

They gave the term N_a to the aeration number, which, they claimed, would provide a clue for judging the degree of dispersion of bubbles throughout the system. They determined experimentally with an air-water system the form of function, f, in Eq. (6.23). The function, f, was also dependent on the type of impeller used (see Fig. 6.5). The values of N_a in their experiments ranged from 0 to 12×10^{-2}, while those of P_g/P were in a range from 1.0 to 0.3.

The experimental correlation between P_g and operating variables was presented recently by Michel *et al.*[19] as follows:

$$P_g \propto \left(\frac{P^2 n D_i^3}{Q^{0.56}} \right)^{0.45} \tag{6.24}$$

They studied the values of P_g with the standard flat-blade turbine in an air-water system. The physical properties of the liquids used were as follows:

liquid density,	$\rho = 0.8 \sim 1.65$ g/cm^3	
liquid viscosity,	$\mu = 0.9 \sim 100$ c.p.	
surface tension,	$\sigma = 27 \sim 72$ dynes/cm	

It is interesting to note from the correlation (not shown) that geometrically dissimilar systems were also expressed by Eq. (6.24). The physical properties of the liquids used did not affect explicitly the correlation with Eq. (6.24), the effects of the aeration devices (ring sparger and open nozzle) being also implicit. However, the original correlation of Eq. (6.24) must be used carefully as a means of scale-up, because the correlation was made in absolute values of each term, rather than in dimensionless numbers. According to Michel et al.,[19] the data of Ohyama et al.[23] agreed favorably with the curves extrapolated from Eq. (6.24).

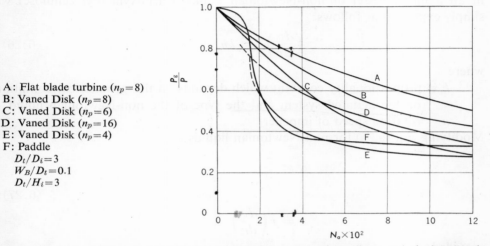

A: Flat blade turbine ($n_p=8$)
B: Vaned Disk ($n_p=8$)
C: Vaned Disk ($n_p=6$)
D: Vaned Disk ($n_p=16$)
E: Vaned Disk ($n_p=4$)
F: Paddle
$D_t/D_i=3$
$W_B/D_t=0.1$
$D_t/H_i=3$

Fig. 6.5. Power requirements for agitation in a gassed system. The ordinate and abscissa are the degree of power decrease, P_g/P, and the aeration number, N_a. Parameters are the types of impellers, whose representative geometrical ratios in agitated vessels are also shown in the figure.

6.2.2.3. Power requirements in non-Newtonian liquids [5, 18]

The difference between Newtonian and non-Newtonian liquids is that fluid viscosity, μ, which is defined by the following equation, is dependent on shear rate, dv/dr, in a non-Newtonian liquid:

$$\tau = \mu \frac{dv}{dr} \tag{6.25}$$

where

τ = shear stress in absolute units per unit area of a plane which is parallel to v direction

dv/dr = rate of shear in r direction

μ = viscosity

The so-called flow diagram is necessary for the study of non-Newtonian characteristics; in this diagram, τ is plotted against dv/dr with a certain viscometer, for example with a double-cylinder type of viscometer. The relation between τ and dv/dr is always represented by a straight line in a Newtonian liquid, starting from the origin of the rectangular coordinates (τ, dv/dr), the slope of which is equal to the viscosity, μ.

A detailed description of the flow diagram of various non-Newtonian liquids will be given in the next chapter. The discussion in this section will deal with a convenient procedure for estimating power requirements for the agitation of non-Newtonian liquids. The procedure was suggested by Metzner *et al.*[18] based on their study of Bingham and pseudoplastic liquids. (For the terms of Bingham and pseudoplastic, see Chapter 7.)

According also to Metzner *et al.*,[17] the average value of shear rate, $(dv/dr)_{av}$ in an agitated vessel of non-Newtonian liquid (Carboxymethyl cellulose) was simply expressed as follows:

$$\left(\frac{dv}{dr}\right)_{av.} = kn \tag{6.26}$$

where

k = proportionality constant which depends on the geometrical condition of the agitated system and the type of the non-Newtonian liquid

n = rotation speed of impeller

Modifying Eq. (6.25) for non-Newtonian liquids:

$$\left.\begin{aligned} \mu_a &= \frac{\tau}{\dfrac{dv}{dr}} \\[2em] \tau &= f\left(\frac{dv}{dr}\right) \end{aligned}\right\} \tag{6.27}$$

provided:

μ_a = apparent viscosity of the non-Newtonian liquid

Since the point is how to define the value of μ_a for a non-Newtonian liquid in an agitated vessel, the procedure proposed by Metzner *et al.*[18] for evaluating the value of μ_a is:

(1) First, by varying the rotation speed, n, of the impeller, measure the power requirements, P, in an agitated vessel of laboratory scale filled with a non-Newtonian liquid. Values of the Power number, N_P, are then calculated.

(2) Replace the non-Newtonian liquid with a highly viscous Newtonian liquid whose values (ρ, μ) are known; then, using the same impeller and vessel, experimentally measure the power consumed in agitating the liquid. For the Newtonian liquid, determine the relation between the Power number, N_P, and the modified Reynolds number, N_{Re} (see Fig. 6.4).

(3) The modified Reynolds number, $nD_i^2\rho/\mu_a$, which incorporates the apparent viscosity, μ_a, for each value of rotation speed, n, of the impeller can be determined by equating both values of N_P—the one calculated in accordance with Step 1 above and the other in accordance with Step 2 using the relation between N_P and N_{Re}—provided the latter values of $N_{Re}=nD_i^2\rho/\mu$ are for the Newtonian liquid examined as a reference.

It is, now, necessary to determine the value of k in Eq. (6.26):

(1)' Values of μ_a determined in Step 3 are substituted into Eq. (6.27) to assess the the values of dv/dr for each value of n, provided that the function, $f(dv/dr)$, is given.

(2)' By equating the values of dv/dr to $(dv/dr)_{av.}$ of Eq. (6.26), the value of k is determined.

If the value of k is determined, the estimation of P will be made conversely as follows:

(1)'' At a given value of rotation speed, n, of the impeller, the value of $(dv/dr)_{av.}$ is determined with Eq. (6.26).

(2)'' The value of μ_a is determined with Eq. (6.27), followed by the calculation of the Reynolds number, $nD_i^2\rho/\mu_a$.

(3)'' With the correlation secured earlier between the Power number, N_P, and the modified Reynolds number, N_{Re}, for the Newtonian liquid, the value of N_P, for the non-Newtonian liquid is determined for each value of the modified Reynolds number, $nD_i^2\rho/\mu_a$.

In the above approximate procedure of calculating the power requirements for agitating a non-Newtonian liquid, the step of equating the value of $(dv/dr)_{av.}$ in Eq. (6.26) to that of dv/dr in Eq. (6.27) is only for convenience. It is because the former value is related to flow patterns of the non-Newtonian liquid in an agitated vessel, while the latter is related to that which must be assessed with a certain viscometer. However, if the coupling of Eq. (6.27) with Eq. (6.26) to determine the value of k is only for the power estimation of this particular problem, such a convenient procedure may be acceptable. It may then be inferred that the relation between the Power number, N_P, and the modified Reynolds number, N_{Re}, for a given Newtonian liquid is used to connect the rheological characteristic of the non-Newtonian liquid with the flow pattern of the material in an agitated vessel.

6.2.2.4. *Hold-up of bubbles in an aeration vessel*

Richards et al.[25] studied the hold-up of air bubbles in water-filled agitated vessels. The abscissa of Fig. 6.6 is hold-up, H_0, in per cent, while the ordinate represents $(P/V)^{0.4} \times v_s^{0.5}$.

$$P/V = \text{power input per unit volume of ungassed liquid, } \text{HP}/\text{m}^3$$
$$v_s = \text{linear velocity of air based on the empty cross-sectional area}$$
$$\text{of the vessel, m/sec}$$

The empirical relationship shown in Fig. 6.6 is a simplification of a publication of Calderbank who correlated the hold-up in an aerated vessel with operating variables including physical properties of liquids.[4] According to Richards et al.,[25] a straight line drawn through the data points in Fig. 6.6 approximate Calderbank's correlation. They also claimed that the values of H_0 were affected slightly by the geometrical dissimilarities of agitating vessels, because the data points in Fig. 6.6 were made available using widely different vessels.

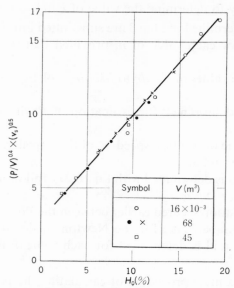

FIG. 6.6.   Estimation of hold-up, H_0, with power input per unit volume of ungassed liquid, P/V, and nominal linear velocity, v_s, of air.[25]

6.3.   CORRELATION BETWEEN MASS-TRANSFER COEFFICIENTS AND OPERATING VARIABLES

6.3.1.   Bubble aeration

Using all the data published to date on the values of k_L by the many workers who have dealt with rising bubbles through water, Eckenfelder recalculated and replotted the values of both the Sherwood and the Reynolds numbers of the bubble with the results shown in Fig. 6.7. These data on k_L in bubble aeration of water were determined with the sulfite-oxidation method by varying water depth, H_L. The sizes of bubbles in these experiments ranged from $d_B = 0.5$ to 2.0 mm. Although the data points in Fig. 6.7 have been omitted for simplicity, the values of N_{Sh} were also dependent on the values of H_L, as may be seen in the figure. This fact is primarily due to the experimental procedure for determining the value of k_L which involves both oxygen transfer from the surface of bubbling water and the rapid rate of oxygen absorption in the transient state associated with the generation of bubbles. These ambiguous factors apparently contributed to the larger values of k_L (and N_{Sh}) as the liquid depth, H_L, was lowered.

The fact that the value of k_L depends on the "age" of bubbles after they are released from orifices has also been recognized experimentally by other workers such as Deindoerfer et al.[10] and Aiba et al.[2] This fact must be given due consideration if the value of k_L free of the transient effect is to be estimated correctly.

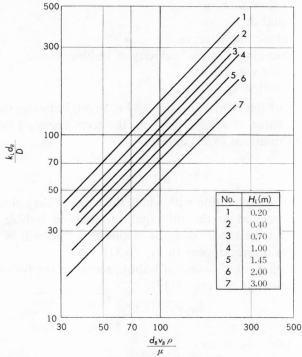

FIG. 6.7. N_{Sh} vs. N_{Re} in bubble aeration; the Sherwood number, $k_L d_B/D$, of single bubbles is plotted against the Reynolds number, $d_B v_B \rho/\mu$; parameters being liquid (water) depth.

Eckenfelder presented the following equation to summarize the data of k_L in bubble aeration as shown in Fig. 6.7, tentatively incorporating the effect of the Schmidt number:

$$\frac{k_L d_B}{D} H_L^{1/3} = \beta \frac{d_B v_B \rho}{\mu} \left(\frac{\mu}{\rho D}\right)^{1/2} = \beta N_{\text{Re}} N_{\text{Sc}}^{1/2} \tag{6.28}$$

where

β = empirical coefficient which is affected by types of aerators

Rearranging Eq. (6.28),

$$k_L = \frac{\beta v_B}{H_L^{1/3}} \frac{1}{N_{\text{Sc}}^{1/2}} \tag{6.29}$$

On the other hand,

$$a = \frac{Q H_L}{10 d_B v_B V} + \beta' \frac{1}{H_L} \tag{6.30}$$

provided:

a = interfacial area between bubbles and liquid per unit volume of liquid, m²/m³

Q = air flow rate, m³/min

H_L = liquid depth, m

d_B = bubble diameter, m

v_B = ascending terminal velocity of bubble, m/sec

V = liquid volume, m³

β' = empirical constant

The second term of the right-hand side of Eq. (6.30) indicates the effect of liquid surface. When the value of H_L is 3 to 5 m, the term becomes negligibly small.[12] Then, combining Equations (6.29) and (6.30),

$$k_L a = \frac{\beta H_L^{2/3} Q}{10 V d_B N_{Sc}^{1/2}} \qquad (6.31)$$

Eq. (6.31) is an empirical equation with which the value of the volumetric (capacity) coefficient, $k_L a$, is related to the principal variables in bubble aeration. Other variables which affect the values of k_L or of the term "a" will be discussed later, though the variables do not appear in Eq. (6.31).

In considering a particular system of bubble aeration, the following equation is derived from Equations (6.31) and (6.17):

$$k_L a V = \beta'' Q^{1-n'} \qquad (6.32)$$

provided:

β'' = empirical constant

Experimental work to prove Eq. (6.32) was made by Eckenfelder[11] with the sulfite-oxidation method (see Fig. 6.8). He studied the performance of a typical aeration device as shown in Fig. 6.8, keeping water volume, $V\,(= 8.5\text{ m}^3)$, constant.

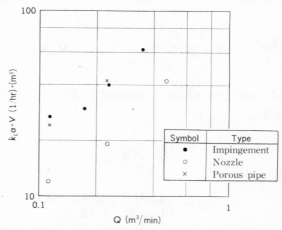

FIG. 6.8. Effect of the aeration rate, Q, on the value of the capacity coefficient of oxygen transfer, $k_L a$, times the volume of the aeration vessel, V. The symbols indicate respective types of aeration devices. Since the value of V in each aeration device was constant, this figure exemplifies the effect of Q on $k_L a$. This sort of representation is only for ease of design.

It is evident then that Fig. 6.8 indicates the effect of Q on the value of k_La in each aeration device. By and large, the experimental data of Fig. 6.8 can support the general form of Eq. (6.32).

6.3.2. Bubble aeration with mechanical agitation

Dimensional analysis of this problem shows:[26]

$$\frac{k_LD_i}{D} \propto \left(\frac{nD_i^2\rho}{\mu}\right)^\alpha \left(\frac{\mu}{\rho D}\right)^\gamma \tag{6.33}$$

Eq. (6.33) corresponds to Eq. (6.28) in bubble aeration. Eq. (6.33) can be simplified by keeping constant the values of liquid viscosity, μ, liquid density, ρ, and molecular diffusivity of gas (oxygen), D:

$$k_LD_i \propto (nD_i^2)^\alpha$$

The literature shows:

$$\alpha = 0.5 \quad {}^{25}$$

Then,

$$k_L \propto n^{0.5} \tag{6.34}$$

According to Calderbank,[4] the value of term "a" in a stirred vessel is:

$$a \propto \left\{\frac{(P_g/V)^{0.4}\rho^{0.2}}{\sigma^{0.6}}\right\}\left(\frac{v_s}{v_B}\right)^{0.5} \tag{6.35}$$

If the values of liquid density, ρ, surface tension of liquid, σ, and ascending velocity of bubble, v_B, are regarded as constant, Eq. (6.35) is reduced as follows:

$$a \propto (P_g/V)^{0.4}v_s^{0.5} \tag{6.36}$$

Richards et al.[25] derived the following equation from Equations (6.34) and (6.36):

$$k_La \propto (P_g/V)^{0.4}v_s^{0.5}n^{0.5} \tag{6.37}$$

They correlated their experimental data on k_La in agitated vessels using Eq. (6.37).[25] Eq. (6.37), they urged, can also represent the data on k_La which Cooper et al. presented.[7]

Cooper, Fernstrom, and Miller initiated the measurement of mass (oxygen)-transfer coefficient in an aerated vessel with the sulfite-oxidation method. Vaned-disk and paddle types of impellers and a series of different size vessels were used. As shown in Fig. 6.9, they correlated the absorption number with the power consumed per unit volume of liquid, this latter measurement having frequently been used for solving problems of scale-up (see Chapter 7).

Fig. 6.9 shows one of the experiments published by Cooper et al.[7] It may be seen in the figure that identical values of the absorption number result, irrespective of vessel size, if the values of power consumed per unit volume of liquid are equated in a series of geometrically similar systems.

To avoid the inconsistency of units in Fig. 6.9, the values of K_v and other factors were converted to metric units to obtain the following equations.

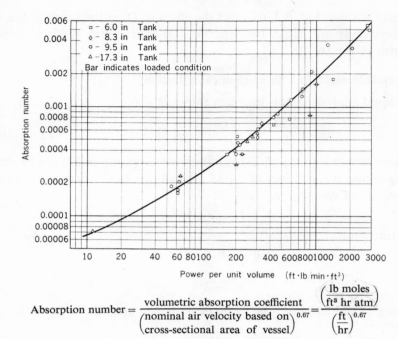

$$\text{Absorption number} = \frac{\text{volumetric absorption coefficient}}{\left(\begin{array}{c}\text{nominal air velocity based on}\\ \text{cross-sectional area of vessel}\end{array}\right)^{0.67}} = \frac{\left(\dfrac{\text{lb moles}}{\text{ft}^3 \text{ hr atm}}\right)}{\left(\dfrac{\text{ft}}{\text{hr}}\right)^{0.67}}$$

Fig. 6.9. Experimental data of Cooper et al.[7] The ordinate is the absorption number, defined as described in the figure, while the abscissa is the value of power requirements for agitation per unit volume of aerated liquid (water). Various symbols in the figure indicate different sizes of agitated vessels. The aeration device used was a single orifice located at the center of the bottom of each aeration vessel.

For a vaned-disk impeller:

$$K_v = 0.0635 (P_g/V)^{0.95} v_s^{0.67} \tag{6.38}$$

where

K_v = oxygen-transfer coefficient, kg mole/hr m³ atm

P_g/V = power input per unit volume of liquid in gassed system, HP/m³

v_s = nominal air velocity based on empty cross-sectional area of vessel, m/hr

It is recommended that Eq. (6.38) be applied under the following conditions:[8]

For one set of impellers, $v_s < 90$ m/hr

For two sets of impellers, $v_s < 150$ m/hr

provided:

$P_g/V > 0.1$ HP/m³

$H_L/D_t = 1.0$

For a paddle impeller:

$$K_v = 0.038 (P_g/V)^{0.53} v_s^{0.67} \tag{6.39}$$

provided:[8]

$v_s < 21$ m/hr

$P_g/V > 0.06$ HP/m³

$H_L/D_t = 1.0$

An empirical factor, f_c, was presented by Cooper et al.[7] as shown in Fig. 6.10 to correct for the case in which the ratio of liquid height to vessel diameter, H_L/D_t, deviates from 1.0. Then,

$$K_v = f_c(K_v)_{H_L/D_t=1.0} \tag{6.40}$$

Equations (6.38) and (6.39), or Fig. 6.9, have been used in designing fermentors when no appropriate data on the volumetric coefficient of oxygen transfer, k_La or K_v, have been available.

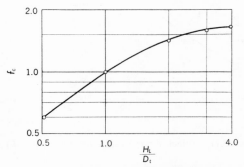

FIG. 6.10. f_c vs. H_L/D_t; empirical chart to obtain the value of f_c if the value of H_L/D_t deviates from unity.

6.4.   OTHER FACTORS AFFECTING THE VALUES OF MASS-TRANSFER COEFFICIENTS

6.4.1.   Temperature

O'Connor studied the effect of temperature on the value of k_La. His semi-theoretical equation is as follows:[22]

$$\frac{k_La(t_1)}{k_La(t_2)} = \sqrt{\frac{T_1\mu_2}{T_2\mu_1}} \tag{6.41}$$

where
$k_La(t_1), \ k_La(t_2) = k_La$ at t_1 and t_2
$\mu_1, \ \mu_2 =$ viscosity of liquid at t_1 and t_2
$t_1, \ t_2 =$ temperature, °C
$T_1, \ T_2 =$ absolute temperature, °K

Eq. (6.41) is plotted in Fig. 6.11 assuming water to be the liquid. The equation was derived on the basis of oxygen transfer in bubble aeration in the activated-sludge process in the biological treatment of waste. Other data which have been published concerning the effect of temperature on the value of k_La in bubble aeration do not significantly change Eq. (6.41). However, this equation has not yet been applied under actual working conditions in the fermentation industry, and further study of the equation needs to be made from this point of view.

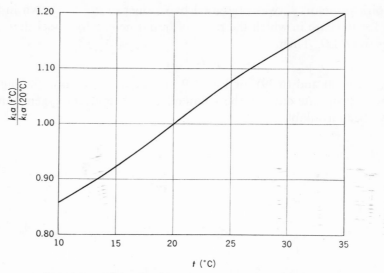

FIG. 6.11.   Effect of temperature on the value of $k_L a$.

6.4.2.   Organic substance

According to Eckenfelder, the value of k_L in bubble aeration of water decreased considerably when a small amount of peptone was added.[13] For instance, the value of k_L decreased to about one-third its initial value when peptone was added to water to the extent of 10,000 ppm. The bubble diameter also decreased in this instance by about 15%. The value of $k_L a$ then became about 40% of that without the organic substance.

Zieminski et al.[30] studied the effect of various kinds of alcohol, ketone, and ester on the value of $k_L a$ in bubble aeration of distilled water. They found that the value of $k_L a$ in distilled water increased conversely by 50 to 100% with the addition of these substances in water to the extent of about 20 ppm in each case. This trend was most clear for n-buthyl and isoamylacetate. A marked increase of the interfacial area between bubbles and liquid per unit volume of liquid, "a", predominating over the decrease of k_L values, accounts for the experimental results mentioned above.

The effect of other organic substances which are usual constituents of fermentation broths are shown in Fig. 6.12.[1] Although the data points which were obtained by measuring polarographically the values of $k_L a$ and by estimating photographically the values of "a" are scattered considerably in the figure, the effects of organic substances on the values of k_L are also shown. A reason to account for the scattering of the data points emerges from the photographic estimation of "a". When aeration such as that shown in Fig. 6.12 is studied, the experimental determination of k_L by the above-mentioned procedure is not feasible technically, and is lacking in good reproducibility of data. It may also be remarked from Fig. 6.12

that the value of k_L was nearly unaffected by the value of v_s in this example of bubble aeration.

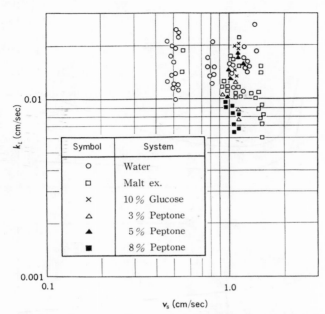

Symbol	System
○	Water
□	Malt ex.
×	10 % Glucose
△	3 % Peptone
▲	5 % Peptone
■	8 % Peptone

v_s (cm/sec)

FIG. 6.12. Effect of organic substance on the value of k_L; the ordinate is k_L, while the abscissa shows the superficial velocity, v_B, of air flow through the sectional area of the aeration vessel.[1]

6.4.3. Surface active agents

Due to the widespread household use of surface active agents in recent times, a preponderance of foam as well as deterioration of oxygen-transfer rate in bubble aeration are causing serious troubles in the activated-sludge process of sewage treatment. Many workers have been engaged in measuring the effect of the surface active agents on the value of k_La. Fig. 6.13 is an example demonstrating how a surface active agent adversely affects the value of k_L and k_La in bubble aeration.[13] An addition to water of a small amount of sodium lauryl sulfate resulted in a sharp decrease of the value of k_L in this example. The value of k_La, on the other hand, first decreased sharply and then gradually recovered with the increased addition of the agent as shown in Fig. 6.13. This might have been caused by the fact that air bubbles decreased in size with the addition of $NaLSO_4$ (see lower section of Fig. 6.13).

Table 6.1 summarizes the results of experiments by several workers who have studied the effect of surfactants. As seen in the table, in the case of each surfactant the value of k_L drops sharply when a small amount of surfactant is added to the

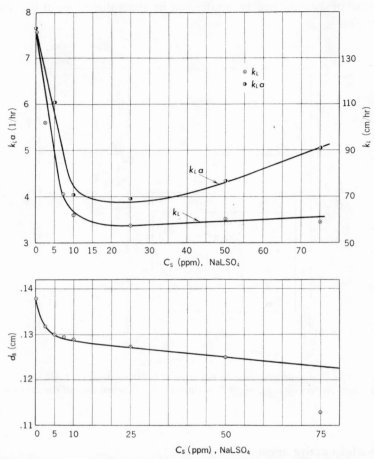

FIG. 6.13.   Effect of surface active agent on k_La and k_L; the upper section of the figure shows the value of k_La is deteriorated by adding sodium lauryl sulfate (a surfactant); the lower section indicates the bubble size, d_B, as affected by adding the surfactant. The abscissae of both sections are the concentration, C_S, of sodium lauryl sulfate in water.[13]

water, the degree of each addition being far below the critical micell concentration, C_S (see the seventh column of the table). The critical concentration, C_S, implies that the surface tension of the liquid (water) decreases with increased addition of surfactant into liquid, leveling off, however, beyond a critical value of C_S (critical micell concentration).

Several different explanations have been put forward to account for this adverse effect of surfactant on the value of k_L. For example, in the surface-drag theory proposed by Timson et al.,[28] it is inferred that surfactant adsorbed onto air-liquid interphase does not necessarily cause resistance to oxygen diffusion from gas into liquid phase, but that the principal controlling factor may be a calming effect of surfactant in dampening complicated movement of the interphase.

TABLE 6.1

EFFECT OF SURFACE ACTIVE AGENT ON THE VALUE OF k_L (cont'd).

Surface Active agent	Experimental condition			k_L cm/sec		C_S ppm		Author
	d_B cm	Q cm³/min	H_L cm	k_L at $C_S=0$	$k_{L\min}$	C_S at $\sigma_{\min}$	C_S at $k_{L\min}$	
Sodium dioctyl sulfosuccinate	—	—	—	0.028	0.012	300–600	10–20	MANCY and OKUN[16]
Alkyl benzene sulfonate	—	—	—	0.017	0.007	—	20	MCKEOWN and OKUN[21]
Pentapropyl benzene sulfonate	0.55	—	—	0.017–0.027	0.014–0.016	—	15	TIMSON and DUNN[28]
Sodium lauryl sulfate	0.12–0.14	40	110	0.039	0.017	1000	10	ECKENFELDER and BARNHART[13]
Synthetic detergent	0.16	128	114	0.056	0.013	—	50	CARVER[6]
Sodium lauryl sulfate	0.70–0.85	40–70	11–85	0.028–0.042	0.005–0.016	100	25	AIBA and TODA[2]

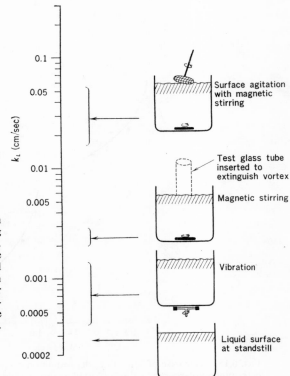

FIG. 6.14.   Spectrum of k_L values for an air-water system; various ways of agitating the water surface are shown schematically. The range of k_L values obtained in each type of surface agitation is shown by the left-hand side of the spectrum. Factors involved in assessing correctly the value of air-water interfacial area in each case were "incorporated" into the value of "k_L" because the "static" value of interfacial area was taken.

A spectrum of k_L values is shown in Fig. 6.14.[2] The spectrum was prepared from the measurement of k_L in an air-water system using a definite interfacial area which could be calculated on a non-agitation basis for each configuration in the figure. It may be urged from the spectrum that the values of k_L varied appreciably from case to case, depending on the dynamic situation of the interphase. One can easily envisage from the spectrum that the decrease of k_L by one-half or by one-third the value of k_L without surfactant can be ascribed to the fact that the interfacial movement was made "quiescent" to a certain extent.

As contradictory as this assumption may appear, the facts that k_L values in bubble aeration in water with and without surfactant have been determined experimentally based on quiescent interfacial area and that dynamic deformation of interphase has not been taken into account will justify the above-mentioned assumption.

6.4.4. Mycelium

It can be inferred that physical properties, especially viscosity, μ, or apparent viscosity, μ_a, of fluid affect the value of $k_L a$. This inference holds true for mycelial fermentation broth. Fig. 6.15, presented by Brierley et al.,[3] shows how a mould

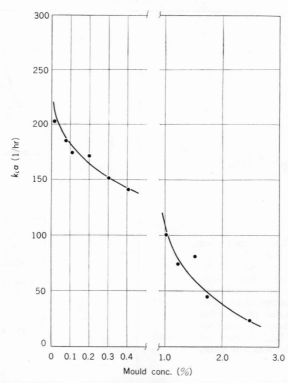

FIG. 6.15. Decrease of $k_L a$ values depending on mycelial concentration in broth; the value determined polarographically is plotted against mould concentration, % (*Aspergillus niger*).[3]

concentration of *Aspergillus niger* affected markedly the value of k_La. They suspended newly prepared mycelia of *Aspergillus niger* in a medium of sucrose, salts, and corn steep liquor using a 8-liter Waldhof-type fermentor. They measured the value of k_La polarographically. The abscissa of Fig. 6.15 represents the mycelium concentration in dry weight. It is surmised that the mould suspension, especially for more than 1% in concentration, might have strongly exhibited non-Newtonian characteristics. Although Brierley *et al.*[3] studied experimentally how to cultivate such mycelia successfully from the viewpoint of oxygen supply, no mention was made of the non-Newtonian characters of the broth. Much work on this specific aspect of oxygen transfer into non-Newtonian liquid is needed.

6.4.5. Type of sparger

Many workers have experimentally studied the oxygen-transfer capacities of various types of aerators in their search for one which would produce a rapid rate of oxygen transfer from air bubbles to liquid. However, it is still difficult to designate the most effective device for a particular fermentor or aeration basin because of the necessity of taking into consideration such aspects of the different devices as their durability or their susceptibility to damage (principally clogging) caused by microbial cells. The basis for assessing such aspects differs from case to case. According to Eckenfelder, the value of k_La measured with various types of aerators by the sulfite-oxidation method did not differ appreciably when compared on the basis of power consumption per unit volume of liquid (see Fig. 6.16).[11] His purpose was to determine the most effective type of aeration basin in the activated-sludge process. For details of designations of sparger types in the figure, see his original paper.[11] No mechanical agitators were used in the categories from "Impingement"

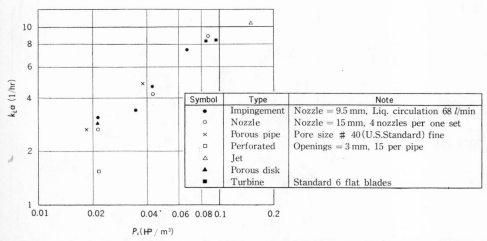

Symbol	Type	Note
●	Impingement	Nozzle = 9.5 mm, Liq. circulation 68 *l*/min
○	Nozzle	Nozzle = 15 mm, 4 nozzles per one set
×	Porous pipe	Pore size ♯ 40 (U.S.Standard) fine
□	Perforated	Openings = 3 mm, 15 per pipe
△	Jet	
▲	Porous disk	
■	Turbine	Standard 6 flat blades

FIG. 6.16. Performance of various types of aeration devices. The value of k_La is plotted against power, P_v, consumed per unit volume of liquid (water). Symbols indicate various types of aeration devices. The value of P_v was principally supplied by air compressors with the exception of the inclusion of turbine power.[11]

to "Porous disk" as shown in the figure. The power requirements for all of the spargers except the turbine are primarily the power consumed in sparging air into liquid, while the power for the turbine represents presumably the figure required for surface agitation of liquid without sparging air bubbles from the vessel bottom.

6.5. An Example of Calculation

Dimensions of a fermentor equipped with two sets of standard flat-blade turbines and four baffle plates are:

$$
\begin{aligned}
\text{Fermentor diameter,} \quad & D_t = 3 \text{ m} \\
\text{Impeller diameter,} \quad & D_i = 1.5 \text{ m} \\
\text{Baffle plate width,} \quad & W_b = 0.3 \text{ m} \\
\text{Liquid depth,} \quad & H_L = 5 \text{ m}
\end{aligned}
$$

The fermentor is used for a specific fermentation. The viscosity, μ, and the density, ρ, of the broth are:

$$ \rho = 1{,}200 \text{ kg/m}^3, \qquad \mu = 0.02 \text{ kg/m sec} $$

Rotation speed of impellers and aeration rate are $N=60$ rpm and 0.40 vvm respectively.

Calculate

(a) Power requirements, P, for ungassed system,
(b) Power requirements, P_g, when aerated,
(c) Volumetric coefficient, K_v, of oxygen transfer, and
(d) Hold-up, H_0 of bubbles.

Solution

(a)
$$ \frac{D_t}{D_i} = \frac{3}{1.5} = 2.0 $$

$$ \frac{H_L}{D_i} = \frac{5}{1.5} = 3.33 $$

$$ n = 1.0 \text{ rps} $$

$$ N_{\text{Re}} = \frac{n D_i^2 \rho}{\mu} = \frac{1 \times 1.5^2 \times 1.2 \times 10^3}{2 \times 10^{-2}} = 1.35 \times 10^5 $$

From Fig. 6.4,

$$ N_P = 6 $$

$$ P = \frac{\rho n^3 D_i^5 N_P}{g_c} = \frac{1.2 \times 10^3 \times 1^3 \times 1.5^5 \times 6}{9.81} $$

$$ = 5.57 \times 10^3 \text{ Kg m/sec} = 73.3 \text{ HP} $$

Since the geometrical ratios, $(D_t/D_i)^*$ and $(H_L/D_i)^*$, of this problem deviate from D_t/D_i and H_L/D_i in Fig. 6.4, a correction factor, f_c, which is approximately expressed as shown below will be calculated.

$$f_c = \sqrt{\frac{(D_t/D_i)^*(H_L/D_i)^*}{(D_t/D_i)(H_L/D_i)}} = \sqrt{\frac{2.0 \times 3.33}{3.0 \times 3.0}} = 0.86$$

Then,

$$P^* = Pf_c = 73.3 \times 0.86 = 63 \text{ HP}$$

If power requirements, P, with two sets of impellers can be estimated by multiplying the value of P for one set of impellers with a factor of $\sqrt{2}$, the total power requirements, P^{**} will be:

$$P^{**} = P^* \sqrt{2} = 63 \times \sqrt{2} = 89.1 \text{ HP}$$

(b) The aeration number, N_a, is calculated as follows:

$$N_a = \frac{Q}{nD_i^3} = \frac{0.40 \times \frac{\pi}{4} \times 3^2 \times 5 \times \left(\frac{1}{60}\right)}{1 \times 1.5^3} = 6.95 \times 10^{-2}$$

Assuming that Curve A in Fig. 6.5 can be used,

$$\frac{P_g}{P^{**}} = 0.65, \qquad P_g = P^{**} \times 0.65 = 89.1 \times 0.65 = 58 \text{ HP}$$

(c)
$$Q = \frac{2}{5} \times \frac{\pi}{4} \times 3^2 \times 5 = 14.1 \text{ m}^3/\text{min}$$

$$v_s = \frac{14.1 \times 60}{\frac{\pi}{4} \times 3^2} = 119.7 \text{ m/hr}$$

From Eq. (6.38),

$$K_v = 0.0635 \times \left(\frac{58}{(\pi/4) \times 3^2 \times 5}\right)^{0.95} \times (119.7)^{0.67}$$

$$= 2.50 \text{ kg mole/m}^3 \text{ hr atm}$$

The correction factor, f_c, will become (see Fig. 6.10):

$$\frac{H_L}{D_t} = \frac{5}{3} = 1.67$$

$$f_c = 1.3$$

Then, the volumetric coefficient, K_v^*, of oxygen transfer is:

$$K_v^* = K_v f_c = 2.50 \times 1.3 = 3.25 \text{ kg mole/m}^3 \text{ hr atm}$$

It must be remembered that the above value of capacity coefficient is maximum in terms of oxygen-transfer coefficient, because Eq. (6.38) based on the sulfite-oxidation experiment is applied in the calculation.

(d) Fig. 6.6 is used to calculate the hold-up, H_0.
From Fig. 6.6,

$$\left(\frac{P}{V}\right)^{0.4} v_s^{0.5} = \left(\frac{89.1}{(\pi/4) \times 3^2 \times 5}\right)^{0.4} \times 119.7^{0.5} = 15.9$$

Then,

$$H_0 = 18.5\%$$

NOMENCLATURE

a = interfacial area between liquid and gas per unit volume of liquid, m^2/m^3

C = concentration of dissolved gas (oxygen), kg mole/m^3

$\bar{C}$ = concentration of dissolved gas (oxygen) in bulk liquid, kg mole/m^3

C_i = concentration of dissolved gas (oxygen) at gas-liquid interphase, kg mole/m^3

C_S = concentration of surface active agent in liquid, ppm

C^* = concentration of dissolved gas (oxygen) which is in equilibrium with partial pressure, $\bar{p}$, in gas phase in bulk, kg mole/m^3

D = diffusivity of dissolved gas (oxygen) in water, cm^2/sec, m^2/hr

d = orifice diameter, m

D_t = vessel diameter, m

D'_i = disk diameter of turbine, m

D_i = impeller diameter, m

d_B = bubble diameter, m, mm

f = function

f_c = correction factor

g = acceleration due to gravity, m/sec^2

g_c = conversion factor, kg m/Kg sec^2

H = Henry's constant, kg mole/m^3 atm

H_i = location of impeller from bottom of vessel, m

H_L = liquid depth, m

H'_0 = empirical constant

H_0 = gas (air) hold-up in liquid (water), % or fraction

k = proportionality constant

K_L = over-all coefficient of mass transfer based on liquid film, m/hr

K_G = over-all coefficient of mass transfer based on gas film, kg mole/m^2 hr atm

k_g = mass-transfer coefficient of gas film, kg mole/m^2 hr atm

k_L = mass-transfer coefficient of liquid film, m/hr

K_v = volumetric absorption coefficient, kg mole/m^3 hr atm

$k_L a$ = volumetric absorption coefficient, 1/hr

L_i = blade length of impeller, m

N = rotation speed of impeller, 1/min

$\dot{n}$ = rotation speed of impeller, 1/sec

n_p = number of blades

N_a = aeration number ($= Q/nD_i^3$)

N_b = number of baffle plates

N_P = Power number ($= Pg_c/\rho n^3 D_i^5$)

N_{Re} = Reynolds number ($= nD_i^2\rho/\mu$, $d_B v_B \rho/\mu$, $nD_i^2\rho/\mu_a$)

N_{Sc} = Schmidt number ($= \mu/\rho D$)

N_{Sh} = Sherwood number ($= k_L d_B/D$, $k_L D_i/D$)

n' = experimental exponent

N_A, N'_A, N''_A = mass transfer per unit time per unit interfacial area, kg mole/m^2 hr, kg mole/m^2 sec

P = power consumption of liquid agitation in ungassed system, Kg m/sec, HP

P_g = power consumption of liquid agitation in gassed system, Kg m/sec, HP

$\bar{p}$ = partial pressure of gas component in gas phase in bulk, atm

p_i = partial pressure of gas component at gas-liquid interphase, atm
p^* = partial pressure of gas component which is in equilibrium with bulk concentration in liquid phase, atm
P_v = power requirements per unit volume of liquid, HP/m³, Fig. 6.16
Q = gas (air) flow rate, m³/min, m³/sec
r = radial distance in vessel, m
s = surface renewal rate, Eq. (6.14)
t = temperature, °C
T = absolute temperature, °K
V = liquid volume, m³
v_B = ascending (terminal) velocity of bubbles, m/sec, cm/sec
v_s = nominal velocity of gas (air) based on cross-sectional area of vessel, m/hr
v = liquid velocity, Eq. (6.19)
W_b = width of baffle plate, m
W_i = impeller width, m
x = coordinate

Subscript: min
minimum value

Greek letters
α = empirical exponent
β = proportionality constant
β',β'' = empirical constant
γ = empirical exponent
θ = time
μ = liquid viscosity, kg/m sec, g/cm sec
μ_a = apparent viscosity of liquid, kg/m sec
ρ = liquid density, kg/m³, g/cm³
$\Delta\rho$ = density difference between gas and liquid, Eq. (6.16)
σ = surface tension, dyne/cm
$\Delta\tau$ = replacement time of liquid film, Eq. (6.15)
τ = shear stress, Eq. (6.25)

REFERENCES

1. AIBA, S., and YAMADA, T. (1961). "Oxygen absorption in bubble aeration. Part 1." *J. Gen. Appl. Microbiol.* **7**, 100.
2. AIBA, S., and TODA, K. (1963). "The effect of surface active agent on oxygen absorption in bubble aeration I." *ibid.* **9**, 443.
3. BRIERLEY, M.R., and STEEL, R. (1959). "Agitation-aeration in submerged fermentation. Part 2. Effect of solid disperse phase on oxygen absorption in a fermentor." *Appl. Microbiol.* **7**, 57.
4. CALDERBANK, P.H. (1958). "Physical rate processes in industrial fermentation. Part 1. The interfacial area in gas-liquid contacting with mechanical agitation." *Trans. Instn. Chem. Engrs.* **36**, 443.
5. CALDERBANK, P.H., and MOO-YOUNG, M.B. (1959), and (1961). "The prediction of power consumption in the agitation of non-Newtonian fluids." *ibid.* **37**, 26. "The power characteristics of agitators for the mixing of Newtonian and non-Newtonian fluids." *ibid.* **39**, 337.
6. CARVER, C.E., JR. (1955). "Absorption of oxygen in bubble aeration." *Biological Treatment*

of Sewage and Industrial Wastes (Eds.). ECKENFELDER, W.W., and MCCABE, J. **1**, 149 Reinhold, N.Y.

7. COOPER, C.M., FERNSTROM, G.A., and MILLER, S.A. (1944). "Performance of agitated gas-liquid contactors." *Ind. Eng. Chem.* **36**, 504.
8. Chem. Engrs' Handbook p.814 (1958). Maruzen Book. Co., Tokyo.
9. DANCKWERTS, P.V. (1951). "Significance of liquid-film coefficient in gas absorption." *Ind. Eng. Chem.* **43**, 1460.
10. DEINDOERFER, F.H., and HUMPHREY, A.E. (1961). "Mass transfer from individual gas bubbles." *ibid.* **53**, 755.
11. ECKENFELDER, W.W., JR. (1956). "Process design of aeration system for biological waste treatment." *Chem. Eng. Progress* **52**, 286.
12. ECKENFELDER, W.W., JR. (1959). "Absorption of oxygen from air bubbles in water." *J. Sanitary Eng. Division, Proc. A.S.C.E.* **85**, No. SA 4.
13. ECKENFELDER, W.W., JR., and BARNHART, E.L. (1961). "The effect of organic substances on the transfer of oxygen from air bubbles in water." *A.I.Ch.E. Journal* **7**, 631.
14. HIGBIE, R. (1935). "The rate of absorption of a pure gas into a still liquid during short periods of exposure." *Trans. Am. Inst. Chem. Engrs.* **31**, 365.
15. LEWIS, W.K., and WHITMAN, W.G. (1924). "Principles of gas absorption." *Ind. Eng. Chem* **16**, 1215.
16. MANCY, K.H., and OKUN, D.A. (1963). "Effect of surface active agents on the rate of oxygen transfer." *Advances in Biological Waste Treatment* (Eds.). ECKENFELDER, W.W., and MCCABE J. p. 111. Pergamon, Oxford.
17. METZNER, A.B., and TAYLOR, J.S. (1960). "Flow patterns in agitated vessels." *A.I.Ch.E Journal* **6**, 109.
18. METZNER, A.B., FEEHS, R.H., RAMOS, H.P., OTTO, R.E., and TUTHILL, J.D. (1961). "Agitation of viscous Newtonian and non-Newtonian fluids." *ibid.* **7**, 3.
19. MICHEL, B.J., and MILLER, S.A. (1962). "Power requirements of gas-liquid agitated systems." *ibid.* **8**, 262.
20. MOCHAVOLA, L.A., and KISHINEVSKII, M.H. (1958). "Mass transfer—gas absorption by bubbling." *J. Appl. Chem. (U.S.S.R.)* **31**, 1013.
21. MCKEOWN, J.J., and OKUN, D.A. (1963). "Effects of surface active agents on oxygen bubble characteristics." *Advances in Biological Waste Treatment* (Eds.). ECKENFELDER, W.W., and MCCABE, J. p.113. Pergamon, Oxford.
22. O'CONNOR, D.J. (1955). D. Sc. Thesis, N.Y. Univ.
23. OHYAMA, Y., and ENDOH, K. (1955). "Power characteristics of gas-liquid contacting mixers." *Chem. Eng. (Japan)* **19**, 2.
24. PEEBLES, F.N., and GARBER, H.J. (1953). "Studies on the motion of gas bubbles in liquids." *Chem. Eng. Progress* **49**, 88.
25. RICHARDS, J.W. (1961). "Studies in aeration and agitation." *Progress in Industrial Microbiology* **3**, 143.
26. RUSHTON, J.H. (1951). "The use of pilot plant mixing data." *Chem. Eng. Progress* **47**, 485.
27. RUSHTON, J.H., COSTICH, E.W., and EVERETT, H.J. (1950). "Power characteristics of mixing impellers. Part 2." *Chem. Eng. Progress* **46**, 467.
28. TIMSON, W.J., and DUNN, C.G. (1960). "Mechanism of gas absorption from bubbles under shear." *Ind. Eng. Chem.* **52**, 799.
29. VAN KREVELEN, D.W., and HOFTIJZER, P.J. (1950). "Studies of gas-bubble formation. Calculation of interfacial area in bubble contactors." *Chem. Eng. Progress* **46**, 29.
30. ZIEMINSKI, S.A., GOODWIN, C.C., and HILL, R.L. (1960). "The effect of some organic substances on oxygen absorption in bubble aeration." *Tappi* **43**, 1029.

CHAPTER 7

SCALE-UP

Scale-up is the study of the problems associated with transferring data obtained in laboratory and pilot-plant equipment to industrial production. Equipment for the fermentation industry's fermentors, heat exchangers, crystallizers, separators, and so forth, can be designed and operated properly only if scale-up technology is fully appreciated. This problem is not peculiar to biochemical engineering, but is shared by many branches of chemical engineering.

In this chapter, only those problems associated with the scale-up of fermentors will be discussed: the scale-up of other operations will be discussed in their appropriate chapters. To illustrate the types of problems encountered with fermentors, two simple examples will be discussed.

FIG. 7.1.   A series of Fermentors. Each capacity = 60 m³ (*Courtesy   Kaken Chem. Co., Ltd., Fujieda.*)

Suppose the conditions of aeration which give maximum productivity in a specific fermentation have been established using a bench-scale fermentor, and it is then proposed to transfer the fermentation to a large fermentor having the same geometrical design. The problem is to calculate the proper aeration rate in the large vessel, assuming for simplicity no mechanical agitation. Since the physical properties of the broth under consideration are the same in geometrically similar types of fermentors, Eq. (6.31) in Chapter 6 is simplified as follows:

$$k_L a \propto \frac{Q}{V} H_L^{2/3} \frac{1}{d_B}$$ (7.1)

Then,

$$\frac{[k_L a]_1}{[k_L a]_2} = \frac{\left[\dfrac{Q}{V}\right]_1}{\left[\dfrac{Q}{V}\right]_2} \left(\frac{H_{L1}}{H_{L2}}\right)^{2/3} \frac{d_{B2}}{d_{B1}}$$ (7.2)

where subscripts 1 and 2 relate to small- and large-scale equipment respectively. It may be assumed that $d_{B2} \doteqdot d_{B1}$ in Eq. (7.2), because the size of bubbles is considered not to differ appreciably with the size of the fermentor. The aeration rate with the large fermentor can be determined by equating the left-hand side of Eq. (7.2) to unity, then

$$\frac{\left[\dfrac{Q}{V}\right]_2}{\left[\dfrac{Q}{V}\right]_1} = \left(\frac{H_{L2}}{H_{L1}}\right)^{-2/3}$$ (7.3)

Eq. (7.3) signifies, for example, that the aeration rate $[Q/V]_2$ with the large fermentor will be $[Q/V]_2 = 5^{-2/3} \doteqdot 0.34$ vvm, provided the value of $[Q/V]_1 = 1.0$ vvm and the scale-up ratio, $H_{L2}/H_{L1} = 5$ (volumetric scale-up × 125).

Another type of problem in scale-up is encountered where microbial growth is inhibited by a metallic ion electrolytically dissociated from the structural material of the fermentor. The degree of inhibition is usually determined by inserting a test piece of the material into the fermentation in a shaken flask, but the translation of these results to a large fermentor must take into account the fact that unit surface area of fermentor exposed to unit volume of broth will diminish by D_t^{-1} as the scale-up ratio increases.

From the above examples, it is clear that problems of scale-up in a fermentor are associated both with the behavior of the liquid in the fermentor and with the metabolic reactions of the organisms. Although studies from chemical engineering have already provided some insight into the behavior of liquids in stirred vessels, knowledge of the behavior of organisms in fermentation vessels is less well understood, and further investigations of both the biological and technological aspects of the system are required.

At this point, progress in the scale-up of liquid-mixing equipment will be reviewed.

As is well-known, the mixing of liquids has many objectives; for example, it accelerates the rates of mass and heat transfer, it promotes the rate of chemical reaction and provides a uniform suspension of particles in the liquid. The usual procedure of scale-up is to fix one of the following criteria as the basis of design; the choice of criterion will depend on the particular fermentation being studied:

(a) Modified Reynolds number, $nD_i^2 \rho/\mu$,
(b) Power consumed for mixing per unit volume of liquid, P/V,

(c) Energy dissipated per unit mass of liquid,

(d) Mean liquid velocity at a particular point in the vessel,

(e) Liquid circulation rate.

In microbial fermentations, power consumed per unit volume, P/V, and the mean liquid velocity at a particular point in the vessel are two criteria commonly used for scale-up. Other criteria have been used in chemical engineering, and those interested in this approach may refer to the literature.[1]

In this chapter, scale-up based on the power consumed per unit volume will be discussed in some detail; this will be followed by an account of scale-up based on the mass-transfer coefficient of oxygen. It may be noted in passing that the mass-transfer coefficient is closely related to the power requirement of the fermentor.

It should be emphasized that even if the problems of scale-up are successfully solved from an engineering point of view, it cannot be assumed that microorganisms will behave identically in small and large fermentors. It is generally accepted that the scale-up of bacterial or yeast fermentations presents less difficulty than that of mycelial fermentations exhibiting non-Newtonian behavior. Because of the importance of mycelial fermentations, the basic characteristics of non-Newtonian broths have been included in this chapter. The viscosity of microbial suspensions which is related to their non-Newtonian behavior will be dealt with in detail in Chapter 10.

7.1. POWER PER UNIT VOLUME OF LIQUID

7.1.1. General scheme

The dimensional analysis of the mass-transfer coefficient in agitated and geometrically similar systems, as outlined in the preceding chapter, is:

$$\frac{k_L D_i}{D} \propto \left(\frac{D_i^2 n \rho}{\mu}\right)^\alpha \left(\frac{\mu}{\rho D}\right)^\gamma \tag{7.4}$$

where

k_L = mass-transfer coefficient

D_i = impeller diameter

D = molecular diffusivity of the specific substance under consideration in the liquid

n = rotation speed of impeller

μ = liquid viscosity

ρ = liquid density

α, γ = empirical exponents

Two significant points must be remembered throughout the following discussion. First, Eq. (7.4) can be applied to cases other than mass transfer. For example, if the Sherwood number $(k_L D_i/D)$ is replaced by the Nusselt number $(hD_i/k$; where h=film coefficient of heat transfer, and k=thermal conductivity) and the Schmidt number $(\mu/\rho D)$ by the Prandtl number $(C_p\mu/k$; where C_p=specific heat), the analogous equation thus obtained can be used to evaluate the liquid-mixing performance of an impeller in terms of heat transfer. Therefore, it may not be unreasonable to infer that a dimensionless equation similar to Eq. (7.4) applies to the performance of impellers in fermentors. Needless to say, the exact representation of such equations must be left open at the present time for further investigation, primarily because of the difficulty of assessing quantitatively the effect the impeller may have on the metabolic activity of the organisms in the fermentation. Secondly, the discussion will assume that the aeration conditions in the fermentor are such that the aeration number (N_a) is the same, or at least not significantly different, from one geometrically similar system to the next. As seen in Fig. 6.5 in Chapter 6, the power requirements of an impeller in gassed systems, which most fermentors are, can be represented in geometrically similar systems by P (the power consumed in ungassed systems).

In order to achieve the same value for k_L in Eq. (7.4) in two geometrically similar systems, the following relation must hold (assuming the physical properties of the liquid are constant):

$$\frac{n_1}{n_2} = \left(\frac{D_{i2}}{D_{i1}}\right)^{\frac{2\alpha-1}{\alpha}} \tag{7.5}$$

where subscripts 1 and 2 relate to small- and large-scale equipment respectively. For scaling-up in turbulent, agitated liquids in fully baffled vessels (see Fig. 6.4),

$$P \propto n^3 D_i^5 \tag{7.6}$$

Then,

$$\frac{P_2}{P_1} = \left(\frac{n_2}{n_1}\right)^3 \left(\frac{D_{i2}}{D_{i1}}\right)^5 \tag{7.7}$$

From Equations (7.5) and (7.7),

$$\frac{P_2}{P_1} = \left(\frac{D_{i2}}{D_{i1}}\right)^{5-3\left(\frac{2\alpha-1}{\alpha}\right)} \tag{7.8}$$

$$\frac{P_2/V_2}{P_1/V_1} = \left(\frac{D_{i2}}{D_{i1}}\right)^{2-3\left(\frac{2\alpha-1}{\alpha}\right)} \tag{7.9}$$

In Fig. 7.2, the left-hand side of Eq. (7.9) is plotted against α, parameters being the scale-up ratio, D_{i2}/D_{i1}. It is apparent from the figure that the "equal power per unit volume" concept can be applied effectively to the scale-up, irrespective of the ratio of D_{i2}/D_{i1}, when the value of α is equal to 0.75.

Despite this observation, it is known from a recent study of liquid agitation that much more power per unit volume is required in gas-liquid agitation as the vessel increases in size, whereas the reverse is true for mass transfer, heat transfer, and liquid droplet dispersion in liquid agitation systems.[13]

It might be inferred from the above discussion that the value of α differs from case to case. It is estimated that the value of α for the mass transfer of oxygen in fermentors would be around 0.75 if the equation is expressed in terms similar to Eq.

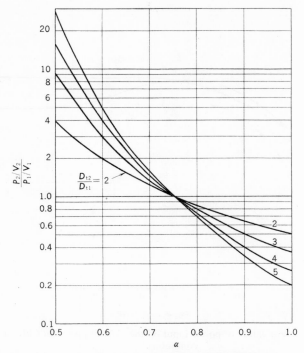

FIG. 7.2. P/V vs. α in scale-up;[12] parameters are scale-up ratio, D_{t_2}/D_{t_1}.

7.4) and if the "equal power per unit volume" concept applies to fermentation systems.

7.1.2.   Examples

Although many people have suggested that the "power per unit volume" concept is useful for scaling-up systems involving liquid agitation, experimental data in support of this are surprisingly scarce. With the recent development of strain gauges which can be applied as torsion dynamometers on agitators, more data on the power consumption in fermentors should soon be available. Figs. 7.3 and 7.4 are examples of fermentations where productivity has been correlated with the power input for different sized fermentors.

The penicillin titre at the 108th hour of fermentation is plotted against power input (HP/m³) in Fig. 7.3; the volumetric ratio of scale-up was 1:10, while the values of v_s were roughly doubled in each fermentor tested. Within the range of these data, it appears that scale-up was successful provided the power input exceeded 1.5 HP/m³. It is also noted from Fig. 7.3 that the yield of penicillin fell sharply with a power input of less than 1.0 HP/m³.

In principle, it is known that the performance of impellers can be assessed accurately, irrespective of the geometrical similarity or dissimilarity of the system, if the power imposed by the impeller on unit volume of agitated liquid is selected

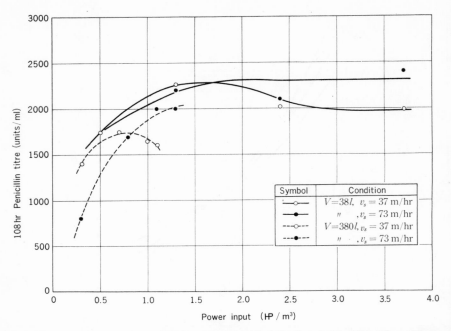

FIG. 7.3.   Effect of different values of power input on the yield of penicillin with different fermentation conditions.[7]

as the basis of comparison.[1] Therefore, the geometrical properties of the system from which the data points of Fig. 7.3 were derived are not of primary importance.

However, in Fig. 7.4, where novobiocin production was related to power input, the above-mentioned fact may not necessarily apply; standard flat blade turbines whose sizes ranged from 2.02 to 3.42 in terms of D_t/D_i were used in this case; it can be seen that the three curves drawn through the data points in Fig. 7.4 are approximately parallel to each other. It is seen from the figure that for equal values of HP/m^3 the larger impeller gave lower yields of novobiocin compared with other sizes of impeller. These experimental facts suggest that the type of mycelium in the fermentation broth may be another factor to be considered in scale-up, besides the factors associated with the hydrodynamical behavior of the broth. It is interesting to note also that values of $\text{HP}/\text{m}^3 > 1.5\ \text{HP}/\text{m}^3$ gave the best yields of antibiotic.

From reports of the values of power input in general use in chemical processes, the degree of liquid agitation with impellers may be classified as follows:[17]

	$P/V\ \text{HP}/\text{m}^3$
mild agitation	$0.3 \sim 1.0$
strong agitation	$1.0 \sim 3.0$

Judging from these figures, penicillin and novobiocin fermentations, where the titres of antibiotic are unaffected by values of HP/m^3, belong to the category of strongly agitated fermentations.

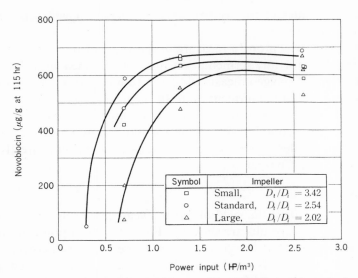

FIG. 7.4.   Effect of different values of power input on the yield of novobiocin in fermentors fitted
with different sized impellers.[10]

7.2.   VOLUMETRIC MASS (OXYGEN)-TRANSFER COEFFICIENT

7.2.1.   Background

As reported earlier, Cooper *et al.* studied oxygen-transfer rates from bubbles into
liquid by the sulfite-oxidation method (see Reference 7 in Chapter 6). Their principal
objective was to present a basis for the rational design and operation of aerators in
various vessels.

The sulfite-oxidation method was first applied to the study of fermentations by
Hixson *et al.*[8] and Bartholomew *et al.*;[3] they correlated the value of the oxygen-
transfer coefficient, measured with the sulfite-oxidation method, with the subsequent
performance of the fermentor during an actual fermentation. Since then, many
people have used the sulfite method to study equipment for various kinds of fermentation.

The physical properties of dilute aqueous solutions of sulfite, with which the
value of the oxygen-transfer coefficient is determined, differ appreciably from those
of fermentation broths. In other words, the values of the oxygen-transfer coefficient
measured by this method may not represent those applicable to fermentation broths.
Nevertheless, there are examples of successful scale-up based on the oxygen-transfer
coefficient measured by the sulfite method (see Figs. 7.5 to 7.9).

The rates of growth and of the formation of product by many microorganisms
are likely to be inhibited if the concentration of dissolved oxygen in the medium
falls below certain critical levels, but microbial activity is unaffected by concentrations of dissolved oxygen above the critical level. It is probable that dissolved

oxygen at lower values of the oxygen-transfer coefficient will become the factor limiting microbial activity.

In the design of fermentors, a measure of the value of the critical concentration of oxygen required for any fermentation may be obtained by using the over-all transfer coefficient of oxygen measured by the sulfite method, and correlating this with the productivity of the fermentation. In the next section, specific cases will be mentioned where this method was applied satisfactorily to scale-up.

To provide a really sound basis for control and design, however, it is preferable to use methods that determine the oxygen-transfer coefficient directly in the fermentation broth (see Chapter 10).

7.2.2. Examples

Strohm *et al.* measured the yield of baker's yeast in vessels with different sulfite oxidation values; these results are shown in Fig. 7.5.[16] Data points in the figure are scattered considerably, but the yield appears to be fairly well correlated with the sulfite oxidation value. This good correlation was a little unexpected, because the experiments were conducted in both geometrically similar and dissimilar vessels, with and without mechanical agitation. The results reported in Fig. 7.5 suggest that the type of fermentor and the method of aeration did not affect the yield of baker's yeast appreciably if the sulfite oxidation value was greater than 150 m moles O_2/liter/hr.

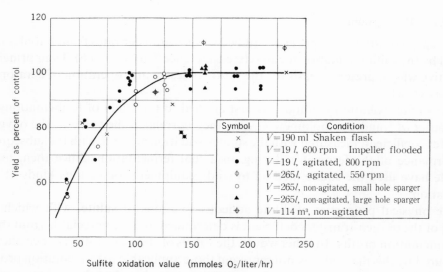

FIG. 7.5.   The effect of sulfite oxidation value on the yield of baker's yeast.[16]

The production of ustilagic acid provides another example of a good correlation between the yield of product and the sulfite oxidation value, as shown in Fig. 7.6.[15] All data in the figure, except one with the + symbol, were obtained using 5-liter fermentors; the yield of ustilagic acid from a medium containing 7.5% glucose monohydrate was determined in fermentations using different degrees of aeration and agitation. The yield was plotted against the corresponding value of sulfite oxidation. Here, the yield increased with increase in sulfite oxidation value, until it approached 125 m moles O_2/liter/hr; above this value, there was no improvement in yield. A similar trend was seen in Fig. 7.5 for the production of baker's yeast.

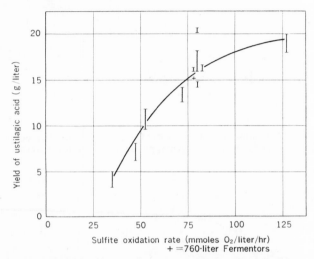

FIG. 7.6.   The effect of sulfite oxidation value on the yield of ustilagic acid.[15]

In Figs. 7.7 to 7.9, the abscissae represent values of K_vp, which is the product of the volumetric oxygen-transfer coefficient by the mean pressure of the incoming air. The principal reason for this representation is to correct for the driving force expressed by the pressure term, because, in large-scale fermentors, the pressure greatly exceeds 1 atmosphere; this results in inconsistencies when comparing the results of large-scale fermentors with those from bench-scale experiments.

In Figs. 7.7 and 7.8, the values of K_v for production equipment were calculated from the empirical equation presented by Cooper et al. (see Eq. (6.38) in Chapter 6).

Although the calculation of K_vp from Eq. (6.38) is only an approximation, the calculated values correlate well with the final titres of streptomycin (Fig. 7.7) and penicillin (Fig. 7.8) obtained experimentally.[9] These figures clearly indicate that above certain minimum values of K_vp, the yields of antibiotic leveled off, as was found in Figs. 7.5 and 7.6. However, these critical values of K_vp are several times larger than those for the baker's yeast and ustilagic acid fermentations, calculated for $p=1$ atm in the data in Figs. 7.5 and 7.6 respectively. It is probable that in penicillin and streptomycin fermentations, a network of hyphae forms and offers greater resistance to oxygen transfer than the single-cell fermentations described in Fig. 7.5. Differences in the way cells grow in a fermentor may offer some explanation of differences in the critical values of K_v observed with different species of

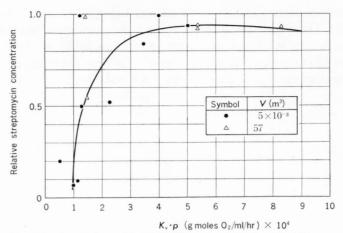

FIG. 7.7. Comparison of the yields of streptomycin at different mass-transfer coefficients of oxygen applying in vessels of different size.[9]

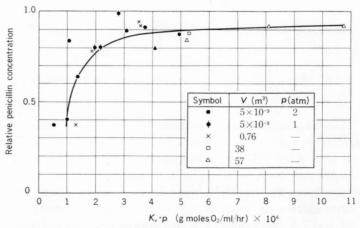

FIG. 7.8. Comparison of the yields of penicillin at different mass-transfer coefficients of oxygen applying in vessels of different size.[9]

microbes. However, this interpretation cannot be applied to the case of *Ustilago zeae*, which produces ustilagic acid; here, the critical value of K_v was about the same as that for yeast (*cf.* Figs. 7.5 and 7.6). It can only be suggested that the form of growth which a fungal mycelium exhibits may be affected considerably by the particular strain in use and by the conditions in the vessel. The data suggest that the penicillin and streptomycin fermentations can be scaled-up from Figs. 7.7 and 7.8 if the aeration rate and agitator speed are fixed such that the values of $K_v p$ calculated from Cooper's equation are beyond the critical value of about (5 to 6) $\times$ 10^{-4} g moles O_2/ml/hr.

In the scale-up of a bacterial fermentation for the production of vitamin B_{12}, some peculiar phenomena were observed by Bartholomew et al.[4] These are shown in Fig. 7.9, where the dotted and solid curves correspond to bench-scale and production-scale fermentors respectively. These two curves imply that scale-up based on the value of $K_v p$ was not satisfactory in this case. However, this conclusion may not be completely reliable, because it is possible to draw a single curve through these same points if a degree of scattering of the data around the curve is accepted.

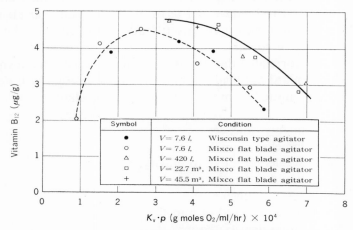

Symbol	Condition	
●	$V = 7.6$ l.	Wisconsin type agitator
○	$V = 7.6$ l.	Mixco flat blade agitator
△	$V = 420$ l.	Mixco flat blade agitator
□	$V = 22.7$ m³,	Mixco flat blade agitator
+	$V = 45.5$ m³,	Mixco flat blade agitator

FIG. 7.9. Yield of vitamin B_{12} in different sized fermentors with different values of mass-transfer coefficient.

The fact that the production of vitamin B_{12} is adversely affected at high values of $K_v p$ is probably more significant. This suggests that the possible advantage of the higher rates of aeration corresponding to high values of $K_v p$ is counterbalanced by damage to the organisms in highly turbulent fermentation broth. At the same time, it can be seen from Fig. 7.9 that the optimum value of K_v ($p=1$) in the bacterial fermentation is similar to the critical value of K_v applying to the production of yeast (see Fig. 7.5), but is quite different from the value of K_v applying to the fungal fermentation.

7.3. MIXING TIME CONCEPT

7.3.1. Significance

Mixing time is defined as the period of time which is needed for a liquid droplet passing into an agitated vessel filled with a fluid with the same physical properties as the droplet to be completely mixed with the bulk of the fluid; the mixing under consideration is at the molecular level. As could be expected, mixing in a small agitated vessel filled with liquid of low viscosity will be instantaneous. However, the time of mixing will markedly increase as the size of the vessel and the viscosity of the fluid are increased.

From a practical point of view, mixing time may serve as a qualitative measure o
the degree of fluid turbulence in a vessel. Even in a series of geometrically simila
vessels of different sizes, mixing time may assist in scale-up when it is necessary to
check the values of mixing times in different sized vessels and to adjust the mixing
conditions in large vessels.

There has been a recent report of experiments where the mixing time, t, was
correlated with the various factors involved in a single agitated vessel or a series of
vessels.[2] In most of these studies the value of t was determined under different
conditions using simple techniques such as the neutralization of an alkaline solution
with acid, electrochemical measurements, (the addition of an electrolyte to a liquid)
or the disappearance of colour.

Norwood et al.[11] correlated the mixing-time factor, ϕ, with the Reynolds number
of the impeller (standard flat blade turbine) as shown in Fig. 7.10. For simplicity,
the data points are omitted from the figure; the nomenclature used in Fig. 7.10 is
as follows:

$$t = \text{mixing time, sec}$$
$$D_i = \text{impeller diameter, m}$$
$$g = \text{acceleration due to gravity, m/sec}^2$$
$$H_L = \text{liquid depth, m}$$
$$D_t = \text{vessel diameter, m}$$
$$n = \text{rotation speed of impeller, 1/sec}$$
$$\rho = \text{liquid density, kg/m}^3$$
$$\mu = \text{liquid viscosity, kg/m sec}$$

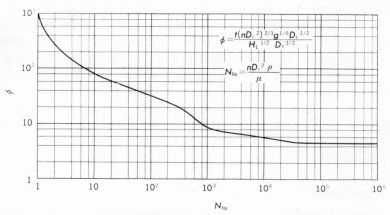

FIG. 7.10. Effect of impeller dimension, impeller speed, and physical
properties of liquid on the mixing time characteristic of a flat blade turbine.[11]

This type of dimensionless correlation was similar to that already published by Fox
et al. for jet mixing and for propeller type of impellers.[6]

These mixing-time data, and those published by other workers, deal exclusively
with Newtonian liquids. Experimental data about non-Newtonian fluids are needed,

especially with regard to the behavior and scale-up of mycelial fermentations which usually exhibit non-Newtonian characteristics.

It is interesting to note that the curve in Fig. 7.10 resembles that of N_P (the Power number) vs. N_{Re} (the Reynolds number) shown in Fig. 6.4 in Chapter 6, and moreover, that $\phi \doteqdot 6$ at higher values of N_{Re} corresponds with the situation where $N_P \doteqdot 6$ in the turbulent region of the power chart for a standard flat blade turbine.

Table 7.1 illustrates the values of t for geometrically similar vessels and shows the difference in values of t as the size of vessel and the rotation speed of the impeller are increased.

TABLE 7.1

VALUES OF MIXING TIME, t, AT DIFFERENT IMPELLER SPEEDS IN 5-LITER AND 40,000-LITER VESSELS.*

N (rpm)	Mixing Time, t, sec			
	$\phi = 100$ (Laminar Region)		$\phi = 6$ (Turbulent Region)	
	3 liter	24,000 liter	3 liter	24,000 liter
30	680	1,100	40	66
60	417	683	35	41
120	260	425	16	26
300	140	230	9	14
750	73	118	5	8

* Provided: $H_L = 1.2 D_t$, $D_i = (1/3) D_t$, $V_1 = 3$ liter, and $V_2 = 24,000$ liter.

7.3.2. Discussion of the above three indices for scale-up

As was stated in Section 7.1, the following discussion will assume that the power, P, consumed by ungassed systems is proportional to the power, P_g, consumed in gassed systems, provided geometrically similar fermentor vessels are used; it is also assumed that the physical properties of the liquids in the vessels remain constant.

In turbulent conditions in agitated vessels,

$$\frac{P_1}{N_1^3 D_{i1}^5} = \frac{P_2}{N_2^3 D_{i2}^5} \qquad \text{(see Eq. (6.22) in Chapter 6)}$$

Since $D_i \propto D_t$,

$$\frac{P_1}{D_{t1}^3} \frac{D_{t1}}{N_1^3 D_{t1}^3} = \frac{P_2}{D_{t2}^3} \frac{D_{t2}}{N_2^3 D_{t2}^3}$$

From the concept of equal power per unit volume of liquid,

$$\frac{P_1}{D_{t1}^3} = \frac{P_2}{D_{t2}^3}$$

Then,

$$\frac{N_1 D_{t1}}{N_2 D_{t2}} = \frac{N_1 D_{i1}}{N_2 D_{i2}} = \frac{\text{(Tip velocity of impeller)}_1}{\text{(Tip velocity of impeller)}_2}$$

$$= \left(\frac{D_{t1}}{D_{t2}}\right)^{1/3} \tag{7.10}$$

Eq. (7.10) shows that the tip velocity of the impeller which is a measure of the liquid velocity in an agitated vessel increases with the cube root of the ratio of the diameters of the two vessels. For example,

$$V_1 = 3 \text{ liter}, \quad V_2 = 24{,}000 \text{ liter}$$

$$\frac{D_{t1}}{D_{t2}} = \left(\frac{3}{24{,}000}\right)^{1/3} = \frac{1}{20}$$

$$N_2 D_{i2} = N_1 D_{i1}\left(\frac{D_{t2}}{D_{t1}}\right)^{1/3} = N_1 D_{i1} \times 20^{1/3}$$

$$\doteq 2.72 N_1 D_{i1}$$

The representative velocity of the liquid in the larger vessel ($V_2 = 24{,}000$ liter) is about three times greater than that of the smaller one ($V_1 = 3$ liter). Therefore, if scale-up is attempted on the basis of equal power per unit volume of liquid, the tip velocity or representative liquid velocity increases appreciably with increase in the scale-up ratio. The increase of liquid velocity beyond a certain limit may, however, affect microbial activity in some fermentations. In the studies of the production of vitamin B_{12} shown in Fig. 7.9, it was seen that equal values of K_v obtained in different sized vessels did not provide a satisfactory basis for scale-up. Incidentally these equal values of K_v approximately correspond to equal values of P/V; the introduction to this chapter and Eq. (6.38) in Chapter 6 suggest that this basis for scale-up does not always lead to a successful result. In the vitamin B_{12} fermentation, the organisms may have been damaged by the high liquid velocity which accompanied increase in the scale-up ratio.

If the same assumptions as were outlined at the beginning of this section are made about geometrically similar vessels and turbulent conditions in agitated liquid, the following equation relating to the mixing time, t, may be derived from Fig. 7.10:

$$t n^{\frac{2}{3}} D_t^{-\frac{1}{6}} = \text{constant} \tag{7.11}$$

Eq. (7.12) below is another form of expression of equal power per unit volume of liquid.

$$n^3 D_t^2 = \text{constant} \tag{7.12}$$

Cancelling n from Equations (7.11) and (7.12),

$$t_2 = t_1\left(\frac{D_{t2}}{D_{t1}}\right)^{11/18} \tag{7.13}$$

Table 7.2 clearly indicates that the "power per unit volume" concept cannot always be applied to large ratios of scale-up, since the values of t in large vessels are greatly increased compared with those in small ones. If a fermentation can be scaled-up successfully, say from 5 liter to 40,000 liter, on the basis of equal power per unit liquid volume, the fermentation concerned is probably one which is less sensitive to the inevitable increase in the velocity at the tip of the impeller and the mixing time.

TABLE 7.2

SCALE-UP VS. MIXING TIME.

Scale-up Ratio (Volumetric)	Ratio of Diameters of the Vessels (D_{t2}/D_{t1})	Ratio of Mixing Times $\left(\dfrac{t_2}{t_1}\right)^*$
8,000	20	6.3
1,000	10	4.1
125	5	2.7
64	4	2.4
27	3	2.0
8	2	1.5

* From Eq. (7.13)

7.4. INTRODUCTORY COMMENTS ON NON-NEWTONIAN FLUIDS

7.4.1. Definition

The viscosity of Newtonian fluids is defined as follows:

$$\tau = \mu \frac{dv}{dr} \tag{7.14}$$

where

μ = liquid viscosity
τ = shear stress
dv/dr = velocity gradient = shear rate

The value of μ in a Newtonian fluid is independent of shear rate, dv/dr, and is usually dependent on the temperature of the fluid. Therefore, in a plot of τ against dv/dr as shown in Fig. 7.11, the flow characteristic of a Newtonian fluid is represented by a straight line passing through the origin of the figure; the tangent, δ_1, is equal to the fluid viscosity, μ.

On the other hand, there are materials that have other flow characteristics; fluids with flow curves exhibiting shapes other than the straight line passing through the origin are called non-Newtonian. Such characteristic curves have been designated

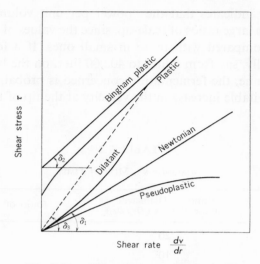

FIG. 7.11.   Shear stress vs. shear rate. Flow
curves of non-Newtonian and Newtonian fluids.

as Bingham plastic, plastic, pseudoplastic, and dilatant (see Fig. 7.11). The flow
curve for a Bingham plastic is expressed as follows:

$$\tau - \tau_y = \eta \left(\frac{dv}{dr} \right) \tag{7.15}$$

where

τ_y = yield value of stress, which means that the fluid will not "flow"
unless a stress larger than τ_y is imposed upon it

η = coefficient of rigidity or plastic viscosity, the value of which is independent of dv/dr

If the value of apparent viscosity, μ_a, is defined by the tangent of the angle subtended between the abscissa and an imaginary straight line connecting any point on
the non-Newtonian flow curves with the origin of Fig. 7.11, it can be seen from the
figure that the value of μ_a is dependent on dv/dr. For Bingham plastic, plastic,
and pseudoplastic fluids, the values of μ_a will decrease with increase of dv/dr; the
situation is reversed in a dilatant fluid.

In some non-Newtonian fluids, the flow curves may be approximated by:

$$\tau = K \left(\frac{dv}{dr} \right)^{n'} \tag{7.16}$$

where

K = consistency index
n' = flow behavior index

Flow curves like those illustrated in Fig. 7.11 are usually determined with one of
the rotational types of viscometer (cf. Chapter 10).

Another type of non-Newtonian flow, not shown in Fig. 7.11, is called thixotropic flow. Such fluids exhibit a hysteresis loop (the curve of viscosity obtained when dv/dr is increased gradually differs from that obtained by the reverse procedure).

Generally, mycelial fermentation broths exhibit non-Newtonian characters, but only a few rheological studies of these broths have been published so far.[5,14]

7.4.2.   Non-Newtonian characteristics of fermentation broths

The rheological character of *Streptomyces griseus* broth is shown in Fig. 7.12, in which the viscometer reading (corresponding to shear stress) is plotted against the shear rate, which was represented by the rotation speed of the viscometer.[14] It can be seen by comparison with Fig. 7.11 that this flow curve belongs to the category of pseudoplastic flow. For simplicity of analysis and calculation, the curve will be assumed to be a straight line at lower values of shear rate, extrapolating to the ordinate with a broken line as shown in the figure; the broth thus simulates a Bingham plastic.

Assuming that the *Streptomyces griseus* broth behaves like a Bingham plastic, if the values of η and τ_y are determined in broth sampled at intervals during the fermentation and plotted against time, θ, the results are as shown in Figs. 7.13 and 7.14 respectively. It is seen from the figures that the values of both η and τ_y are

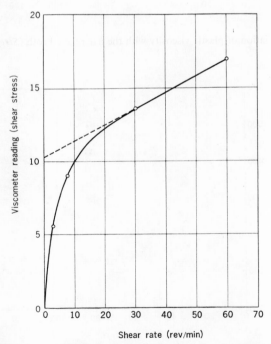

FIG. 7.12.   Non-Newtonian character of *Streptomyces griseus* broth.[14]

closely dependent on the age of the mycelium. The clear dependence of η and τ_y o
the stage of the fermentation may permit such curves to be used to gauge the pro
gress of the fermentation, in other words, as a means of controlling the fermentation
(*cf.* Chapter 10).

Although there are examples (see Figs. 7.3, 7.7, and 7.8) where the scale-up o

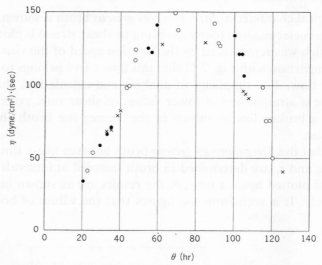

FIG. 7.13. Variation of plastic viscosity with the age of the broth (*Streptomyces griseus*).

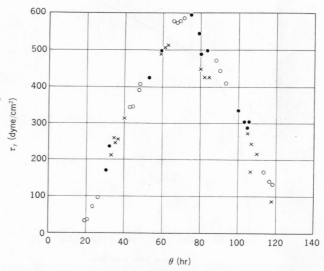

FIG. 7.14. Variation of yield stress with the age of the broth (*Streptomyces griseus*).

ycelial fermentations has been accomplished successfully using as a basis either
ne power input per unit volume or the over-all oxygen-transfer coefficient, this
oes not preclude further study of the scale-up of non-Newtonian fermentation
roths. On the contrary, much more information about properties like oxygen-
ransfer rates in bubble aeration, bubble motion, and mixing time in non-New-
onian fermentation broths are needed to provide a better understanding of scale-
p as a whole.

7.5. DESIGN EXAMPLE OF SCALE-UP

The optimum conditions for a bacterial fermentation were established with a
ench-scale fermentor, 30 liter, as follows:

$$V_1 = 18 \text{ liter}$$

$$\left[\frac{Q}{V}\right]_1 = 1.0 \text{ vvm}$$

$$K_v p = 250 \text{ m mole } O_2/\text{hr/liter (sulfite oxidation value)}$$

$$H_L = 1.2 \, D_t$$

Impeller: standard flat blade turbine (Two sets)

$$D_i = 1/3 \, D_t$$

Production is to be transferred to a large fermentor (40,000 liter) and it is desired
o estimate the operating conditions required for the production fermentor,
specially the rotation speed of impeller and the power requirements, assuming
he physical properties of the broth are the same as those of water at room
emperatures in the scale-up calculation.

Solution

$$V_1 = \frac{\pi}{4} D_{t1}^2 H_{L1} = 1.2 \frac{\pi}{4} D_{t1}^3$$

$$D_{t1} = \left(\frac{V_1}{1.2(\pi/4)}\right)^{1/3} = \left(\frac{30,000 \times 0.6^*}{1.2 \times 0.785}\right)^{1/3}$$

$$= 26.7 \text{ cm} = 0.267 \text{ m}$$

$$D_{t2} = \left(\frac{V_2}{1.2(\pi/4)}\right)^{1/3} = \left(\frac{40 \times 0.6}{1.2 \times 0.785}\right)^{1/3}$$

$$= 2.94 \text{ m}$$

$$H_{L2} = 1.2 \times 2.94 = 3.52 \text{ m}$$

Assuming that Eq. (7.3) can be used in this case,

$$\left[\frac{Q}{V}\right]_2 = \left[\frac{Q}{V}\right]_1 \left(\frac{H_{L2}}{H_{L1}}\right)^{-2/3}$$

Actual working volume is assumed to be 60% of the nominal volume.

$$= \left[\frac{Q}{V}\right]_1 \left(\frac{D_{t2}}{D_{t1}}\right)^{-2/3} = 1 \times \left(\frac{2.94}{0.267}\right)^{-2/3}$$

$$= 0.202 \text{ vvm}$$

$$(v_S)_2 = \frac{Q_2}{(\pi/4)\,D_{t2}^2} = \frac{0.202 V_2 \times 60}{(\pi/4)\,D_{t2}^2} = \frac{0.202 \times 24 \times 60}{0.785 \times (2.94)^2}$$

$$= 42.7 \text{ m/hr}$$

$$[K_v p]_1 = 250 \frac{\text{m mole } O_2}{\text{hr liter}}$$

$$= 250 \frac{10^{-6} \text{ kg mole } O_2}{\text{hr } 10^{-3} \text{ m}^3}$$

$$= 2.5 \times 10^{-1} \frac{\text{kg mole } O_2}{\text{hr m}^3} = [K_v p]_2$$

$$p_2 = \frac{1 + \left(1 + \dfrac{H_{L2}}{10.3}\right)}{2} = \frac{1 + \left(1 + \dfrac{3.52}{10.3}\right)}{2} = 1.17 \text{ atm}$$

$$[K_v]_2 = \frac{2.5 \times 10^{-1}}{1.17} = 2.14 \times 10^{-1} \frac{\text{kg mole } O_2}{\text{hr m}^3 \text{ atm}}$$

$$[K_v]_2 = K_{v2} f_c$$

$$= K_{v2} \times 1.1 \qquad \text{(see Fig. 6.10)}$$

$$[K_v]_2 = \frac{2.14 \times 10^{-1}}{1.1} = 1.94 \times 10^{-1} \frac{\text{kg mole } O_2}{\text{hr m}^3 \text{ atm}}$$

From Eq. (6.38) in Chapter 6,

$$1.94 \times 10^{-1} = 0.0635 \left(\frac{P_g}{V}\right)_2^{0.95} (v_s)_2^{0.67}$$

$$\left(\frac{P_g}{V}\right)_2^{0.95} = \frac{1.94 \times 10^{-1}}{0.0635 \times (42.7)^{0.67}} = 2.47 \times 10^{-1}$$

$$(P_g)_2 = (2.47 \times 10^{-1})^{\frac{1}{0.95}} \times 24 = 5.51 \text{ HP}$$

Assuming that,

$$\left(\frac{Pg_c}{n^3 D_{i\ell}^5 \rho}\right)_2 = 6$$

$$(P)_2 = \frac{6 n^3 \left(\dfrac{2.94}{3}\right)^5 \times 10^3}{9.81} = 552 \times n^3 \text{ Kg m/sec}$$

$$= 7.26 \times n^3 \text{ HP}$$

$$\therefore \quad \left(\frac{P_g}{P}\right)_2 = \frac{5.51}{7.26 \times n^3} = 0.759 \times \frac{1}{n^3} \qquad (7.17)$$

On the other hand, from Eq. (6.23) in Chapter 6,

$$N_a = \frac{Q_2}{60n\left(\frac{2.94}{3}\right)^3} = \frac{0.202 \times 24}{60n\left(\frac{2.94}{3}\right)^3} = 8.60 \times 10^{-2} \times \frac{1}{n} \qquad (7.18)$$

From Equations (7.17) and (7.18) and Curve A in Fig. 6.5 in Chapter 6, the value of n (rotation speed of the impeller in the large vessel) was found by a trial and error method as follows:

Take,

$$n = 1.05 \text{ rps}$$

From Eq. (7.18),

$$N_a = 8.60 \times 10^{-2} \times \frac{1}{1.05} = 8.20 \times 10^{-2}$$

From Eq. (7.17),

$$\left(\frac{P_g}{P}\right)_2 = 0.759 \times \frac{1}{(1.05)^3} = 0.656$$

From Fig. 6.5,

$$\left(\frac{P_g}{P}\right)_2 = 0.62$$

$$\therefore \quad N = 1.05 \times 60 = 63 \text{ rpm}$$

$$(P)_2 = \frac{5.51}{0.62} = 8.9 \text{ P}$$

$$\left(\frac{P_g}{V}\right)_2 = \frac{5.51}{24} = 0.23 \text{ P/m}^3 > 0.1 \text{ P/m}^3$$

$$\left(\frac{nD_i^2\rho}{\mu}\right)_2 = \frac{1.05 \times (0.98)^2 \times 10^3}{10^{-3}} \doteq 10^6$$

Therefore, the use of both Eq. (6.38) and the Power number $= 6$ is permissible. However, the application of Eq. (7.3) and Fig. 6.5 to this problem is only an approximation, since the former deals with an estimation of aeration rate in a system without mechanical agitation, while the latter is relevant to a fermentor with only one impeller. Despite the approximations adopted, these are not considered to introduce grave errors in calculation.

NOMENCLATURE

$b =$ empirical exponent
$C_p =$ specific heat, kcal/kg °C
$d_B =$ bubble size, m
$D =$ molecular diffusivity, m²/sec
$D_i =$ impeller diameter, m
$D_t =$ vessel diameter, m

g = acceleration due to gravity, m/sec^2
g_c = conversion factor, kg m/Kg sec^2
H_L = liquid depth, m
h = heat-transfer coefficient, kcal/m^2 hr °C
k = thermal conductivity, kcal/m hr °C
K_v = volumetric oxygen-transfer coefficient, kg mole O_2/m^3 hr atm
k_L = mass-transfer coefficient, m/hr
$k_L a$ = volumetric mass (oxygen)-transfer coefficient, 1/hr
K = consistency index, g cm^{-1} sec$^{n'-2}$
n = rotation speed of impeller, 1/sec
n' = flow behavior index
N = rotation speed of impeller, 1/min
N_a = aeration number
N_P = Power number $\left(= \dfrac{P g_c}{n^3 D_i^5 \rho} \right)$
N_{Re} = Reynolds number $\left(= \dfrac{n D_i^2 \rho}{\mu} \right)$
N_{Sh} = Sherwod number $\left(= \dfrac{k_L D_i}{D} \right)$
N_{Nu} = Nusselt number $\left(= \dfrac{h D_i}{k} \right)$
p = pressure of gas, atm
P = power consumed for agitation in ungassed system, Kg m/sec, HP
P_g = power consumed for agitation in gassed system, Kg m/sec, HP
Q = aeration rate, m^3/sec, m^3/min
t = mixing time, sec
v_s = nominal air velocity, m/hr
dv/dr = shear rate, 1/sec
V = liquid volume, m^3

subscripts: 1,2
    small and large vessels respectively

Greek letters
α = experimental exponent
γ = experimental exponent
δ = angle subtended between τ and dv/dr (Fig. 7.11)
η = plastic viscosity, dyne/cm^2 sec (Fig. 7.13), g/cm sec
θ = fermentation time, hr
μ = liquid viscosity, kg/m sec
μ_a = apparent viscosity, kg/m sec
ρ = liquid density, kg/m^3
τ = shear stress, dyne/cm^2, g/cm sec^2
τ_y = yield value of shear stress, dyne/cm^2 (Fig. 7.14)
ϕ = mixing-time factor, dimensionless

REFERENCES

1. AIBA, S. (1957). "Reassessment of heat and mass transfer data in agitation, as viewed, in particular, from the point of liquid flow pattern." *Chem. Eng. (Japan)* **21**, 130.

2. AIBA, S., SUZUKI, K., and KITAI, S. (1963). "Mixing time studies with non-Newtonian and Newtonian fluids." *Progress Rept. No. 27* Biochem. Eng. Lab., Univ. of Tokyo.

3. BARTHOLOMEW, W.H., KAROW, E.O., SFAT, M.R., and WILHELM, R.H. (1950). "Oxygen transfer and agitation in submerged fermentations." *Ind. Eng. Chem.* **42**, 1801.

4. BARTHOLOMEW, W.H. (1960). "Scale-up of submerged fermentation." *Advances in Applied Microbiology* (Ed.). UMBREIT, W.W. **2**, 289. Academic, N.Y.

5. DEINDOERFER, F.H., and WEST, J.M. (1960). "Rheological examination of some fermentation broths." *J. Biochem. Microbiol. Tech. & Eng.* **2**, 165.

6. FOX, E.A., and GEX, V.E. (1956). "Single-phase blending of liquids." *A.I.Ch.E. Journal* **2**, 539.

7. GADEN, E.L., JR. (1961). "Aeration and agitation in fermentation." *Sci. Repts. Istituto Superiore di Sanita* **1**, 161.

8. HIXSON, A.W., and GADEN, E.L., JR. (1950). "Oxygen transfer in submerged fermentation." *Ind. Eng. Chem.* **42**, 1792.

9. KAROW, E.O., BARTHOLOMEW, W.H., and SFAT, M.R. (1953). "Oxygen transfer and agitation in submerged fermentations." *J. Agr. Food Chem.* **1**, 302.

10. MAXON, W.D. (1959). "Aeration-agitation studies on the novobiocin fermentation." *J. Biochem. Microbiol. Tech. & Eng.* **1**, 311.

11. NORWOOD, K.W., and METZNER, A.B. (1960). "Flow patterns and mixing rates in agitated vessels." *A.I.Ch.E. Journal* **6**, 432.

12. RUSHTON, J.H. (1951). "The use of pilot plant mixing data." *Chem. Eng. Progress* **47**, 485.

13. RUSHTON, J.H. (1962). Comment presented at the 25th Anniversary of Soc. Chem. Eng. (Japan). *Chem. Eng. (Japan)* **26**, 958.

14. RICHARDS, J.W. (1961). "Studies in aeration and agitation." *Progress in Industrial Microbiology* **3**, 143.

15. ROXBURGH, J.M., SPENCER, J.F.T., and SALANS, H.R. (1954). "Factors affecting the production of ustilagic acid by *Ustilago zeae*." *J. Agr. Food Chem.* **2**, 1121.

16. STROHM, J., DALE, H.F., and PEPPLER, H.J. (1959). "Polarographic measurement of dissolved oxygen in yeast fermentation." *Appl. Microbiol.* **7**, 235.

17. Society of Chem. Eng. (Japan)
    Sub-committee of liquid mixing survey (1956). "Survey of agitators used in the chemical industry in Japan." *Chem. Eng. (Japan)* **20**, 634.

CHAPTER 8

MEDIA STERILIZATION

Microorganisms can be removed from fluids by mechanical methods, for example, by filtration, centrifugation, flotation, or electrostatically. They may also be destroyed by heat, chemical agents, or electromagnetic waves. Although cells may be disrupted and killed by mechanical abrasion on a small scale, this method is not satisfactory industrially. Similarly, X-rays, β-rays, ultra-violet light, and sonic radiations, while useful for laboratory purposes, are not applicable to the sterilization of large volumes of fluids. γ-rays on the other hand may prove useful, particularly in the food industry.

FIG. 8.1.　Continuous Media Sterilizer for Fermentors (60 m³).
Pipe diameter = 314 mm *i.d.*
Pipe length　　= 45.8 m
(*Courtesy　　Ajinomoto Co., Kawasaki.*)

Antibacterial agents have an important place in the fermentation industry, particularly for the production of a pure-water supply but have little application for the sterilization of fermentation media. Therefore, a discussion of antibacterial chemicals is beyond the scope of this book. This chapter will be confined to a discussion of the application of moist heat to fermentation media. Despite the fact that heat sterilization of media is the most common method, little attention has been paid until recently to the engineering aspects of heat sterilization.[4]
Interest in continuous methods of sterilizing media is increasing, but for the

successful operation of a continuous sterilizer, foaming of the medium must be carefully controlled and the viscosity of the media must be relatively low.[7] The advantages of continuous sterilization of media are as follows:

(1) Increase of productivity since the short period of exposure to heat minimizes damage to media constituents,
(2) Better control of quality,
(3) Leveling of the demand for process steam,
(4) Suitability for automatic control.

At present, most media in the fermentation industry are sterilized by batch methods. Over-exposure of the medium to heat is inherent in batch-sterilization processes. Procedures which minimize damage to the medium will be outlined later, but before discussing the design and operation of equipment for sterilizing media, the concept of thermal death of microorganisms will be introduced. This is important since the rational design of sterilizers must be based on knowledge of the kinetics of the death of microorganisms. Although it is known that metallic ions, amino acids, and the pH of the medium all affect the resistance of microorganisms to heat, detailed discussions of these topics are beyond the scope of this book (see reference 1).

8.1. THERMAL DEATH OF MICROORGANISMS

8.1.1. Theory

The destruction of microorganisms by heat implies loss of viability, not destruction in the physical sense. The destruction of organisms by heat at a specific temperature follows a monomolecular rate of reaction as shown in Eq. (8.1).

$$\frac{dN}{d\theta} = -kN \qquad (8.1)$$

where

k = reaction rate constant, min^{-1} (function of temperature; see Section 8.1.2)
N = number of viable organisms
θ = time

Microbiologists sometimes prefer the term decimal reduction time, D, meaning the time of exposure to heat during which the original number of viable microbes is reduced by one-tenth.[2] Integrating Eq. (8.1) under the condition of

$$N = N_0 \quad \text{at } \theta = 0$$
$$N = N_0 e^{-k\theta} \qquad (8.2)$$

From the above definition of D,

$$\frac{N}{N_0} = \frac{1}{10} = e^{-kD}$$

$$D = \frac{2.303}{k} \qquad (8.3)$$

It is well known that spores are much more resistant to heat than are vegetative cells; in other words, k values for vegetative cells are much greater than those for spores. Although some workers consider that the dipicolinic acid present in spores may be responsible for their increased resistance to heat,[1] further study is necessary before definite conclusions can be drawn as to the mechanism of their increased resistance to heat.

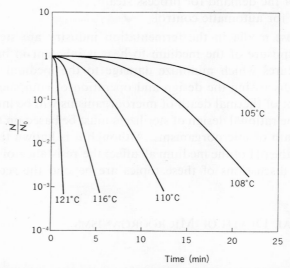

FIG. 8.2. Typical death rate data for spores of *Bacillus stearothermophilus* Fs 7954 in distilled water, where N=number of viable spores at any time, N_0=original number of viable spores.

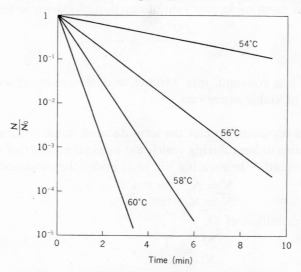

FIG. 8.3. Typical death rate data for *E. coli* in buffer,
where N=number of viable cells at any time
and N_0=original number of viable cells.

Figs. 8.2 and 8.3 show typical death rate data for bacterial spores and vegetative cells respectively; the parameters are different temperatures. For simplicity,
data points have been excluded from these figures. It is apparent from Figs. 8.2 and
8.3 that the resistance of bacterial spores to heat is much more marked than that
of vegetative cells. It is clear from Fig. 8.2 that the logarithmic rate of death, as
stated in Eq. (8.1), does not always hold for bacterial spores, particularly during the
short period immediately following exposure to heat. On the contrary, there are
cases reported where the number of viable spores actually increased immediately
after exposure to heat and then dropped sharply as sterilization proceeded. This
deviation from the logarithmic rate of death is ascribed to the "activation" of
dormant spores by heat, but these phenomena are not fully understood.

8.1.2.   Effect of temperature on specific death rate

The effect of temperature on the values of the reaction rate constant, k, is exemplified in Figs. 8.4 (bacterial spores) and 8.5 (vegetative cells). In both figures the
values of k are plotted against reciprocals of absolute temperature, $1/T$. Although
the data points are scattered considerably in the case of vegetative cells (Fig. 8.5),
a linear correlation between k and $1/T$ is shown in these figures.

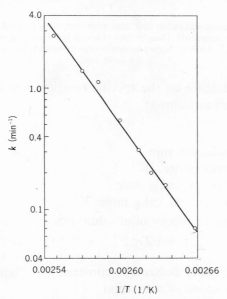

FIG. 8.4.   Correlation of isothermal death rate data for *Bacillus stearothermophilus* Fs 7954,
where $k=$ reaction rate constant and $T=$ absolute temperature.

Regarding the vegetative cells of *E. coli* (Fig. 8.5), two methods of determining
k values were used as indicated in the figure. Since the temperature range for in-
activating vegetative cells is considerably lower than that for spores, some elaborate
techniques are necessary before reliable estimates of k can be obtained. Experimental techniques for measuring k values will be discussed in the following section.

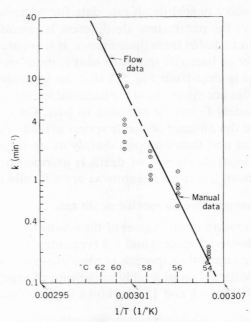

FIG. 8.5.   Correlation of isothermal death rate data with temperature for *E. coli*, where $k=$reaction rate constant and $T=$absolute temperature. Data points at lower temperatures were measured with apparatus like that described in Fig. 8.7, while at higher temperatures apparatus like that described in Figs. 8.8 and 8.9 were used.

The effect of temperature on the specific reaction rate k may be expressed by the Arrhenius equation as follows:

$$k = ae^{-E/RT}$$

(8.4)

where

a = empirical constant, min^{-1}

T = absolute temperature, °K

E = activation energy, cal/g mole

R = gas constant = 1.98, cal/g mole °K

On the basis of Eyring's theory of absolute reaction rate,

$$k = gTe^{-\Delta H^*/RT} e^{\Delta S^*/R}$$
(see Eq. (4.32))   (8.5)

where

g = factor including Boltzmann constant and Planck's constant

ΔH^* = heat of reaction of activation

ΔS^* = entropy change of activation

In 1921, Bigelow published the Q_{10} theory[2] which said

$$D = a' e^{-b't}$$

(8.6)

where

a', b' = empirical constants

t = temperature

Thus, the value of the reaction rate constant, k, may be calculated by Eq. (8.4) or Eq. (8.5), and the value of the decimal reduction time, D, may be calculated by Eq. (8.6), and the relation of D to k is given in Eq. (8.3). To determine whether these different bases of calculation give significantly different results, an organism that has D equal to 7.18 min at 115°C and equal to 2.27 min at 126.5°C will be used for the comparison of calculations; ΔS^* in Eq. (8.5) is assumed to be independent of temperature.

In Fig. 8.6, the calculated values of D are plotted against temperature, t; this shows the values of D calculated from k using the Arrhenius theory (Eq. (8.4)) or the Eyring theory (Eq. (8.5)) are not significantly different from each other. Eq. (8.6), based on the Q_{10} theory, however, cannot be used to calculate D over a wide range of temperatures.

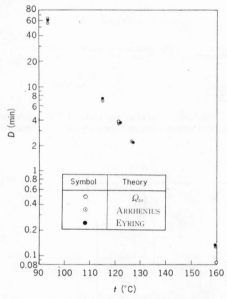

FIG. 8.6. Comparison of the Arrhenius, Eyring, and Q_{10} theories for the calculation of the decimal reduction time, D. Here D is plotted against temperature, t.

8.1.3. Experimental determination of microbial death rate

The important points in determining microbial death rates are that
(1) the cell or spore suspension must be free of aggregates,
(2) there must be no lag in heating or cooling the samples under examination,
(3) the composition and pH value of the suspending medium must be such as to have the minimum inhibitory effect on the test organism in order to isolate the effect of temperature on the death rate of the organism.

It has been observed by many workers that clumps of spores or cells have increased resistance to heat compared with single cells. Accordingly, each suspension should be filtered to remove clumps and its uniformity checked microscopically.

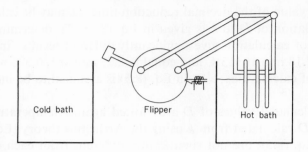

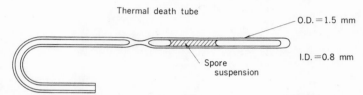

Thermal death tube

O.D. = 1.5 mm

I.D. = 0.8 mm

Spore
suspension

Fig. 8.7.   Manually operated apparatus for the determination
of thermal death rates at relatively low temperatures.

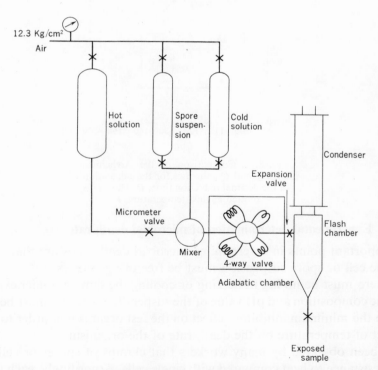

12.3 Kg/cm²

Air

Hot
solution

Spore
suspen-
sion

Cold
solution

Condenser

Expansion
valve

Micrometer
valve

Flash
chamber

Mixer

4-way valve

Adiabatic chamber

Exposed
sample

Fig. 8.8.   Apparatus, operated by air pressure with a flash-cooling chamber,
used for the determination of thermal death rates of organisms.

The problem of lag in the time to heat and cool samples may be solved with the apparatus shown in Figs. 8.7 to 8.9.

In Fig. 8.7, the test suspension is sealed in a capillary and a number of capillaries hung over a cage on a "flipper" arm. The "flipper" allows the capillaries to be dipped into either a hot or a cold bath for a given time; the small volume in the capillary minimizes the time lag for the temperature to increase or decrease in the sample. This kind of apparatus can be operated manually and is suitable for experiments at lower temperatures (cf. Fig. 8.5). The number of viable organisms before and after exposure to elevated temperatures is usually determined biologically with a plate count.

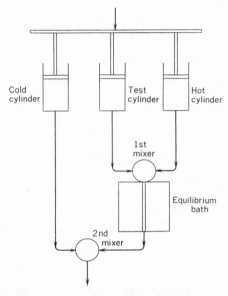

FIG. 8.9. Apparatus, operated by air pressure with a mixing chamber and an equilibrium bath, used for the determination of thermal death rates of organisms.

More elaborate methods to avoid the lag in change of temperature are shown in Figs. 8.8 and 8.9. In the former example, the spore suspension is mixed with either a hot or a cold solution, the volume of each solution depending on the temperature desired. After the mixing, the suspension passes through an adiabatic chamber where its retention time is controlled by a 4-way valve as seen in the figure; the sample is cooled instantly in a flash chamber.

The apparatus shown in Fig. 8.9 is similar in principle; heating or cooling of the sample is achieved by mixing it with either a hot or a cold solution in a test cylinder as shown in Fig. 8.9. The time of exposure of the sample to a particular temperature can be adjusted by controlling the velocity of the sample through the equilibrium bath.

TABLE 8.1

THE REACTION RATE CONSTANTS (k) AND DECIMAL REDUCTION TIMES (D)
OF SPORES OF DIFFERENT BACTERIA SUSPENDED IN BUFFER AT 121 °C.

Species	k at 121 °C (min^{-1})	D at 121 °C (min)
Bacillus subtilis FS 5230	~3.8 – 2.6~	~0.6 – 0.9~
Bacillus stearothermophilus FS 1518	~0.77~	~3.0~
Bacillus stearothermophilus FS 617	~2.9~	~0.8~
Clostridium sporogenes PA 3679	~1.8~	~1.3~

8.2.   USE OF MICROBIAL DEATH RATE AND LEVEL OF CONTAMINATION IN THE DESIGN OF STERILIZING EQUIPMENT

It may be concluded that the value of k for bacterial spores is of the order of 1 min^{-1} at 121°C. On the other hand, it is difficult to give accurate values of k for vegetative cells at 121°C, as they lose viability almost instantaneously at this temperature; from Fig. 8.5, the value of k at 121°C for *E. coli* is of the order of 10^{13} min^{-1}.

Other values of k at 121°C for vegetative cells vary from 10 to about 10^{10} depending on the particular organism.

The value of E (activation energy) in Eq. (8.4) is considered to range from 50 to about 100 kcal/g mole with respect to vegetative cells and spores. These figures are considerably larger than those for enzymes or vitamins which are in a range 2 to 20 kcal/g mole.

To design a sterilizer, it is necessary to establish the degree of residual contamination which is acceptable for a particular fermentation.

Fig. 8.10 shows the reduction of a microbial population in a medium, assuming that there are 10^5 vegetative cells/ml and 10^2 spores/ml of medium, that the total volume of the medium is 10^8 ml, and that the temperature is 121°C. The death rates of vegetative cells and spores are assumed to be 10 and 1 min^{-1} respectively. This figure shows that the time required for sterilization should obviously be based on the time required to reduce the number of viable spores to the desired limit.

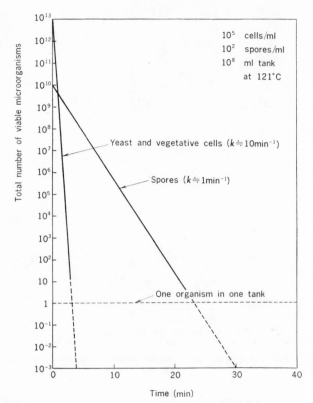

FIG. 8.10.   Destruction of vegetative cells ($k=10$ min^{-1}) and spores ($k=1$ min^{-1}) with time. Original population, 10^5 vegetative cells/ml and 10^2 spores/ml in a tank of 10^8 ml.

Although it may be debated whether death rate curves should be extrapolated over such a wide range of population, the logarithmic death rate will be assumed to apply irrespective of the numbers of organisms originally present (N_0).

It is impossible to fix a level of sterility which will apply to media for all types of fermentation. In future calculations it will be assumed, however, that microbial contamination must be reduced to the level where one viable organism remains per 1,000 tanks processed.

8.3.   Batch Sterilization of Media

8.3.1.   Temperature-time profile and design calculation

Fig. 8.11 shows different types of equipment for the batch sterilization of media, while Table 8.2 summarizes the design equations with which the temperature-time profile can be calculated for each type of equipment. Heat losses are neglected in these equations.

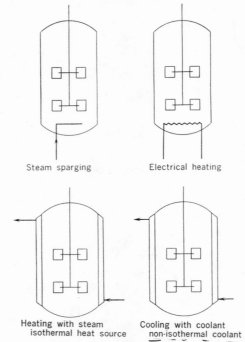

Steam sparging   Electrical heating

Heating with steam   Cooling with coolant
isothermal heat source   non-isothermal coolant

FIG. 8.11. Types of equipment for batch sterilization of media.[5]

From Equations (8.1) and (8.4),

$$\frac{dN}{d\theta} = -kN = -ae^{-E/RT}N$$

Integrating,

$$\nabla_{\text{total}} = \ln\frac{N_0}{N} = a\int_0^\theta e^{-E/RT}d\theta \qquad (8.11)$$

where

∇_{total} = design criterion

It is apparent from Table 8.2 that the values of absolute temperature, T, are functions of the time of exposure, θ. In the design of batch sterilizers, the time, θ, applying Eq.(8.11) must be determined. It is clear that some of the contaminating microbes will be inactivated during the time required to heat (θ_1) and cool (θ_3) the bulk of the medium. Consequently, Eq. (8.11) can be subdivided as follows:

$$\nabla_{\text{total}} = \ln\frac{N_0}{N} = \nabla_{\text{heating}} + \nabla_{\text{holding}} + \nabla_{\text{cooling}} \qquad (8.12)$$

$$\nabla_{\text{heating}} = \ln\frac{N_0}{N_1} = a\int_0^{\theta_1} e^{-E/RT}d\theta \qquad (8.13)$$

TABLE 8.2

TEMPERATURE-TIME PROFILE IN BATCH STERILIZATION.[5]

Type of Heat Transfer	Temperature-time Profile	α, β, or γ
Steam Sparging	$T = T_0\left(1 + \dfrac{\alpha\theta}{1+\gamma\theta}\right)$ (Hyperbolic) (8.7)	$\alpha = \dfrac{hs}{McT_0}$ $\gamma = \dfrac{s}{M}$
Electrical Heating	$T = T_0(1+\alpha\theta)$ (Linear)　(8.8)	$\alpha = \dfrac{q}{McT_0}$
Heating with Steam	$T = T_H(1+\beta e^{-\alpha\theta})$ (Exponential) (8.9)	$\alpha = \dfrac{UA}{Mc}$ $\beta = \dfrac{T_0 - T_H}{T_H}$
Cooling with Coolant	$T = T_{CO}(1+\beta e^{-\alpha\theta})$ (Exponential)　(8.10)	$\alpha = \left(\dfrac{wc'}{Mc}\right)\left(1 - e^{-\frac{UA}{wc'}}\right)$ $\beta = \dfrac{T_0 - T_{CO}}{T_{CO}}$

$$\nabla_{\text{holding}} = \ln \frac{N_1}{N_2} = a \int_0^{\theta_2} e^{-E/RT} d\theta$$

$$= ae^{-E/RT}\theta_2 \tag{8.14}$$

$$\nabla_{\text{cooling}} = \ln \frac{N_2}{N} = a \int_0^{\theta_3} e^{-E/RT} d\theta \tag{8.15}$$

$$\theta = \theta_1 + \theta_2 + \theta_3 \tag{8.16}$$

where

N = sterility level (number of contaminating microbes after sterilization)

N_0 = contamination level (number of contaminating microbes before sterilization)

N_1 = number of contaminating microbes after heating period, θ_1

N_2 = number of contaminating microbes after holding period, θ_2

Calculation of ∇_{heating}

(a)　Hyperbolic profile

Substituting Eq. (8.7) into Eq. (8.13),

$$\nabla_{\text{heating}} = a \int_0^{\theta_1} \exp\left[-\frac{E}{RT_0}\,\frac{1}{1+\alpha\theta/(1+\gamma\theta)}\right]d\theta$$

$$= a \int_0^{\theta_1} \exp\left[-\delta\left(\frac{1+\gamma\theta}{1+p\theta}\right)\right]d\theta \qquad (8.17)$$

where

$$\delta = \frac{E}{RT_0}, \qquad p = \alpha+\gamma$$

Setting

$$x = \frac{1+\gamma\theta}{1+p\theta}, \qquad d\theta = \frac{(1+p\theta)^2}{\gamma-p}\,dx$$

$$\nabla_{\text{heating}} = a\,(\gamma-p)\int_1^{\frac{1+\gamma\theta_1}{1+p\theta_1}} \frac{e^{-\delta x}}{(\gamma-xp)^2}\,dx = a(\gamma-p)\frac{1}{\delta}\int_\delta^{\delta\left(\frac{1+\gamma\theta_1}{1+p\theta_1}\right)} \frac{e^{-X}}{(\gamma-\frac{X}{\delta}p)^2}\,dX$$

$$= a(\gamma-p)\frac{\delta}{p^2}\int_\delta^{\delta\left(\frac{1+\gamma\theta_1}{1+p\theta_1}\right)} \frac{e^{-X}}{(m-X)^2}\,dX$$

provided:

$$\delta x = X, \qquad m = \frac{\delta\gamma}{p}$$

Replacing $(X-m)$ with Y, the above equation is simplified as follows:

$$\nabla_{\text{heating}} = a(\gamma-p)\frac{\delta}{p^2}\int_{\delta-m}^{\delta\left(\frac{1+\gamma\theta_1}{1+p\theta_1}\right)-m} \frac{e^{-Y-m}}{Y^2}\,dY$$

$$= \frac{a(\gamma-p)\delta}{p^2}e^{-m}\int_{\delta-m}^{\delta\left(\frac{1+\gamma\theta_1}{1+p\theta_1}\right)-m} \frac{e^{-Y}}{Y^2}\,dY = -\frac{a\alpha\delta}{p^2}e^{-m}\left[\int_{\delta-m}^{\infty} \frac{e^{-Y}}{Y^2}\,dY - \int_{\delta\left(\frac{1+\gamma\theta_1}{1+p\theta_1}\right)-m}^{\infty} \frac{e^{-Y}}{Y^2}\,dY\right]$$

$$= \frac{a\alpha\delta}{p^2}e^{-m}\left[E_2\left\{\delta\left(\frac{1+\gamma\theta_1}{1+p\theta_1}\right)-m\right\}-E_2(\delta-m)\right] \qquad (8.18)$$

where

$$E_n(Z) = \int_Z^\infty \frac{e^{-x}}{x^n}\, dx \qquad (8.19)$$

(Integral exponential function)

(b) Linear profile

Substituting Eq. (8.8) into Eq. (8.13),

$$\nabla_{\text{heating}} = a \int_0^{\theta_1} \exp\left[-\frac{E}{RT_0}\,\frac{1}{1+\alpha\theta}\right] d\theta$$

$$= a \int_0^{\theta_1} \exp\left[\left(-\frac{\delta}{1+\alpha\theta}\right)\right] d\theta$$

Changing the variable from θ to x,

$$x = \frac{\delta}{1+\alpha\theta}$$

$$d\theta = -\frac{\delta}{\alpha}\,\frac{dx}{x^2}$$

$$\nabla_{\text{heating}} = -\frac{a\delta}{\alpha} \int_\delta^{\frac{\delta}{1+\alpha\theta_1}} \frac{e^{-x}}{x^2}\, dx$$

$$= -\frac{a\delta}{\alpha} \int_\delta^\infty \frac{e^{-x}}{x^2}\, dx + \frac{a\delta}{\alpha} \int_{\frac{\delta}{1+\alpha\theta_1}}^\infty \frac{e^{-x}}{x^2}\, dx$$

$$= \frac{a\delta}{\alpha}\left[E_2\!\left(\frac{\delta}{1+\alpha\theta_1}\right) - E_2(\delta)\right] \qquad (8.20)$$

(c) Exponential profile

From Equations (8.9) and (8.13),

$$\nabla_{\text{heating}} = a \int_0^{\theta_1} \exp\left[-\frac{E}{RT_{\text{H}}(1+\beta e^{-\alpha\theta})}\right] d\theta$$

$$= \frac{a\delta}{\alpha} \int_{\frac{\delta}{1+\beta}}^{\frac{\delta}{1+\beta e^{-\alpha\theta_1}}} \frac{e^{-x}}{x(\delta-x)}\, dx$$

provided:

$$\delta = \frac{E}{RT_H}, \quad x = \frac{\delta}{1+\beta e^{-a\theta}}, \quad d\theta = \frac{(1+\beta e^{-a\theta})^2}{a\beta\delta e^{-a\theta}}dx$$

Arranging further the above equation of ∇_{heating},

$$\nabla_{\text{heating}} = \frac{a}{\alpha}\int_{\frac{\delta}{1+\beta}}^{\frac{\delta}{1+\beta e^{-a\theta_1}}}\frac{e^{-x}}{x}dx + \frac{a}{\alpha}\int_{\frac{\delta}{1+\beta}}^{\frac{\delta}{1+\beta e^{-a\theta_1}}}\frac{e^{-x}}{(\delta-x)}dx$$

$$= \frac{a}{\alpha}\int_{\frac{\delta}{1+\beta}}^{\infty}\frac{e^{-x}}{x}dx - \frac{a}{\alpha}\int_{\frac{\delta}{1+\beta e^{-a\theta_1}}}^{\infty}\frac{e^{-x}}{x}dx + \frac{a}{\alpha}\int_{-\frac{\delta\beta}{1+\beta}}^{-\frac{\delta\beta e^{-a\theta_1}}{1+\beta e^{-a\theta_1}}}\frac{e^{-X-\delta}}{-X}dX$$

provided:

$$x - \delta = X$$

$$\nabla_{\text{heating}} = \frac{a}{\alpha}\left[E_1\left(\frac{\delta}{1+\beta}\right) - E_1\left(\frac{\delta}{1+\beta e^{-a\theta_1}}\right)\right] - \frac{a}{\alpha}e^{-\delta}\int_{-\frac{\delta\beta}{1+\beta}}^{-\frac{\delta\beta e^{-a\theta_1}}{1+\beta e^{-a\theta_1}}}\frac{e^{-X}}{X}dX$$

$$= \frac{a}{\alpha}\left[E_1\left(\frac{\delta}{1+\beta}\right) - E_1\left(\frac{\delta}{1+\beta e^{-a\theta_1}}\right)\right] - \frac{a}{\alpha}e^{-\delta}\left[\int_{-\frac{\delta\beta}{1+\beta}}^{\infty}\frac{e^{-X}}{X}dX - \int_{-\frac{\delta\beta e^{-a\theta_1}}{1+\beta e^{-a\theta_1}}}^{\infty}\frac{e^{-X}}{X}dX\right]$$

$$= \frac{a}{\alpha}\left[E_1\left(\frac{\delta}{1+\beta}\right) - E_1\left(\frac{\delta}{1+\beta e^{-a\theta_1}}\right)\right]$$

$$- \frac{a}{\alpha}e^{-\delta}\left[E_1\left(\frac{\delta}{1+\beta}-\delta\right) - E_1\left(\frac{\delta}{1+\beta e^{-a\theta_1}}-\delta\right)\right] \quad (8.21)$$

Calculation of ∇_{cooling}

It is evident from Equations (8.10) and (8.9) that Eq. (8.21) can also be used for evaluating the values of ∇_{cooling} provided that $\delta = E/RT_{CO}$ is adopted instead of $\delta = E/RT_H$ in Eq. (8.21). Then, the values of α and β in Eq. (8.21) should be used as indicated by Eq. (8.10).

8.3.2. Example of calculation

A medium (60,000 kg, 40°C) in a fermentor is sterilized batch-wise at 120°C. Calculate the time the medium must remain at 120°C. Operating conditions are assumed to be as follows:

(a)   Contamination level:
$$10^5/\text{ml}$$
(b)   Sterility level:
$$10^{-3} \ /TANK$$
(c)   Specific denaturation rate of bacterial spores:
$$k = 7.94 \times 10^{38} e^{-\frac{68.7 \times 10^3}{RT}} \ \text{min}^{-1} \qquad (cf. \text{ Fig. 8.4})$$
(d)   Heating: steam entering at a rate of 180 kg/min at 4 Kg/cm² gauge
(e)   Cooling: water (20°C) circulation at a rate of 4×10^3 kg/min
       The medium is cooled from 120°C to 35°C.
       Heat transfer area of the fermentor: 240 m²
       Over-all heat transfer coefficient: 600 kcal/m²hr°C
(f)   The values of specific heat and specific gravity of the medium are 1.0 kcal/kg°C and 1.0 respectively.

Solution
$$N_0 = 10^5 \times 60 \times 10^3 \times 10^3 = 6 \times 10^{12} \ \leftarrow \# \ bacteria$$
$$N = 10^{-3} \ /TANK$$

From Eq. (8.12),
$$\nabla_{\text{total}} = \ln \frac{6 \times 10^{12}}{10^{-3}} = 2.303 \log (6 \times 10^{15}) \qquad (8.22)$$
$$= 36.4$$

(i)   Heating (hyperbolic temperature-time profile)
$$\delta = \frac{E}{RT_0} = \frac{68.7 \times 10^3}{1.98 \times (273 + 40)} = 111$$

Enthalpy of steam, h, for the medium, 40°C,
$$h = 656.3 - 40 = 616.3 \quad \text{kcal/kg}$$

From Eq. (8.7) in Table 8.2,
$$\alpha = \frac{hs}{McT_0} = \frac{616.3 \times 180}{(60 \times 10^3) \times 1.0 \times (273 + 40)} = 5.90 \times 10^{-3} \ \text{min}^{-1}$$
$$\gamma = \frac{s}{M} = \frac{180}{60 \times 10^3} = 3 \times 10^{-3} \ \text{min}^{-1}$$

From Eq. (8.17),
$$m = \frac{\delta \gamma}{p} = \frac{\delta \gamma}{\alpha + \gamma} = \frac{111 \times (3 \times 10^{-3})}{(5.90 \times 10^{-3}) + (3 \times 10^{-3})} = 37.4$$
$$e^{-m} = e^{-37.4} = 5.62 \times 10^{-17}$$
$$10^5 /ml \qquad 60 \ kg/m$$

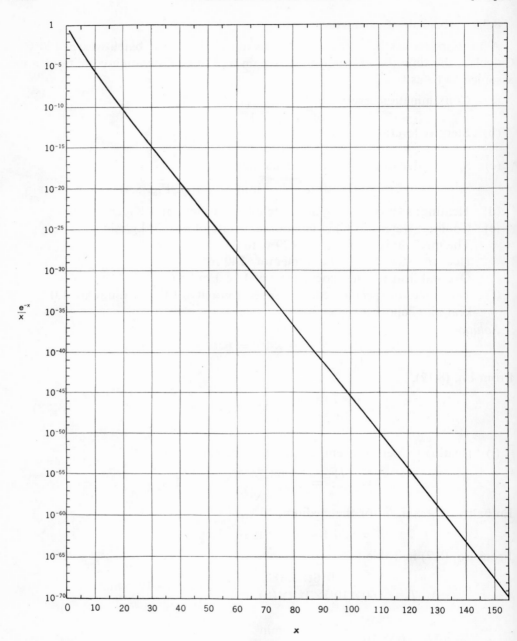

FIG. 8.12. e^{-x}/x vs. x $(x>0)$. The values of e^{-x}/x is plotted against x to facilitate the numerical calculation of the integral exponential function, $E_1(z)$ (see Eq. (8.19)).

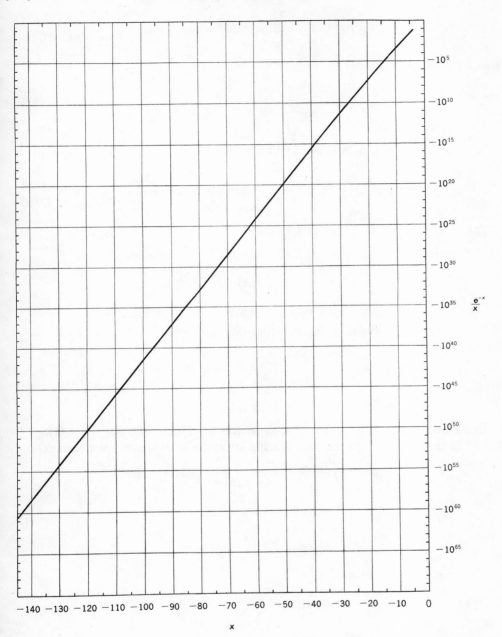

FIG. 8.13. e^{-x}/x vs. x $(x<0)$. The value of e^{-x}/x is plotted against x to facilitate the numerical calculation of the integral exponential function, $E_1(z)$ (see Eq. (8.19)).

$$\frac{a\delta\alpha}{p^2}e^{-m} = \frac{(7.94\times10^{38})\,(111)\,(5.90\times10^{-3})\,(5.62\times10^{-17})}{(8.90\times10^{-3})^2} = 3.68\times10^{26}$$

From Eq. (8.7),

$$\theta_1 = \frac{T-T_0}{T_0\alpha-(T-T_0)\gamma}$$

$$= \frac{393-313}{313\times(5.90\times10^{-3})-(393-313)\,(3\times10^{-3})} = 49.8 \text{ min}$$

From Eq. (8.18),

$$E_2\left\{\delta\left(\frac{1+\gamma\theta_1}{1+p\theta_1}\right)-m\right\} = E_2\left\{111\times\frac{1+(3\times10^{-3})\times49.8}{1+(8.90\times10^{-3})\times49.8}-37.4\right\} = E_2(51)$$

$$E_2(\delta-m) = E_2(111-37.4) = E_2(73.6)$$

It is clear that only the value of $E_2(51)$ needs to be estimated.

$$E_2(51) \doteq \frac{e^{-51}}{(51)^2} = 3.05\times10^{-26}$$

$$\nabla_{\text{heating}} = (3.68\times10^{26})\,(3.05\times10^{-26}) = 11.2$$

(ii)   Cooling (exponential temperature-time profile)
From Eq. (8.10),

$$308 = 293\left[1+\left(\frac{393-293}{293}\right)\exp\left\{-\left(\frac{240\times10^3}{(60+9)\times10^3}\right)\left(1-e^{-\frac{600\times240}{240\times10^3}}\right)\theta_3\right\}\right]$$

$$\theta_3 = 72 \text{ min}$$

In the above calculation, the value of M was assumed: $M = 60\times10^3+(180\times50)$ kg, including the volume increase during sparging with steam for about 50 min.

$$\alpha = \frac{(4\times10^3)\,(1.0)}{\{(60+9)\times10^3\}(1.0)}\left\{1-\exp\left(-\frac{600\times240}{240\times10^3\times1.0}\right)\right\}$$

$$= 2.61\times10^{-2} \text{ min}^{-1}$$

$$\delta = \frac{E}{RT_{\text{co}}} = \frac{68.7\times10^3}{1.98\times293} = 118$$

$$e^{-\delta} = e^{-118} = 5.01\times10^{-52}$$

$$\beta = \frac{393-293}{293} = 0.342$$

$$\frac{a}{\alpha} = \frac{7.94\times10^{38}}{2.61\times10^{-2}} = 3.04\times10^{40}$$

$$\frac{a}{\alpha}e^{-\delta} = (3.04\times10^{40})\,(5.01\times10^{-52}) = 1.52\times10^{-11}$$

$$e^{-\alpha\theta_3} = e^{-(2.61\times10^{-2})\,(72)} = 1.51\times10^{-1}$$

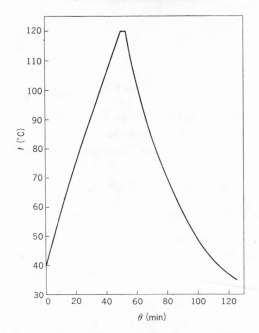

FIG. 8.14.　Temperature-time profile of this example of a batch-sterilization cycle.

$$E_1\left(\frac{\delta}{1+\beta}\right) = E_1\left(\frac{118}{1+0.342}\right) = E_1(87.9)$$

$$E_1\left(\frac{\delta}{1+\beta e^{-\alpha\theta_3}}\right) = E_1\left(\frac{118}{1+0.342\times0.151}\right) = E_1(112)$$

$$E_1(87.9) \gg E_1(112)$$

$$E_1(87.9) \doteq \frac{e^{-87.9}}{87.9} = 7\times10^{-41} \quad \text{(see Fig. 8.12)}$$

$$E_1\left(\frac{\delta}{1+\beta}-\delta\right) = E_1(87.9-118) = E_1(-30.1)$$

$$E_1\left(\frac{\delta}{1+\beta e^{-\alpha\theta_3}}-\delta\right) = E_1(112-118) = E_1(-6)$$

$$|E_1(-30.1)| \gg |E_1(-6)|$$

$$E_1(-30.1) \doteq -3\times10^{11} \quad \text{(see Fig. 8.13)}$$

$$\therefore \nabla_{\text{cooling}} = (3.04\times10^{40})(7\times10^{-41})-(1.52\times10^{-11})(-3\times10^{11})$$

$$= 6.69$$

From Equations (8.12) and (8.22),

$$\nabla_{\text{holding}} = 36.4-11.2-6.69$$

$$= 18.5$$

$$k_{\text{at120°C}} = (7.94\times10^{38})e^{-68.7\times10^8/1.98\times393}$$

$$= 3.55 \quad \text{min}^{-1}$$

From Eq. (8.14),

$$\theta_2 = \frac{18.5}{3.55}$$

$$\doteqdot 5 \text{ min}$$

The temperature-time profile for the batch-sterilization process outlined in this example is shown in Fig. 8.14. It is clear that the times required to heat and cool the medium contributed about 67% to the required destruction of the organisms.

8.4. CONTINUOUS STERILIZATION OF MEDIA

8.4.1. Equipment and temperature-time profile

Fig. 8.15 shows equipment for continuous sterilization of fermentation media. The upper part, A, of the figure shows an injection type of sterilizer; steam is injected directly into the raw medium; therefore the temperature rises almost instantaneously to the predetermined sterilizing temperature. The time for which the medium is held at this temperature is governed by the length of a pipe in the holding section. The sterilized medium is cooled instantly by passing through an expansion valve into a vacuum chamber, as shown in the figure.

An example of the temperature-time profile obtained with the injection type of equipment is shown in the left profile of Fig. 8.16. The numerical values given in the figure have no general significance; these will depend on the particular sterilization problem. Because of the short period of exposure to heat, it is possible to raise the temperature as high as 140°C without serious damage to the medium.

The lower part, B, of Fig. 8.15 shows a plate heat exchanger type frequently employed in the fermentation industry for the continuous sterilization of media.

Steam heated plates raise the temperature of the raw medium, the medium is maintained at the elevated temperature for a certain period of time, and then cooled in another section of the plate exchanger, as shown in Fig. 8.15.

Although the time required to heat and cool the raw medium is much longer than with the steam injection type of continuous sterilization, the contribution of these periods to the sterilizing cycle will be much smaller (around 1 or 2%) than is the case with batch sterilization (cf. the right profile in Fig. 8.16 and Fig. 8.14).

8.4.2. Residence time concept

To design and evaluate a continuous media sterilizer where the raw medium passes through round pipes, it is important to appreciate that not all portions of the medium spend the same length of time in the holding section of the sterilizer. This is because, in both turbulent and viscous flow, the mean velocity (u) of the fluid is a function of the radial distribution of fluid velocities occurring across the pipe. The mean velocity of a viscous-fluid flow through a pipe is one-half the maximum velocity found at the axis of the pipe (radial distribution of velocities is

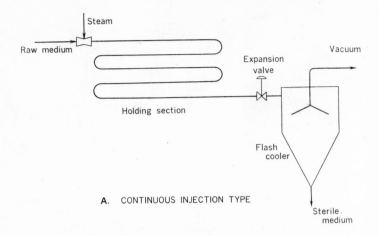

A.   CONTINUOUS INJECTION TYPE

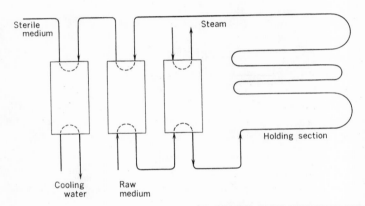

B.   CONTINUOUS PLATE EXCHANGER TYPE

FIG. 8.15.   Continuous sterilizers.

parabolic); in the turbulent condition, the mean velocity is 82% of the maximum value (radial distribution of velocities is governed by Carman-Prandtl's power law); these types of flow are illustrated in the two lower diagrams of Fig. 8.17.

With piston flow, the mean time in the holding section is exactly equal to the time of exposure to heat in all portions of the medium; this makes it easier to calculate the length of the holding section required to give a desired level of sterility. However, in practice it is difficult to realize ideal piston flow, although it would be most desirable, since it avoids both over-cooking and under-cooking the medium.

It is difficult to predict the distribution of residence times in advance, so this must be determined empirically. This can be done by discharging a "marker" material and observing the pattern of its recovery at the outlet of the pipe; this pattern will, of course, be dependent on the type of flow in the pipe.

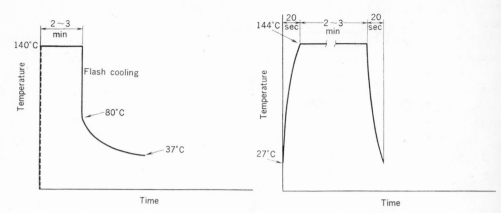

FIG. 8.16.   Temperature-time profiles in continuous sterilizers;
the left profile applies to a steam-injection sterilizer
and the right profile to a plate-exchanger sterilizer

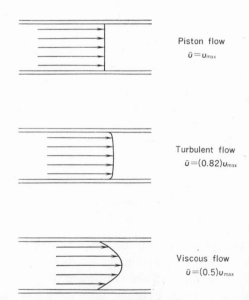

FIG. 8.17.   Distribution of velocities in fluids exhibiting different
types of flow inside round pipes; $\bar{u}$=mean velocity of the fluid.

Before proceeding to the following discussion, it is important to make some underlying assumptions clear. The first assumption is that, as the length of pipe in the holding section becomes longer, the property of effective dispersion is more satisfactory than the distribution of velocities to describe the performance of sterilizers. This is particularly true for sterilizers where elbows or valves are present, to say nothing of the more complicated pathways existing in the plate type of heat exchanger.

The second assumption is that, although the mixing characteristics of equipment with respect to effective dispersion apply to the mixing of molecules, it is assumed that they apply also to the behavior of microbes suspended in the medium. So far, there are no experimental data to support or refute this assumption.

For simplicity, the residence time curve with a pipe will be considered. A differential equation is derived from the material balance as follows:

$$E_z \frac{\partial^2 n}{\partial x^2} - \bar{u}\frac{\partial n}{\partial x} = \frac{\partial n}{\partial \theta} \tag{8.23}$$

Setting

$$\bar{n} = n/n_0, \qquad \chi = x/L, \qquad PeB = \bar{u}L/E_z, \qquad \phi = \theta/\theta_T$$

where

E_z = axial dispersion coefficient
n_0 = inlet concentration
L = pipe (reactor) length
PeB = Péclet number (or Bodenstein number)
x = axial direction
θ_T = nominal holding time

Rearranging Eq. (8.23),

$$\frac{\partial^2 \bar{n}}{\partial \chi^2} - PeB\frac{\partial \bar{n}}{\partial \chi} - PeB\frac{\partial \bar{n}}{\partial \phi} = 0 \tag{8.24}$$

Initial and boundary conditions are:

$$
\left.
\begin{array}{ll}
\chi > 0, & \bar{n}_{\phi=0} = 1 \\
\chi < 0, & \bar{n}_{\phi=0} = 0
\end{array}
\right\} \text{ initial conditions}
$$

$$
\left.
\begin{array}{ll}
\chi \to 0^+, & \dfrac{\partial \bar{n}}{\partial \chi} - PeB\bar{n} = 0 \\[2ex]
\chi \to 1, & \dfrac{\partial \bar{n}}{\partial \chi} = 0
\end{array}
\right\} \text{ boundary conditions}
$$

Solving for $\bar{n}$ [3.8]

$$\bar{n} = 32\sum_{\tau=1}^{\infty} \frac{PeB\lambda_\tau(4\lambda_\tau^2 \cos 2\lambda_\tau\chi + PeB \sin 2\lambda_\tau\chi)}{(16\lambda_\tau^2 + 4PeB + PeB^2)\,(16\lambda_\tau^2 + PeB^2)}\exp\left[\frac{PeB}{2}\chi - \frac{PeB^2 + 16\lambda_\tau^2}{4PeB}\phi\right] \tag{8.25}$$

provided: the λ_τ ($\tau = 1, 2, 3, \ldots$) are the positive roots, taken in order of magnitude, of the transcendental equation

$$\tan 2\lambda = \frac{8\lambda PeB}{16\lambda^2 - PeB^2} \tag{8.26}$$

The exit concentration, $\bar{n}_{\chi=1}$, is given from Eq. (8.25) by setting $\chi=1$.

$$\bar{n}_{\chi=1} = R(\phi)$$

$$= 16\sum_{\tau=1}^{\infty} \frac{\lambda_\tau \sin 2\lambda_\tau}{(16\lambda_\tau^2 + 4PeB + PeB^2)}\exp\left[\frac{PeB}{2} - \frac{PeB^2 + 16\lambda_\tau^2}{4PeB}\phi\right] \tag{8.27}$$

where

$$\int_0^\infty R(\phi)\, d\phi = 1.0 \qquad (8.28)$$

Numerical correlations between $R(\phi)$ and ϕ are plotted from Eq. (8.27) as shown in Fig. 8.18,[3] in which the values of PeB are taken as parameters.

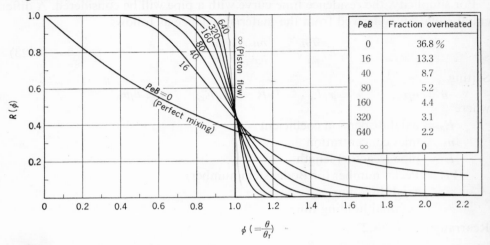

PeB	Fraction overheated
0	36.8 %
16	13.3
40	8.7
80	5.2
160	4.4
320	3.1
640	2.2
∞	0

FIG. 8.18.   Effect of different types of flow (as shown by different PeB values and different ratios of the holding time (θ) to the nominal holding time (θ_T)) in continuous sterilization of media.

It is seen from the figure that the flow in the reactor approaches the piston type of flow as the values of PeB are increased. Assuming that the medium is not over-

heated at all in the case of piston flow and that the area $\int_1^\infty R(\phi)d\phi$ under any curve

in the figure is a measure of overheating of that medium, the relative amount of overheating for any type of flow can be calculated; several examples have been

listed in Fig. 8.18. In each estimation of $\int_1^\infty R(\phi)d\phi = 1.0 - \int_0^{1.0} R(\phi)d\phi$, numerical

data of electronic computations of Eq. (8.27)[3] and Simpson's formula of approximations were used.

It is also clear from Fig. 8.18 that continuous sterilizers should be designed and operated so that the flow of medium in the reactor approaches the piston type of flow.

Next, the inactivation of organisms by heat in continuous sterilizers will be considered. Since the rate of microbial death is expressed by Eq. (8.1), the material balance within a continuous sterilizer (straight pipe) at steady state is as follows:

$$E_z \frac{d^2n}{dx^2} - \bar{u} \frac{dn}{dx} - kn = 0 \tag{8.29}$$

Changing the variables as shown previously in connection with Eq. (8.23) and rearranging Eq. (8.29),

$$\frac{d^2\bar{n}}{d\chi^2} - PeB \frac{d\bar{n}}{d\chi} - PeBN_r\bar{n} = 0 \tag{8.30}$$

where

$$N_r = kL/\bar{u} \qquad \text{Damköhler}$$

Boundary conditions are:

$$\chi \to 0^+, \qquad \frac{d\bar{n}}{d\chi} + PeB(1-\bar{n}) = 0$$

$$\chi = 1, \qquad \frac{d\bar{n}}{d\chi} = 0$$

The solution of Eq. (8.30) with the above-mentioned boundary conditions is:[9]

$$\bar{n}_{\chi=1} = \left(\frac{n}{n_0}\right)_{x=L} = \frac{4\zeta \exp\left(\frac{PeB}{2}\right)}{(1+\zeta)^2 \exp\left(\frac{PeB}{2}\zeta\right) - (1-\zeta)^2 \exp\left(-\frac{PeB}{2}\zeta\right)} \tag{8.31}$$

provided:

$$\zeta = \sqrt{1 + \frac{4N_r}{PeB}}$$

A degree of sterility (N/N_0) is plotted against $N_r(=kL/\bar{u})$ in Fig. 8.19 according to Eq. (8.31), parameters being PeB ($=\bar{u}L/E_z$).

It is also evident from Fig. 8.19 that where $PeB=\infty$, in other words with ideal piston flow, conditions are most desirable for designing continuous sterilizers, since this reduces the length of pipe required to produce a given degree of sterility in a given mass of medium. However, it is difficult in practice to realize ideal piston flow and so the data in Fig. 8.19 may assist in designing and assessing the efficiency of continuous sterilizers.

Finally, the time required for microbial particles in a continuous sterilizer to attain the sterilizing temperature following the injection of steam will be mentioned briefly. Although this time is of the order of microseconds for particles several microns in size, the response time, $0.632(T_H - T_0)$, where T_H is the temperature of the heat source and T_0 is the temperature of the medium, will be of the order of seconds for solids several millimeters in size. It is urged, therefore, that raw media be clarified as much as possible before entering a continuous sterilization system.

8.4.3. Example of calculation

It is desired to sterilize a medium (60,000 kg, 40°C) within 40 minutes using in parallel two continuous sterilizers. The pipes of the reactor have an inner diameter, $d=0.155$ m and a length, $L=50$ m; the steam which is injected into the

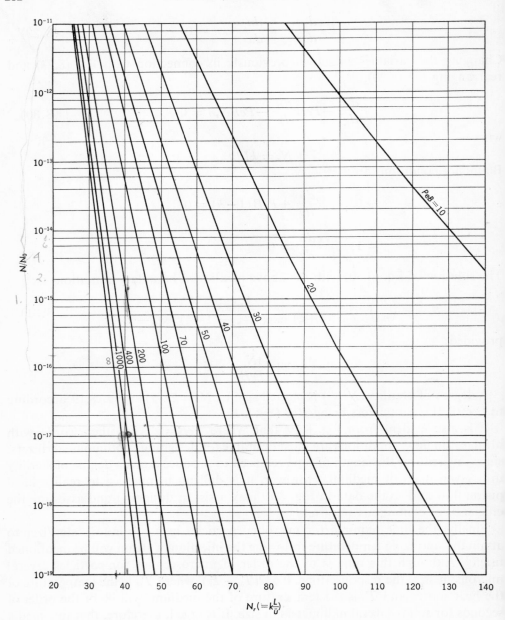

Fig. 8.19.   Effect of different types of flow (as shown by different PeB values) on the destruction of organisms (N/N_0) at different rates of destruction (measured as $N_r = kL/\bar{u}$).

sterilizers elevates the temperature of the raw medium almost instantly. It is desired to estimate the temperature of sterilization which will satisfy this requirement.

The levels of contamination and the sterility desired are the same as those used in a previous problem described in Section 8.3.2. The specific denaturation rate of bacterial spores is also the same as was assumed in Section 8.3.2. The physical properties of this medium at 100°C are $c=1$ kcal/kg°C, $\rho=10^3$ kg/m³ and $\mu=3.6$ kg/m hr.

Sectional area, S, of each sterilizer:

$$S = \frac{\pi}{4}(1.55\times 10^{-1})^2$$

$$= 1.88\times 10^{-2} \text{ m}^2$$

Mean velocity, $\bar{u}$, to satisfy $\theta=2/3$ hr:

$$\bar{u} = \frac{60/2}{S\theta} = \frac{30}{(1.88\times 10^{-2})(2/3)}$$

$$= 2.39\times 10^3 \text{ m/hr}$$

$$N_{\text{Re}} = \frac{d\bar{u}\rho}{\mu} = \frac{(1.55\times 10^{-1})(2.39\times 10^3)(10^3)}{3.6}$$

$$\doteqdot 10^5$$

From the data which have been published by Levenspiel[6] regarding $E_z/\bar{u}d$ vs. N_{Re},

$$E_z/\bar{u}d \doteqdot 0.2 \quad (N_{\text{Re}} = 10^5)$$

Then,

$$PeB = \frac{\bar{u}L}{E_z} = \frac{\bar{u}d}{E_z}\frac{L}{d}$$

$$= \frac{1}{0.2}\frac{50}{0.155} = 1,610$$

From Figs. 8.18 and 8.19, the condition of flow may be regarded approximately as the piston type of flow.

The levels of contamination and the sterility assumed:

$$\frac{N}{N_0} = \frac{1}{\dfrac{60\times 10^3\times 10^3\times 10^3}{10^5}} = 1.67\times 10^{-16} \qquad \text{(see Section 8.3.2)}$$

From Fig. 8.19,

$$N_r = kL/\bar{u}$$

$$= 36$$

$$k = \frac{N_r\bar{u}}{L}$$

$$= \frac{36\times 2.39\times 10^3}{50} = 1.72\times 10^3 \text{ hr}^{-1}$$

$$= 28.7 \text{ min}^{-1}$$

The relation between temperature, $t°C$, and the value of the reaction rate constant, k, min^{-1}, is shown in Fig. 8.20; from this graph the temperature required to give the desired degree of sterility can be shown to be 129. 5°C.

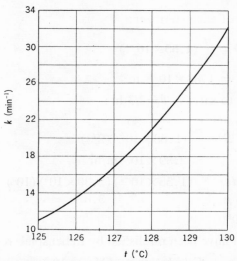

FIG. 8.20.   Values of the reaction rate constant (k) at different sterilization temperatures (t) applying in a sample calculation.

The nominal holding time, θ_T, of the raw medium within the sterilizer,

$$\theta_T = \frac{L}{\bar{u}}$$

$$= \frac{50}{2.39 \times 10^3} = 2.09 \times 10^{-2} \text{ hr}$$

$$= 1.25 \text{ min}$$

If live steam (latent heat of vaporization=481.7 kcal/kg) at 9 Kg/cm^2 gauge is injected into the sterilizer, the mass of steam, s, needed per hr:

$$481.7 \times s = \frac{60}{2} \times 10^3 \times (129.5 - 40)$$

$$s = \frac{30 \times 10^3 \times 89.5}{481.7} \doteqdot 5.6 \times 10^3 \text{ kg/hr}$$

The effect of the increase in the Reynolds number due to s, on the value of $E_z/\bar{u}a$ is negligible.[6]

NOMENCLATURE

a = empirical constant, min^{-1}
a' = empirical constant, Eq. (8.6)
A = heat transfer area, m^2

b' = empirical constant, Eq. (8.6)
c = specific heat of medium, kcal/kg°C
c' = specific heat of coolant, kcal/kg°C
d = inner diameter of pipe, m
D = decimal reduction time, min
E = activation energy, cal/g mole, kcal/g mole
E_Z = axial dispersion coefficient, m²/sec
g = constant, Eq. (8.5)
h = enthalpy of steam relative to raw medium temperature, kcal/kg
ΔH^* = heat of reaction of activation
k = reaction rate constant, min⁻¹, hr⁻¹, sec⁻¹
L = length of reactor pipe, m
M = initial mass of medium in batch sterilizer, kg
n = concentration of dyestuff or electrolyte (simulation of microbial concentration)
n_0 = inlet concentration
N = number of viable microbes
N_0 = initial number of viable microbes (at $\theta=0$)
N_r = $kL/\bar{u}$, dimensionless
N_{Re} = Reynolds number, $(=d\bar{u}\rho/\mu)$
PeB = Péclet number (or Bodenstein number) $(=\bar{u}L/E_Z)$
p = $\alpha+\gamma$
q = rate of heat transfer, kcal/sec
R = gas constant, 1.98 cal/g mole °K
ΔS^* = entropy change of activation
s = mass flow rate of steam, kg/sec, kg/hr, kg/min
S = sectional area of pipe, m²
t = temperature, °C
T = absolute temperature, °K
T_0 = initial temperature of medium, °K
T_H = temperature of heat source, °K
T_{CO} = inlet temperature of coolant, °K
U = over-all heat transfer coefficient, kcal/m² hr °C
$\bar{u}$ = mean velocity of fluid through round pipe, m/hr, m/sec
u_{max} = maximum velocity of fluid through round pipe, m/hr, m/sec
w = mass flow rate of coolant, kg/sec, kg/hr, kg/min
x = axial direction
$R(\phi)$ = function of ϕ, residence time curve
∇ = design criterion

Greek letters

$$\alpha = \frac{hs}{McT_0}, \frac{q}{McT_0}, \left(\frac{wc'}{Mc}\right)\left(1-e^{-\frac{UA}{wc'}}\right)$$

$$\beta = \frac{T_0-T_H}{T_H}, \frac{T_0-T_{CO}}{T_{CO}}$$

$$\gamma = s/M$$
$$\delta = E/RT$$

$$\zeta = \sqrt{1+\frac{4N_r}{PeB}}$$

θ = time
θ_T = nominal holding time
μ = viscosity of medium kg/m hr
ρ = density of medium, kg/m^3
$\phi = \theta/\theta_T$
$\chi = x/L$

REFERENCES

1. AMAHA, M. (1953). "Heat resistance of Cameron's putrefactive anerobe 3679 in phosphate buffer *(Clostridium sporogenes)*." *Food Research* **18**, 411.
2. BIGELOW, W.E. (1921). "The logarithmic nature of thermal death time curves." *J. Infect. Disease* **29**, 528.
3. BRENNER, H. (1962). "The diffusion model of longitudinal mixing in beds of finite length. Numerical values." *Chem. Eng. Sci.* **17**, 229.
4. BURTON, H. (1958). "An analysis of the performance of an ultra-high temperature milk sterilizing plant. Part 1. Introduction and physical measurements. Part 2. Calculation of the bactericidal effectiveness." *J. Dairy Research* **25**, 75; 324.
5. DEINDOERFER, F.H., and HUMPHREY, A.E. (1959). "Analytical method for calculating heat sterilization times." *Appl. Microbiol.* **7**, 256.
6. LEBENSPIEL, O. (1958). "Longitudinal mixing of fluids flowing in circular pipes." *Ind. Eng. Chem.* **50**, 343.
7. PFEIFER, V.F., and VOJNOVICH, C. (1952). "Continuous sterilization of media in biochemical processes." *ibid.* **44**, 1940.
8. YAGI, S., and MIYAUCHI, T. (1953). "On the residence time curves of the continuous reactors." *Chem. Eng. (Japan)* **17**, 382.
9. YAGI, S., and MIYAUCHI, T. (1955). "Operational characteristics of the continuous flow reactors in which the reactants are mixing." *ibid.* **19**, 507.

CHAPTER 9

AIR STERILIZATION

The problem of producing a large quantity of sterile air for aerobic fermentations is peculiar to biochemical engineering. On a laboratory scale, cotton plugs are quite satisfactory in test tubes or shaken flasks, and in pilot-plant fermentors, small fibrous filters present no serious troubles. On an industrial scale, however, fibrous filters have certain disadvantages.

It should be stated at the outset that 100% efficiency of collection of air-borne microorganisms cannot be expected in filters with beds packed with fibers or granular particles.

FIG. 9.1.   Air filter vessel packed with glass wool; auxiliary filter.
Filter bed; 1.24 m in diameter and 1.92 m in height.
(*Courtesy   Fujisawa Pharmaceutical Co., Ltd., Nagoya.*)

The purpose of an air filter is to prolong the interval of time between the passage of one air-borne organism and the next. The length of this interval of time will be governed by the type of fermentation but should be sufficient to protect the fermentation at least for the first critical period of growth.

During the past decade, valuable contributions have been made in both the theoretical and practical aspects of air filtration. A reasonable procedure for the design of filters for air sterilization has been established, provided the over-all collection efficiency required by the process is known. Despite the fact that glass fibers are known to be a better filter medium than cotton fibers or active carbon, these latter materials are still used in some fermentors. This is indicative of a

217

regrettably conservative attitude in the industry to the adoption of the findings of research.

This chapter will largely be concerned with the theory and design of fibrous air filters for the fermentation industry, but in the final section, a new type of air filter will be described; this filter is much smaller and has lower operating costs than the conventional fibrous or particulate filters.

9.1. SPECIES AND NUMBERS OF AIR-BORNE MICROBES

Before discussing the design of filters for air sterilization, a brief review will be made of air-borne microorganisms.

Table 9.1 lists species of bacteria and bacterial spores which are commonly detected in air;[3,15] in addition, yeast, fungi, and viruses are also present. The size of these organisms varies from several millimicrons to several hundreds of microns. Small organisms are, however, often adsorbed onto air-borne dust and can thus be easily removed from the air along with the larger dust particles before attempting air sterilization proper. Therefore, the air-borne particles which have to be destroyed or collected during air sterilization are about the size of small bacteria, namely, 0.5 to 1.0 micron (see Table 9.1). Incidentally, a recent extensive study of

TABLE 9.1

REPRESENTATIVE SPECIES OF AIR-BORNE BACTERIA AND BACTERIAL SPORES.
(AIBA AND HUMPHREY)

Species	Width (microns)	Length (microns)
Aerobacter aerogenes	1.0 – 1.5	1.0 – 2.5
Bacillus cereus	1.3 – 2.0	8.1 – 25.8
Bacillus licheniformis	0.5 – 0.7	1.8 – 3.3
Bacillus megaterium	0.9 – 2.1	2.0 – 10.0
Bacillus mycoides	0.6 – 1.6	1.6 – 13.6
Bacillus subtilis	0.5 – 1.1	1.6 – 4.8
Micrococcus aureus	0.5 – 1.0	0.5 – 1.0
Proteus vulgaris	0.5 – 1.0	1.0 – 3.0
(Spores)		
Bacillus megaterium	0.6 – 1.2	0.9 – 1.7
Bacillus mycoides	0.8 – 1.2	0.8 – 1.8
Bacillus subtilis	0.5 – 1.0	0.9 – 1.8

the dust particles in both indoor and outdoor air shows that the median size of dust particles is around 0.6 micron.[16]

The numbers of air-borne microbes in indoor and outdoor air were determined at the Sanitary Engineering Station, Tokyo, in 471 samples of air taken over a period of one year.[22] In each experiment, 5 liters of air were sucked into a sterile saline solution and shaken vigorously. The solution was then distributed over several Petri dishes containing nutrient agar. After incubation for 2 to 3 days at 30°C, the number of organisms per m³ of air, n, was calculated. This is shown in the abscissa of Fig.9.2, where these data have been rearranged by Aiba to show the frequency of distribution of organisms in a cubic meter of air.[5]

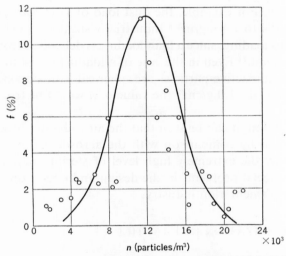

FIG. 9.2.   Frequency of distribution of organisms in air in Tokyo.

Now, suppose N is the total number of microbes which are found in a large volume of air. The probability $W(n)$ with which a unit volume (m³) arbitrarily selected from the bulk air will contain n microbes will be expressed as follows:

$$W(n) = {}_NC_n p^n (1-p)^{N-n} \qquad (9.1)$$

where

p = probability with which each microbe out of N in the total will be found in the unit volume of air arbitrarily selected

Setting

$$Np = \nu \text{ (expected value)}$$

and assuming

$$N \gg 1, \qquad p \ll 1$$

Eq. (9.1) can be rearranged to give:

$$W(n) = \frac{\nu^n e^{-\nu}}{n!} \qquad (9.2)$$

The curve in Fig. 9.2 was obtained from Eq. (9.2) with the value of $\nu = 12 \times 10^3$ particles/m^3.

Although the data points in Fig. 9.2 are scattered considerably around the curve, it appears that the occurrence of air-borne microbes is represented by Poisson's law (Eq. (9.2)). In other words, air-borne microbes are randomly distributed. It is interesting to note that a recent report of the value of $\nu\ (=\bar{n})$ for air in London, was $(3 \text{ to } 9) \times 10^3$ particles/m^3.[13] Humphrey, on the other hand, suggests the use of $\bar{n} \doteqdot 2 \times 10^3$ particles/m^3, if reliable figures of $\bar{n}$ are not available.[15] At any rate, it may be concluded that the number of air-borne microbes is of the order of 10^3 to 10^4 particles/m^3.

The value of $\bar{n} = 10^3$ to 10^4 particles/m^3 indicates that the microbial contamination of air is exceedingly light compared with the usual problem of cleaning dust-laden air in industry. For example, the dust load of stack gas from an atomic reactor ranges from 0.4 to 1.4 mg/m^3.[8] Industrially speaking, such figures are in the category of very low loading, since a light loading is defined as from 3.5 to 35 mg/m^3 according to Silverman.[24] Even in the case of a loading of 0.4 to 1.4 mg/m^3, if it is assumed that the radioactive particles are spherical with a diameter, $d_p = 0.2 \sim 0.7$ micron and a density, $\rho = 1.0$ g/cm^3, the value of $\bar{n}$ would be from 10^9 to 10^{10} particles/m^3.

From this calculation, it can be seen that the air to be sterilized in the fermentation industry is clean by comparison with the aerosols to be processed in other industries. However, the extremely high level of sterility required in air for fermentations poses special problems in the design and operation of air-sterilization equipment for the fermentation industry.

9.2. AIR STERILIZATION IN PRACTICE

9.2.1. Heat

Although bacterial spores are notoriously resistant to dry heat, they can be destroyed if temperatures are high enough. For instance, Decker *et al.* found that bacterial spores suspended in air could be killed at 218°C in 24 sec.[11]

Fig. 9.3 is a simple process which Stark[27] designed for air sterilization. In this system, heat generated by air compression is used to kill air-borne microbes; the outlet temperature of the air in a single-stage and adiabatic compressor operating at 3 Kg/cm^2 gauge rises to 150°C and 220°C, starting from inlet air temperatures of 20°C and 70°C, respectively. Stark carried out successful fermentations for the production of acetone and butanol, amylase and 2,3-butylene glycol using air sterilized by the heat generated during the compression of the air. (Inlet and outlet air temperatures were 21°C and 187°C respectively; outlet air pressure = 7 Kg/cm^2 gauge; fermentor volume = 1 to 30 m^3; air flow rate = 0.01 to 3 m^3/min)

The principle of utilizing heat generated by air compression is promising, especially for the production of large quantities of sterile air. However, before applying this idea to a practical fermentation, several other factors, including the location of the air compressor relative to fermentor, the length of pipe connecting the compressor and the fermentor, and their sterility, must be carefully examined. Due to the complicated factors involved and to the difficulty of assessing them, it is usual to install, in addition to the air compressor, auxiliary equipment to filter the air before it enters the fermentor.

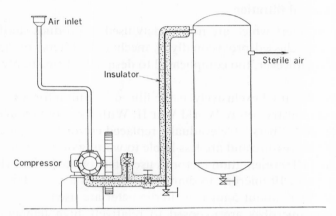

Fig. 9.3.   Sterilization of air with heat generated from the compression of air.[27]

9.2.2. Ultra-violet rays and other electro-magnetic waves

Morgan *et al.* found ultra-violet rays of wave lengths from 2,265 to 3,287Å were the most effective for killing air-borne microbes.[21] Sterile rooms in fermentation factories and operation rooms in hospitals are usually equipped with lamps emitting these rays, but it is questionable whether ultra-violet irradiation can be successfully applied to producing sterile air for fermentations.

Theoretically, sonic energy, high energy cathode rays, and gamma rays could be applied to air sterilization. Practically, however, the investment costs of such devices are high and their reliability for sterilizing large volumes of air has yet to be established.

9.2.3. Corona discharge

The Cottrell precipitator, which applies corona discharge to the removal of air-borne particles, is used successfully, for example, in the cement and sulfuric acid industries. It has possible application in sterilizing air for the fermentation industry, since air-borne organisms commonly adhere to dust particles, but the research has yet to be done to provide detailed information of its effectiveness and reliability in practical fermentations.

9.2.4. Germicidal sprays

Carswell claimed a significant reduction in air-borne bacteria by introducing a small amount of a germicide—for instance, phenol, ethylene oxide, or salts of heavy metals—into water which was sprayed and circulated within air conditioning equipment.[10] Although this method may have application in cleaning air in rooms where aseptic operations are to be performed, it is likely that there will be considerable difficulty in removing all entrained vapors and mists from the treated air before it is used.

9.2.5. Mechanical filtration

The fibrous air filters which are now widely used to produce sterile air for fermentations may be classed provisionally as mechanical filters; the mechanism of their operation is, however, too complicated to designate them simply as "mechanical."

Cotton fibers were used exclusively as the fibrous medium for air sterilization in the fermentation industry before World War II. With the production of antibiotics on a large scale, glass fibers have gradually replaced cotton fibers; glass fibers give a lower drop in air pressure and are less liable to wetting or combustion. In Japan, nowadays, almost all fermentation factories use filters packed with cylindrical pads woven of glass fibers 19 microns in diameter. Methods are similar in the United States, but glass fibers about 5 microns in diameter are used.

Since air-borne microbes are exposed to relatively high temperatures during compression of the air, the current practice of air sterilization is actually a combination of heat inactivation and mechanical filtration.

A few of the papers on filtration of particles from air will now be mentioned. One of the earliest papers was by Kluyver et al., who measured the efficiency of collection of Bacillus cereus on cotton fibers.[18] Gaden and Humphrey determined the distribution of the spores of Bacillus subtilis in a filter consisting of a 3 mm layer of glass fibers and studied the effect of air velocity on the efficiency of collection.[13,14] Aiba et al. measured the distribution of Serratia marcescens labeled with ^{32}P within a 50 mm layer of glass fibers; they found that the distribution of organisms in the filter showed a marked deviation from log-penetration as the bed thickness increased.[1] Mathematical analyses conducted by Aiba et al. allowed estimations to be made of the longitudinal distribution of bacteria within filters of practical size.[4] In addition, Chen has published a review of the theoretical bases of aerosol filtration.[9] In connection with the removal of radioactive particles suspended in exhaust gas from atomic reactors many theoretical as well as technological publications have appeared.[8]

Turning now to the problems that remain to be investigated; first, it should be noted that almost all of the previous publications are concerned with the behavior of thin layers of fibrous material. The over-all efficiency of collection of particles measured with small filters may not apply directly to the prediction of the values of collection efficiences in industrial filters, which are usually from 1 to 2 meters long. Furthermore, the number of particles in the air to be filtered for fermentations is exceedingly small compared with the degree of aerial contamination found in other industries.

In the next sections, theoretical and experimental investigations of the problems of air sterilization, as they apply to the fermentation industry particularly, will be elaborated.

9.3. AIR STERILIZATION BY FIBROUS MEDIA

9.3.1. Theory

The mechanisms of collection of aerosol particles by fibrous media may be classified as follows:

(a)   Inertial impaction
(b)   Interception
(c)   Diffusion
(d)   Settling by gravitational force
(e)   Electrostatic force

With fibrous filters, mechanism (d) (as for d, e, etc., see items of the mechanisms listed before) can be excluded, because the diameter of particles to be collected is of the order of one micron. Humphrey measured the electrostatic charge of *Bacillus subtilis* spores in relation to mechanism (e) and found that about 70% of them had a positive charge of 1 to 60 e.s.u., about 15% of them had a negative charge of 5 to 14 e.s.u., while the remaining spores were neutral.[14] It would be expected that charged organisms would be more effectively collected than neutral ones, and this was indeed shown experimentally by Silverman.[25]

However, there is little quantitative data on the contribution of mechanism (e) to the over-all collection efficiency of fibrous filters. Therefore the discussions which follow will be confined to the remaining mechanisms (a), (b), and (c).

For quantitative evaluation of these mechanisms it will be assumed that single cylindrical fibers are placed perpendicularly to the aerosol flow in an indefinite space, and that the air flow around the cylinders is laminar with no vortices (see Fig. 9.4). The second assumption is that all of the following analyses are two dimensional.

(a)   Inertial impaction

Assuming that the resistance to motion of a spherical particle (diameter$=d_p$ and density$=\rho_p$) moving with a velocity, u, in a stream of air (velocity$=v$ and viscosity $=\mu$) is governed by Stokes' law, the equation of motion with regard to the particle will be shown by either of the following:

$$\left(\frac{\pi}{6}\right) d_p^3 \rho_p \frac{d\bar{u}}{dt} = -\frac{3\pi\mu d_p}{C}(\bar{u}-\bar{v}) \tag{9.3}$$

$$\frac{C\rho_p d_p^2}{18\mu} \frac{d\bar{u}}{dt} = -(\bar{u}-\bar{v}) \tag{9.4}$$

where

  C = Cunningham's correction factor for slip flow

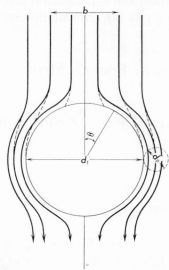

FIG. 9.4. Flow patterns around single cylindrical fibers.
————: Flow pattern of air
- - - - -: Flow pattern of particles
d_f = diameter of fiber
d_p = diameter of particles
b = width of air stream

Introducing the following dimensionless terms with respect to the coordinates, velocity and time, Eq. (9.3) will be rearranged to give:

$$\tilde{x} = \frac{2x}{d_f}, \quad \tilde{y} = \frac{2y}{d_f}, \quad \tilde{v}_x = \frac{v_x}{v_0}, \quad \tilde{v}_y = \frac{v_y}{v_0}, \quad \tilde{t} = \frac{2v_0 t}{d_f}$$

$$\left. \begin{array}{l} 2\phi\dfrac{d^2\tilde{x}}{d\tilde{t}^2} + \dfrac{d\tilde{x}}{d\tilde{t}} - \tilde{v}_x = 0 \\[2mm] 2\phi\dfrac{d^2\tilde{y}}{d\tilde{t}^2} + \dfrac{d\tilde{y}}{d\tilde{t}} - \tilde{v}_y = 0 \end{array} \right\} \tag{9.5}$$

where

  v_0 = upstream velocity of air

  $\phi = \dfrac{C\rho_p d_p^2 v_0}{18\mu d_f}$ — Inertial parameter

Eq. (9.5) can be integrated under appropriate boundary conditions to give the flow patterns of the particle (see broken lines in Fig. 9.4). It is seen from Fig. 9.4 that the flow patterns of the particles deviate from those of the air flow (theoretically calculable), due to the inertia of the particles as they approach the cylindrical surface. In the figure, the width of the upstream air flow is denoted as b; particles that move in the streamline of air beyond b will not touch the cylinder surface even after particles deviate from the air streamline near the cylinder. The theoretical value of the collection efficiency of single fibers due to the inertial effect of the particles, η_0', can be expressed by:

$$\eta_0' = b/d_f \qquad (9.6)$$

According to the calculation of Langmuir, the value of η_0' becomes zero when $\phi = 1/16$,[9] though other investigations have shown theoretically that other relationships exist between the values of η_0' and ϕ for cases in which various shapes of objects, other than the cylinder, are involved.

Designating the critical air velocity as v_c corresponding to the condition of $\phi = 1/16$,

$$v_c = (1.125) \frac{\mu d_f}{C \rho_p d_p^2} \qquad (9.7)$$

Substituting the values of $\rho_p = 1.0$ g/cm³ and $\mu = 1.80 \times 10^{-4}$ g/cm sec (air at 20°C) into Eq. (9.7), Fig. 9.5 is obtained, parameters being fiber diameter, d_f.[3] The value of C is determined from an empirical equation.[20]

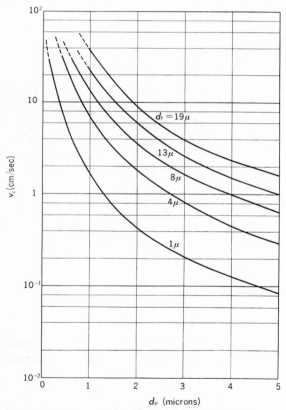

FIG. 9.5. Effect of fiber diameter (d_f) and particle diameter (d_p) on the critical velocity (v_c) for inertial impaction.

Fig. 9.5 is useful in determining quickly the approximate value of v_c, below which inertial impaction of particles may be neglected.

(b) Interception

If particles had no mass, they would follow exactly the streamlines of air flow; and although bacteria have mass, it is so small that they do, in fact, follow closely the streamlines of air flow. When particles entrained in streamlines of air are collected by contact with the fibers (see Fig. 9.4) they are said to be intercepted. The streamline of air which is $d_p/2$ from the fiber surface at a location of $\theta = \pi/2$ (see Fig. 9.4) is a limiting condition for the deposition of entrained particles as they pass a cylindrical fiber. The collection efficiency, η_0'', of particles on single fibers due to interception is calculated using the limiting width of air streamlines, $d_p/2$ from the fiber surface mentioned above.

According to Langmuir, the value of η_0'' can be calculated with the following equation in which $N_R = d_p/d_f$ and the upstream velocity of air, v_0, approximates the air velocity, v, around the cylinder:

$$\eta_0'' = \frac{1}{2(2.00 - \ln N_{Re})}\left\{2(1+N_R)\ln(1+N_R) - (1+N_R) + \frac{1}{1+N_R}\right\} \quad (9.8)$$

where

$N_{Re} = d_f v \rho / \mu$

$\rho = $ density of air

(c) Diffusion

Small particles display Brownian motion and thus may be collected on the surface of fibers as the particles are displaced from their median center of location. If the displacement of the particle is $2x_0$, by replacing d_p in Eq. (9.8) with $2x_0$, the collection efficiency, η_0''', of particles due to diffusion can be calculated from:[9]

$$\eta_0''' = \frac{1}{2(2.00 - \ln N_{Re})}\left\{2\left(1+\frac{2x_0}{d_f}\right)\ln\left(1+\frac{2x_0}{d_f}\right) - \left(1+\frac{2x_0}{d_f}\right) + \frac{1}{1+2x_0/d_f}\right\} \quad (9.9)$$

Assuming $v_0 = v$,

$$\frac{2x_0}{d_f} = \left\{1.12 \times \frac{2(2.00 - \ln N_{Re})D_{BM}}{vd_f}\right\}^{1/3} \quad (9.10)[9]$$

where

$D_{BM} = CkT'/3\pi\mu d_p \quad (9.11)$

$k = $ Boltzmann constant

$T' = $ absolute temperature

$D_{BM} = $ diffusivity of particles

Collection efficiencies, η_0, with single fibers may be expressed by the following equation, assuming that the values of η_0', η_0'' and η_0''' are independent to each other:

$$\eta_0 = \eta_0' + \eta_0'' + \eta_0''' \quad (9.12)$$

To simplify Equations (9.8) and (9.9), the following equation will be used; this holds nearly true over a range of values of N_{Re} from 10^{-4} to 10^{-1}:

$$\frac{1}{2.00 - \ln N_{\text{Re}}} \propto N_{\text{Re}}^{1/6} \tag{9.13}$$

The terms N_{R} and $2x_0/d_f$ in the brackets of Equations (9.8) and (9.9) are then expanded, assuming that each term is small compared with unity and that the second and higher orders of each term can be neglected. Consequently, Equations (9.8) and (9.9) can be simplified as follows:

$$\eta_0'' \propto N_{\text{R}}^2 N_{\text{Re}}^{1/6} \tag{9.14}$$

$$\eta_0''' \propto N_{\text{Sc}}^{-2/3} N_{\text{Re}}^{-11/18} \tag{9.15}$$

where

$$N_{\text{Sc}} = \frac{\mu}{\rho D_{\text{BM}}}$$

Equations (9.14) and (9.15) are similar to the semi-theoretical analysis published by Friedlander.[12]

The experience of practical sterilization of air sometimes suggests that the collection efficiency, η_0', due to inertial impaction of particles can be disregarded in calculating the value of η_0 in Eq. (9.12). Thus, using Equations (9.14) and (9.15), Aiba attempted to rearrange the extensive data published on the efficiencies of collection of various sorts of particles with different fibrous materials.[3,9,14,19,23,26,28,29,30]

Aiba selected data on over-all collection efficiencies, $\bar{\eta}$ (Eq. (9.16), where interception and diffusion probably predominate, see Eq. (9.7)). From the value of $\bar{\eta}$, that of η_α (the collection efficiency of single fibers whose volume fraction in the fibrous bed is α) was calculated with Eq. (9.17).

$$\bar{\eta} = \frac{N_1 - N_2}{N_1} \tag{9.16}$$

provided:

N_1 = numbers of organisms in the original aerosol
N_2 = numbers of organisms in the aerosol leaving the filter

$$\eta_\alpha = \frac{\pi d_f(1-\alpha)}{4L\alpha} \ln \frac{N_1}{N_2} = \frac{\pi d_f(1-\alpha)}{4L\alpha} \ln \left(\frac{1}{1-\bar{\eta}}\right) \tag{9.17}$$

where

L = thickness of filter bed

Eq. (9.17) indicates that the fraction of particles collected in any section within L is constant, the so-called log-penetration relation. All of the data in these calculations were secured with relatively thin filter beds (less than 4 cm) and, under these conditions, Eq. (9.17) is approximately true.

The following equation, which is an empirical relation presented by Chen,[9] was then used by Aiba to convert the values of η_α into η_0 starting from data on $\bar{\eta}$:

$$\eta_\alpha = \eta_0(1 + 4.5\alpha), \qquad 0 < \alpha < 0.10 \tag{9.18}$$

Lastly, the values of $\eta_0 N_{\text{R}} N_{\text{Pe}}$ $(= \eta_0 N_{\text{R}} N_{\text{Sc}} N_{\text{Re}})$ and $N_{\text{R}} N_{\text{Pe}}^{1/3} N_{\text{Re}}^{1/18}$ were calculated and plotted as shown in Fig. 9.6. The data points in the figure are markedly scattered, but this may suggest that a curve with a slope of three can be drawn through points at higher values of the abscissa (>1) and with a slope of one at lower values of the abscissa ($\sim10^{-1}\sim$), except a series of data points presented by Stern et al.[26] If this is accepted, then the curve with a slope of three corresponds to situations where interception predominates and this is expressed by Eq. (9.14),

Symbol	Author	$d_p(\mu)$	$d_f(\mu)$	N_{Re}	Particle	Fiber
●	Aiba	1.0	8~19	$10^{-2}\sim10^{-1}$	Bacteria	Glass
⊙	Chen	0.15~0.52	2.5	$10^{-3}\sim10^{-2}$	—	"
△	Humphrey	1.15	16	$10^{-2}\sim10^{-1}$	Bacteria spore	"
×	Ramskill	0.30	2.0	10^{-2}	—	Paper
▲	Sadoff	0.08	8.5	$10^{-3}\sim10^{-2}$	Bacteriophage	Glass
●	Stern	1.191~0.138	17	$10^{-2}\sim10^{-1}$	Polystyrene	Viscose
♦	Thomas, D. G.	0.40	10.5	$10^{-3}\sim10^{-1}$	—	Glass
○	Thomas, J. W.	0.13~0.56	1.5	$10^{-4}\sim10^{-3}$	DOP	"
□	Wong	0.47	9.6	10^{-1}	Sulfuric acid	"

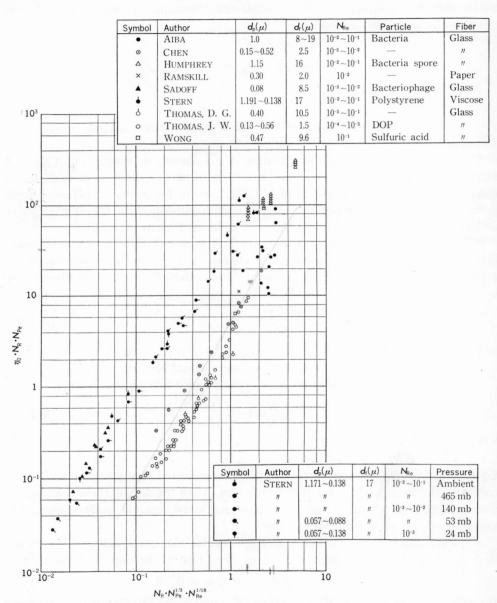

Symbol	Author	$d_p(\mu)$	$d_f(\mu)$	N_{Re}	Pressure
●	Stern	1.171~0.138	17	$10^{-2}\sim10^{-1}$	Ambient
●	"	"	"	"	465 mb
●	"	"	"	$10^{-3}\sim10^{-2}$	140 mb
●	"	0.057~0.088	"	"	53 mb
●	"	0.057~0.138	"	10^{-3}	24 mb

FIG. 9.6.　Single fiber collection efficiencies. The ordinate and abscissa are $\eta_0 N_R N_{Pe}$ and $N_R N_{Pe}^{1/3} N_{Re}^{1/18}$ respectively; where η_0=single fiber collection efficiency, N_R=interception parameter, N_{Pe}=Péclet number and N_{Re}=Reynolds number. For detailed information of these dimensionless terms, see the nomenclature at the end of this chapter.

while the other curve corresponds to situations where diffusion predominates and Eq. (9.15) applies.

In so far as the log-penetration law holds true, Fig. 9.6 indicates a way of determining the thickness of the filter bed required under various operating conditions, i.e., various values of η, d_f, d_p, α, and v_0. The value of η_0 estimated from Fig. 9.6 for a specific set of operating conditions will lead to the determination of L by using Equations (9.17) and (9.18).

9.3.2. Experimental determination of collection efficiencies

Fig. 9.6 was based on experimental data obtained with fibrous filters with thin beds and numbers of particles far in excess of $10^4/m^3$.

Aiba et al.[2] tested longer filter beds for their ability to collect *Serratia marcescens* from air contaminated with 10^4 cells/m³; these experimental conditions simulate industrial conditions much more closely than in the case of experiments previously reported.

Fig. 9.7 is a flow sheet of the apparatus used by Aiba et al. The bacterial suspension was atomized without reducing the viability of the cells. To determine the number of cells that passed the fibrous filter, the aerosol from the filter was directed through a nozzle, 1.8 mm in diameter, onto the surface of nutrient agar with a velocity of about 150 m/sec at atmospheric pressure and room temperature. The distance between the nozzle and the agar surface was 2 mm; the equation reported

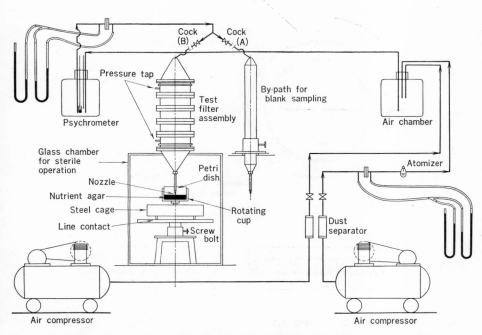

FIG. 9.7.   Flow sheet of a fibrous filter with a device to sample the outflow of air.

by Ranz *et al.*[20] indicates that, at the velocity of impingement used, 98 per cent of the cells were collected on the agar surface due to their inertial impaction. A Petri dish of nutrient agar was rotated at constant speed and replaced with a fresh dish after each complete revolution. The dishes were incubated at 30°C for 24 hours and the colonies on the agar surface were counted (see Fig. 9.8). To sample the original bacterial concentration, Cock A was opened and Cock B closed (see Fig. 9.7), so that the bacterial aerosol was diverted through a second nozzle to plates of nutrient medium. Fig. 9.9 shows the construction of the test-filter assembly, in which glass fibers were packed to give different lengths of filter bed up to 28.5 cm. To change the volume fraction of the bed, several stainless steel collars could be inserted (see Fig. 9.9).

Fig. 9.10 is a histogram showing the frequency of various values of the time interval, T, between the passage of successive bacterial cells from the test filter. The experimental conditions used to obtain the results shown in Fig. 9.10 are listed within the figure, where n' is the total number of colonies observed, $\bar{\nu}'_0$ the number of cells blown into the filter per second, and v_s the nominal velocity of aerosol flow through the filter; for other symbols, see the nomenclature at the end of this chapter.

It is seen from Fig. 9.10 that most of the cells pass the filter within short intervals

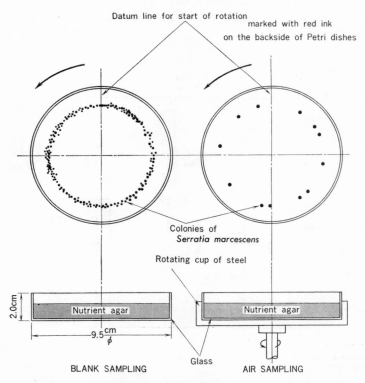

FIG. 9.8.   Plates of colonies which have developed from cells that passed the fibrous filter.

of time; this trend was also observed with other experimental conditions. Since the passage of the bacterial cells through the filter is expected to be a random phenomenon, the mean value, $\bar{T}$, can therefore be determined accurately only after a significant number of bacteria have passed from the filter.

To determine the number of bacteria needed to give a reliable value of $\bar{T}$, the sample ($n'=248$ in the example shown in Fig. 9.10) was divided into small groups, $n'=10, 20, 30$, and so forth. Using each sub-group or a combination of them, the range of $\bar{T}_{n'=\infty}$ (the mean of T in an infinite population of n') was estimated from the t-distribution with a level of significance of 5%. The result of this estimation is shown in Fig. 9.11; it is evident that the range of values of $\bar{T}_{n'=\infty}$ became smaller with increase in n', as could be expected. It was ascertained, from these results and many other experimental data, that the limits of confidence of $\bar{T}_{n'=\infty}$ were about ± $0.2\,T_{n'}$ when n' was greater than 50 and the level of significance was 5%. The deviations from the arithmetical sample averages of $\bar{v}'_0$ and $\bar{T}_{n'=248}$ in Fig. 9.10 were estimated also from the t-distributions with a level of significance of 5%.

Fig. 9.12 shows the effect of fiber diameter on the collection efficiency of the bacterial particles; each data point obtained with samples where $n'\geq 50$. The bed length L (cm) of the test filter is plotted in this figure against the value of $\bar{v}'_0\bar{T}_{n'}$ which is related to the over-all collection efficiency, $\bar{\eta}$, as follows:

$$\bar{\eta} = \frac{\bar{v}'_0\bar{T}_{n'} - 1}{\bar{v}'_0\bar{T}_{n'}} \qquad\qquad (9.19)$$

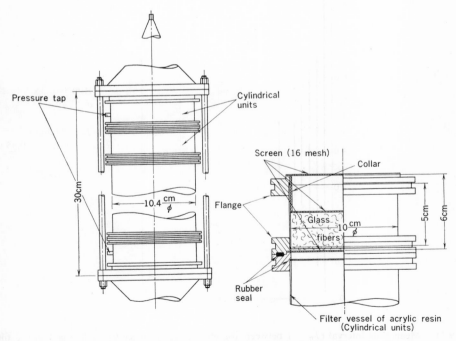

FIG. 9.9.　Details of air filter with variable thickness of filter bed.[2]

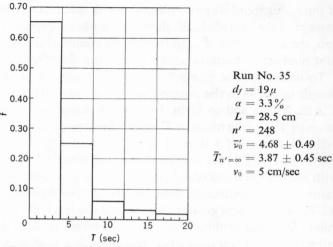

Run No. 35
$d_f = 19\,\mu$
$\alpha = 3.3\%$
$L = 28.5$ cm
$n' = 248$
$\bar{v}_0' = 4.68 \pm 0.49$
$\bar{T}_{n'=\infty} = 3.87 \pm 0.45$ sec
$v_0 = 5$ cm/sec

Fig. 9.10. Frequency distribution of the time interval (T) between the passage of successive bacteria from the filter.

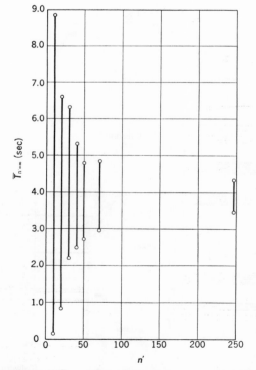

Run No. 35
$d_f = 19\,\mu$
$\alpha = 3.3\%$
$L = 28.5$ cm
$\bar{T}_{n'=248} = 3.87 \pm 0.45$ sec

Fig. 9.11.   Mean time interval ($\bar{T}_{n'=\infty}$) between the emergence of successive bacteria from a filter, exposed to an infinite population ($n' = \infty$).

For example, for $\bar{v}_0'\bar{T}_{n'}=10^2$, the filter has a collection efficiency of $\bar{\eta}=\dfrac{10^2-1}{10^2}=$
$0.99=99(\%)$. For a bacterial concentration in the aerosol of about 10^4 particles/m^3, the solid curves in Fig. 9.12 clearly show that the values of $\bar{\eta}$ for the respective values of d_f increased as L increased. It is also apparent from the figure that the fibers with smaller diameters are more effective in collecting particles than are those with larger diameters.

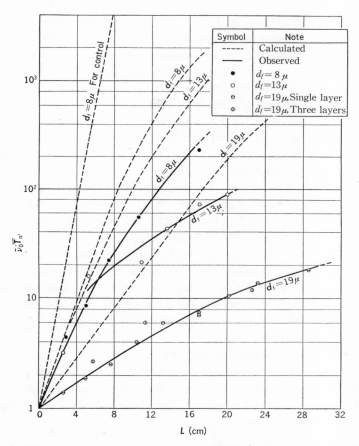

Fig. 9.12.   Effect of fiber diameter (d_f) on the collection efficiency at different depths of filter bed (L). Superficial air velocity, $v_s=5$ cm/sec; volume fraction of the filter, $\alpha=3.3\%$; No. of particles entering filter per sec$=\bar{v}_0'$; mean time interval between the emergence of particles from the filter$=\bar{T}_{n'}$

To determine the effect of different conditions of packing in a filter, fibers 19 microns in diameter were placed in a filter in a single layer and compared with a filter where the fibers were divided into sublayers giving a more uniform flow of the aerosol through the filter. The experimental data in Fig. 9.12 do not indicate a marked difference in the values of $\bar{\eta}$ for the two ways of packing the filters. However, this observation does not mean that in practical air sterilization there is no benefit in dividing the filter bed into several sections with supporters; these are necessary to prevent the fibrous bed from deforming during steam sterilization.

The broken curves in Fig. 9.12 were calculated from measurements of the distribution of bacteria within each filter bed. The experiments were conducted using ^{32}P labeled *Serratia marcescens*, the aerosol concentration of which was about 10^8 particles/m³, and with each bed length being 5 cm. From the theoretical analyses previously reported by Aiba *et al.*[4] the distribution curves could be extrapolated beyond the experimental value of L(5cm). In addition, the values of $\bar{v}_0' \bar{T}_{n'}$ could be calculated from the data on the longitudinal distribution of the particles within the bed. Readers who are especially interested in this calculation may refer to the original publication.[4] For comparison with data points, the resulting curves are shown in Fig. 9.12 as broken lines; the broken line designated as control was calculated assuming the log-penetration law. A remarkable difference of $\bar{\eta}$ is noted between the calculated curve for $d_f = 8$ microns on the one hand and the control on the other, especially as the value of L is increased.

For all fiber sizes, it should be noted that the curves for experimental determinations of $\bar{\eta}$ deviated considerably from those derived by calculation. This may be because the experimental curves were obtained with the aerosol concentration at 10^4 particles/m³, while in the calculations much more concentrated aerosols (10^8 particles/m³) were used. Although the collection efficiency ought to be independent of the aerosol concentration, the non-uniformity of passage of aerosol particles becomes more pronounced as the aerosol contamination is greatly reduced; and this may account for the deviations between these curves. It seems probable, therefore, that the slopes of the broken curves for each fiber size will decrease with increase in bed length L to approximate those of the corresponding solid curves, when the concentration of particles in the aerosol is decreased from 10^8 particles/m³ to 10^4 particles/m³.

If allowance is made for the fact that the concentration of bacteria varied from 10^4 to 10^8/m³ in the situations described in Fig. 9.12, the relation between over-all collection efficiency and bed length is considered to be independent of time within the usual duration of a batch fermentation, and the so-called "bridging" phenomenon would not be expected to occur.

9.3.3. Pressure drop of air flow

The drop in pressure as air flows through fibrous filters is related to the modified drag coefficient C_{Dm} which was introduced by Kimura *et al.*[17] Experimental data plotted in Fig. 9.13 show the effect of changes in the Reynolds number, N_{Re}, on the modified drag coefficient in filters packed with cotton or glass fibers.[5]
When the fiber size is roughly the same, it is seen from Fig. 9.13 that cotton fibers exert more resistance to air flow than do glass fibers.

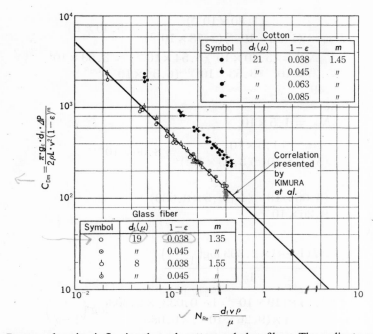

$$N_{Re} = \frac{d_f v \rho}{\mu}$$

FIG. 9.13.   Pressure drop in air flowing through cotton and glass fibers. The ordinate and abscissa are the modified drag coefficient, C_{Dm} and the Reynolds number, N_{Re}. The definitions of these two terms are also described in the figure; however, for detailed information regarding each term, see the nomenclature at the end of this chapter.

9.3.4.   Design example of a filter for air sterilization

Air at 20°C will be assumed to contain 10^4 particles, 1 micron in size, /m³. This dilute aerosol is to be filtered through a bed of glass fibers ($d_f = 19$ microns and $\alpha = 3.3\%$) at an air velocity $v_s = 5$ cm/sec. Calculate the relation between bed length, L, and over-all collection efficiency, $\bar{\eta}$, of the filter. Calculate also the pressure drop, ΔP, in the air flowing through the filter.

Solution

(1)   Calculation from the single fiber collection efficiency (Fig. 9.6)

It is apparent from Fig. 9.5 that $v_s = 5$ cm/sec is far less than the velocity of v_c which should apply to this problem. Therefore, Fig. 9.6 may be used to estimate the value of η_0 (single fiber collection efficiency).

$$N_{Re} = \frac{d_f \rho v}{\mu} = \frac{d_f \rho v_s}{\mu(1-\alpha)} = \frac{(19 \times 10^{-4})(1.20 \times 10^{-3})(5)}{(1.80 \times 10^{-4})(1-0.033)} = 6.54 \times 10^{-2}$$

$$N_R = \frac{d_p}{d_f} = \frac{1.0 \times 10^{-4}}{19 \times 10^{-4}} = 5.27 \times 10^{-2}$$

$$D_{BM} = \frac{CkT'}{3\pi\mu d_p} = \frac{(1.16)(1.38 \times 10^{-16})(273+20)}{(3)(3.14)(1.8 \times 10^{-4})(1.0 \times 10^{-4})} = 2.78 \times 10^{-7} \text{ cm}^2/\text{sec*}$$

* The value of C was calculated from the equation presented by Ranz *et al.*[20]

$$N_{\text{Sc}} = \frac{\mu}{\rho D_{\text{BM}}} = \frac{(1.80 \times 10^{-4})}{(1.20 \times 10^{-3})(2.78 \times 10^{-7})} = 5.40 \times 10^{5}$$

$$N_{\text{Pe}} = N_{\text{Sc}} N_{\text{Re}} = (5.40 \times 10^{5})(6.54 \times 10^{-2}) = 3.53 \times 10^{4}$$

$$N_{\text{R}} N_{\text{Pe}}^{1/3} N_{\text{Re}}^{1/18} = (5.27 \times 10^{-2})(3.53 \times 10^{4})^{1/3}(6.54 \times 10^{-2})^{1/18}$$
$$= 1.49$$

From Fig. 9.6, take

$$\eta_0 N_{\text{R}} N_{\text{Pe}} = 1.5 \times 10$$

$$\therefore \; \eta_0 = \frac{1.5 \times 10}{(5.27 \times 10^{-2})(3.53 \times 10^{4})} = 8.06 \times 10^{-3}$$

From Eq. (9.18),

$$\eta_\alpha = (8.06 \times 10^{-3})(1 + 4.5 \times 0.033)$$
$$= 9.26 \times 10^{-3}$$

From Eq. (9.17),

$$L = \frac{\pi d_f(1-\alpha) \times 2.303 \log\left(\frac{1}{1-\bar{\eta}}\right)}{4\eta_\alpha \alpha}$$

$$= \frac{3.14 \times (19 \times 10^{-4})(1-0.033) \times 2.303}{4 \times (9.26 \times 10^{-3}) \times 0.033} \log\left(\frac{1}{1-\bar{\eta}}\right)$$

$$= 10.9 \times \log\left(\frac{1}{1-\bar{\eta}}\right) \tag{9.20}$$

(2) Empirical equation—the following equation presented by Blasewitz et al.[8] will be used:

$$1 - \bar{\eta} = 10^{-c' L^{a'} \rho_b^{b'} v_s^{c''}} \tag{9.21}$$

provided:

L = bed thickness, inch
ρ_b = packed density of glass fibers, lb/ft³
v_s = superficial velocity of air, ft/min

Corresponding to the operating conditions of this problem,[8]

$$\left. \begin{array}{l} c' = 0.075 \\ a' = 0.9 \\ b' = 1.0 \\ c'' = -0.4 \end{array} \right\}$$

Assuming that the true density of glass fibers is 2.5 g/cm³,

$$\rho_b = 0.033 \times 2.5 \text{ g/cm}^3$$
$$= 82.5 \text{ kg/m}^3 = 5.15 \text{ lb/ft}^3$$
$$v_s = 5 \text{ cm/sec} = 9.84 \text{ ft/min}$$

Substituting the above figures into Eq. (9.21),

$$\bar{\eta} = 1 - 10^{-\{(0.075)L^{0.9}(5.15)(9.84)^{-0.4}\}} \tag{9.22}$$

The results of calculations with Equations (9.20) and (9.22) are shown in Fig.

9.14, in which L is plotted against $\bar{\eta}$. The scale of the abscissa of the figure is derived from Eq. (9.19). The solid curve for a fiber, diameter, $d_f = 19$ microns in Fig. 9.12, can be extrapolated and will become Curve B in this figure. The marked difference between Curves A and B might be ascribed to the fact that the aerosol concentration, $n = 10^4$ particles/m^3, in this example apparently decreased the value of $\bar{\eta}$ compared with the case of $n = 10^8$ particles/m^3, from which Fig. 9.6 or Eq. (9.20) was derived.

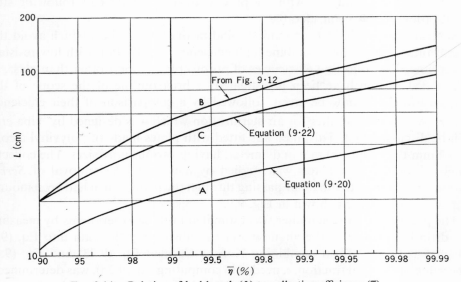

FIG. 9.14.   Relation of bed length (L) to collection efficiency ($\bar{\eta}$)

(3)   Pressure drop of air flow
Corresponding to $N_{\text{Re}} = 6.54 \times 10^{-2}$,

$$C_{\text{Dm}} = \frac{\pi g_c d_f \Delta P}{2\rho L v^2 (1-\varepsilon)^m} = 7.50 \times 10^2 \qquad \text{(Fig. 9.13)}$$

Taking the value of $m = 1.35$ from Fig. 9.13,

$$\frac{\Delta P}{L} = \frac{(7.5 \times 10^2) \times 2 \times 1.20 \left(\frac{0.05}{1-0.033}\right)^2 (1-0.967)^{1.35}}{3.14 \times 9.81 \times (19 \times 10^{-6})} = 82 \text{ Kg/m}^2/\text{m}$$

$$= 82 \text{ mmH}_2\text{O/m}$$

In operating filters for air sterilization, it is suggested that the packed fibers be dried completely after sterilization and that the air to be filtered be of low humidity to prevent the bed from becoming damp.

9.4.   NEW TYPE OF AIR-STERILIZATION FILTER

Although filters packed with glass fibers or other materials are extensively used

for air sterilization in fermentation plants in many countries, they have several
defects. Glass fibers have to be replaced after a period of operation, every one or
two years, depending on the particular operation.

Since exceedingly high collection efficiencies are required in fermentation plant
(the value of $\bar{\eta}$ being more than 99.99%) a large filter vessel is required, of the order
of 1 to 2 meters in length. Accordingly, replacement is expensive and the renewal
operation is often troublesome. Furthermore, the costs associated with producing
steam for sterilization and with the process of drying the fibers following steam
sterilization are also considerable.

Several attempts have been made to find media for air filters which avoid these
disadvantages and which combine high efficiency of collection with low resistance
to air flow. The collection efficiencies of porous plates, fibers other than glass, and
granulated carbon have been investigated; a brief outline of the scope of these
investigations will now be given, followed by a comparison of their efficiencies.

(1) A new type of filter for air sterilization which was designed by Aiba et al.
will be discussed first. This filter was fitted with plates made of polyvinyl alcohol
2 to 3 mm thick and 100 mm in diameter, having various pore sizes. The collection
efficiency of the filter plates was studied by measuring the removal of *Serratia
marcescens* from a stream of air passing through the plate, which had been mounted
in place of the screens shown in Fig. 9.9.

The pore size, d_e, of each filter was estimated in these experiments by measuring
the drop in pressure of the air flow and by substituting the data into Eq. (9.25)
which was derived from combining Kozeny-Carman Eq. (9.23) and Eq. (9.24).
The value of the void fraction, ε, needed in computing Eq. (9.25), was determined by
immersing a known amount of each filter into hot water and measuring its increase
in weight. The value of ε is about 80%.

$$v_s = \frac{\varepsilon}{(1-\varepsilon)^2} \frac{\varDelta P g_c}{\mu S_0^2 \rho_s^2 L K_c} \tag{9.23}$$

$$\frac{d_e}{4} = \frac{\varepsilon}{S_0 \rho_s (1-\varepsilon)} \tag{9.24}$$

$$d_e = 4\sqrt{\frac{v_s \mu L K_c}{\varepsilon \varDelta P g_c}} \tag{9.25}$$

where
ε = void fraction
g_c = conversion factor
S_0 = surface area per unit mass of filter material
K_c = Kozeny-Carman constant ($\doteq 5.0$)
ρ_s = true density of filter material

(2) The performance of a metallic plate, 2.6 mm in thickness and 100 mm in
diameter made of sintered bronze particles, was compared with that of the polyvinyl
alcohol plates. Fig. 9.15 shows photo-micrographs of a section through the poly-

vinyl alcohol plate and the surface of the sintered bronze plate. The measurements
of pore size, d_e, and over-all collection efficiency were made as described previously.

(3)   Aiba *et al.*[7] compared the relative collection efficiencies of several types of

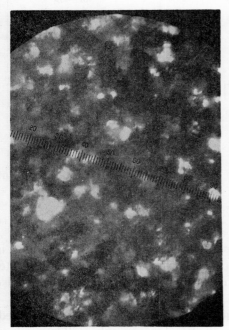
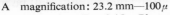

A   magnification: 23.2 mm—100μ B   magnification: 6.4 mm—100μ
FIG. 9.15.   Photo-micrographs of plates for filters;
A: Section of polyvinyl alcohol plate and
B: Surface of sintered bronze plate.

fibers, each with diameter $d_f = 20$ microns, using the apparatus shown in Fig. 9.9.
The fibers tested and the experimental conditions of these studies are indicated in
Fig. 9.16.

(4)   In a further series of tests, Aiba *et al.*[7] replaced glass fibers with activated
carbon particles in the apparatus shown in Fig. 9.9. The bed length of the active
carbon and of each type of fiber tested was adjusted to 7.0 cm; the determination
of the collection efficiencies with *Serratia marcescens* was carried out as previously
described.

Three samples of granular active carbon were examined; one sample of cylindrical carbon granules had been used for air sterilization in a fermentation plant for
about one year; the other two samples were newly manufactured, one of cylindrical
granules made by Japan Carbon Manufacturing Co. and the other of crushed
carbon made by Pittsburgh Co., U.S.A. The cylindrical particles were about 1 to 2
mm in diameter and height; from a sieve analysis, 95% by weight of the crushed
carbon was composed of particles whose size was below $d_{95} = 1.4$ mm. The moisture
contents of the activated carbon ranged from 0.3 to 3%, while the values of ρ_s

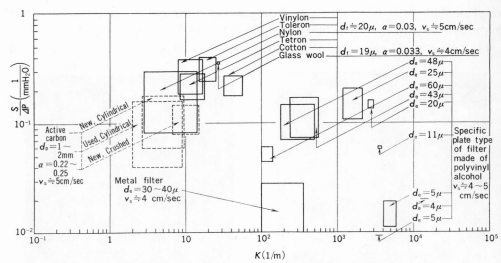

FIG. 9.16. Comparative performances of various filter media in air sterilization.

ranged from 1.91 to 2.02 g/cm³. Other experimental conditions are described in Fig. 9.16. As well as determining the collection efficiencies of these various filter media, the drop in pressure of the air flowing through each filter medium was also measured.[7]

The experimental performance of the various filter media will now be compared. Certain simplifications, assuming the log-penetration law to apply, will be made as shown by the following equation, in which the concepts of stopping criterion and stopping factor are introduced:

$$\bar{\eta} = 1 - e^{-S} = 1 - e^{-KL} \tag{9.26}$$

where

S = stopping criterion
K = stopping factor

The value of K is proportional to the collection efficiency of single fibers for fibrous filters with constant values of d_f and α (see Eq. (9.17)).

Since the thickness L of each type of filter plate was 2 to 3 mm, log-penetration probably applies. In the case of filters of fibrous or granular materials, on the other hand, the log-penetration law of Eq. (9.26) may not be valid, since the bed was 70 mm thick.

However, even in these latter cases, the calculation of K from the experimental data of $\bar{\eta}$, using Eq. (9.26), may be permissible in comparing the relative efficiencies of filters if due attention is paid to the value of L.

In general, it would be expected that the values of $S/\Delta P$ would decrease with increasing values of K; accordingly, an ideal filter is one that fulfils the condition that both K and $S/\Delta P$ have high values. Accordingly, the values of $S/\Delta P$ were calculated for each filter system.

The results of these comparisons are summarized in Fig. 9.16, in which $S/\Delta P$ ($1/\mathrm{mmH_2O}$) is plotted against K ($1/\mathrm{m}$). Rectangular regions in the figure show the extent of errors of mean square associated with respective mean values of K and $S/\Delta P$; these were determined from several replicated experiments, except in the case of the glass-fiber filter.

In the case of glass fibers, the values of K and $S/\Delta P$ were calculated as exemplified in the preceding design example.

It is noted from the figure that all the fibrous materials performed similarly, and that the granular active carbon particles were not as effective as the fibers.

If the value of K required in fermentation practice is considered to be in the range from 10^3 to 10^4, filters made of polyvinyl alcohol, especially those of $d_e = 20 \sim 30$ microns, can be recommended for air sterilization using only a single layer $2 \sim 3$ mm thick (see the values of K and $S/\Delta P$ in the figure). Filters whose effective pore size is $10 \sim 4$ microns are less satisfactory due to the lower value of $S/\Delta P$. For this reason, the metallic filter is not a suitable substitute for the fibrous bed.

Furthermore, if the log-penetration law does not apply to fibrous filters whose bed length exceeds several centimeters, the regions of Fig. 9.16 which apply to fibers or activated carbon will change. In general, the values of K and $S/\Delta P$ would tend to shift towards the origin in Fig. 9.16 when measurements were made with filter beds of fibers or carbon thicker than 7 cm.

Although the fibrous network observed microscopically (Fig. 9.15) may partly account for the excellent performance of plate filters made of polyvinyl alcohol, quantitative explanations have yet to be attempted. Since polyvinyl alcohol plates coated with melamine resin are resistant to repeated steam sterilization, the installation of this type of filter in fermentation plants is promising both from the viewpoint of saving space and of overcoming the various shortcomings of the glass fibers at present in use in the fermentation industry.

NOMENCLATURE

a' = empirical exponent, Eq. (9.21)
b = specific width of air stream, Fig. 9.4
b' = empirical exponent, Eq. (9.21)
C = Cunningham's correction factor for slip flow
c',c'' = empirical exponent, Eq. (9.21)
C_{Dm} = modified drag coefficient
d_f = fiber diameter, microns, cm
d_p = particle diameter, microns, cm
d_e = effective pore size, microns
d_{95} = particles whose size is below d_{95} comprise 95% by weight in sieve analysis
D_{BM} = diffusivity of particles, $\mathrm{cm^2/sec}$
f = frequency
g_c = conversion factor, 9.81 kg m/Kg $\mathrm{sec^2}$, 981 g cm/Gr $\mathrm{sec^2}$
k = Boltzmann constant, 1.38×10^{-16} $\mathrm{cm^2}$ g/$\mathrm{sec^2}$ °K
K_c = Kozeny-Carman constant ($\doteqdot 5.0$)

$K =$ stopping factor, 1/m, Eq. (9.26)

$L =$ thickness of filter (bed), cm, m (inch in Eq. (9.21))

$m =$ empirical exponent, Fig. 9.13

$n =$ particle concentration, particles/m³

$n' =$ number of colonies

$N =$ number of microbes in certain large volume of air

$N_1 =$ number concentration of particles before filter, particles/m³

$N_2 =$ number concentration of particles after filter, particles/m³

$N_{Pe} =$ Péclet number $(= vd_f/D_{BM})$

$N_R =$ Interception parameter $(= d_p/d_f)$

$N_{Re} =$ Reynolds number $(= d_f v\rho/\mu)$

$N_{Sc} =$ Schmidt number $(= \mu/\rho D_{BM})$

$p =$ probability, Eq. (9.1)

$\varDelta P =$ pressure drop of air flow, mmH₂O, Kg/m², Kg/cm²

$S =$ stopping criterion, Eq. (9.26)

$S_0 =$ surface area per unit mass of filter material, Eq. (9.23)

$t =$ time

$T =$ time interval between particles, sec

$T' =$ absolute temperature, Eq. (9.11)

$u =$ particle velocity, Eq. (9.3)

$v =$ air velocity $(= v_s/1 - \alpha)$, Eq. (9.3), cm/sec, m/sec

$v_0 =$ upstream air velocity, cm/sec

$v_c =$ critical value of v, cm/sec, Eq. (9.7)

$v_s =$ superficial air velocity, cm/sec, m/sec; ft/min in Eq. (9.21)

$W(n) =$ probability, Eq. (9.1)

$x, y =$ coordinates

$x_0 =$ effective radius of dispacement of particles due to diffusion, Eq. (9.10)

Superscripts:

— : arithmetical mean

∼ : non-dimensional symbol

→ : vector symbol

Greek letters

$\alpha =$ volume fraction

$\varepsilon =$ void fraction $(= 1 - \alpha)$

$\eta_0 =$ collection efficiency of single fiber

$\eta_0' =$ collection efficiency of single fiber due to inertial impaction

$\eta_0'' =$ collection efficiency of single fiber due to interception

$\eta_0''' =$ collection efficiency of single fiber due to diffusion

$\eta_\alpha =$ collection efficiency of single fiber whose volume fraction is α

$\bar{\eta} =$ over-all collection efficiency of filter

$\theta =$ radian, Fig. 9.4

$\mu =$ viscosity of air, g/cm sec

$\rho =$ density of air, g/cm,³ kg/m³

$\rho_p =$ density of particle, g/cm³

$\rho_s =$ true density of filter material, Eq. (9.23)

$\rho_b =$ packed density of glass fiber, lb/ft³, Eq. (9.21)

$\nu =$ expected value $(= Np)$

$\bar{\nu}_0' =$ number of particles blown into filter per sec

ϕ = inertial parameter ($= \dfrac{C \rho_p d_p^2 v_0}{18 \mu d_f}$), Eq. (9.5)

References

1. AIBA, S., and YAMAMOTO, A. (1959). "Distribution of bacterial cells within fibrous air sterilization filters." *J. Biochem. Microbiol. Tech. & Eng.* **1**, 129.
2. AIBA, S., SHIMASAKI, S., and SUZUKI, S. (1961). "Experimental determination of the collection efficiencies of fibrous air sterilization filter." *J. Gen. Appl. Microbiol.* **7**, 192.
3. AIBA, S. (1961). "Design of air filter." *Chem. Tech. (Japan)* **13**, 43.
4. AIBA, S., SAKAMOTO, H., and KODAMA, T. (1960). "Some analyses of the bacterial distribution within fibrous air sterilization filter." *J. Gen. Appl. Microbiol.* **6**, 15.
5. AIBA, S. (1962). "Design of fibrous air sterilization filters." *ibid.* **8**, 169.
6. AIBA, S., NISHIKAWA, S., and IKEDA, H. (1963). "A new type of air sterilization filter." *ibid.* **9**, 267.
7. AIBA, S., NISHIKAWA, S., and NIIRA, R. (1963). "Comparative studies on the performances of various sorts of materials as the filter media in air sterilization." *Progress Rept. No. 26*, Biochem. Eng. Lab., Inst. Appl. Microbiol., Univ. of Tokyo.
8. BLASEWITZ, A.G., and JUDSON, B.F. (1955). "Filtration of radioactive aerosols by glass fibers." *Chem. Eng. Progress* 6-J.
9. CHEN, C.Y. (1955). "Filtration of aerosols by fibrous media." *Chem. Review* **55**, 595.
10. CARSWELL, T.S., DOUBLY, J.A., and NASON, H.K. (1937). "Bacterial control in air conditioning." *Ind. Eng. Chem.* **29**, 85.
11. DECKER, H.M., CITEK, F.J., HARSTAD, J.B., GROSS, N.H., and PIPER, F.J. (1954). "Time temperature studies of spore penetration through an electric air sterilizer." *Appl. Microbiol.* **2**, 33.
12. FRIEDLANDER, S.K. (1958). "Theory of aerosol filtration." *Ind. Eng. Chem.* **50**, 1161.
13. GADEN, E.L., JR., and HUMPHREY, A.E. (1956). "Fibrous filters for air sterilization." *ibid.* **48**, 2172.
14. HUMPHREY, A.E., and GADEN, E.L. JR. (1955). "Air sterilization by fibrous media." *ibid.* **47**, 924.
15. HUMPHREY, A.E. (1960). Private communication.
16. JACOBS, M.B., MANOHRAN, A., and GOLDWATER, L.J. (1962). "Comparison of dust counts of indoor and outdoor air." *Int. J. Air Wat. Poll.* **6**, 205.
17. KIMURA, N., and IINOYA, G. (1959). "Experimental studies on the pressure drop characteristics of fiber mats." *Chem. Eng. (Japan)* **23**, 792.
18. KLUYVER, A.J., and VISSER, J. (1950). "Some observations on filtration." *Antonie van Leeuwenhoek* **16**, 311.
19. RAMSKILL, E.A., and ANDERSON, W.L. (1951). "The inertial mechanism in the mechanical filtration of aerosols." *J. Colloid Sci.* **6**, 416.
20. RANZ, W.E., and WONG, J.B. (1952). "Impaction of dust and smoke particles on surface and body collectors." *Ind. Eng. Chem.* **44**, 1371.
21. ROBINSON, F.W. (1939). "Ultraviolet air sanitation." *ibid.* **31**, 23.
22. Rept. Sanitary Eng. Station, Tokyo. (1925), (1927), (1928), (1929). "Hygienic examination of air in metropolitan area." 342, 224, 57, 109.
23. SADOFF, H.L., and ALMOLF, J.W. (1956). "Testing of filters for phage removal." *Ind. Eng. Chem.* **48**, 2199.
24. SILVERMAN, L. (1951). "Performance of industrial aerosol filters." *Chem. Eng. Progress* **47**, 462.
25. SILVERMAN, L., CONNERS, E.W., JR., and ANDERSON, D.M. (1955). "Mechanical electrostatic charging of fabrics for air filters." *Ind. Eng. Chem.* **47**, 952.

26. STERN, S.C., ZELLER, H.W., and SCHEKMAN, A.I. (1960). "The aerosol efficiency and pressure drop of a fibrous filter at reduced pressures." *J. Colloid Sci.* **15**, 546.

27. STARK, W.H., and POHLER, G.M. (1950). "Sterile air for industrial fermentations." *Ind. Eng. Chem.* **42**, 1789.

28. THOMAS, D.G. (1953). Ph.D. Thesis in Chem. Eng., Ohio State Univ.

29. THOMAS, J.W., and YODER, R.E. (1956). "Aerosol size for maximum penetration through Fiberglas and sand filters." *A.M.A. Arch. Ind. Health* **13**, 545.

30. WONG, J.B., RANZ, W.E., and JOHNSTONE, H.F. (1956). "Collection of aerosol particles." *J. Appl. Phys.* **27**, 161.

CHAPTER 10

OPERATION, MEASUREMENT AND CONTROL

Measurement and control in fermentation plants have many features in common with other chemical industries; for example, devices for the measurement and control of flow rate, temperature, humidity, pressure, and liquid level are basic equipment in any chemical plant. These topics are, therefore, omitted. Discussion in this chapter will center particularly around those controllable variables peculiar to the fermentation industry. The analytical and quantitative explanations of the mechanisms connecting detection with control will not be attempted. In other words, control in this context means the better management of the fermentation as a whole, rather than control of each variable in the narrow sense of the term. Readers who are interested in the practical and theoretical aspects of control mechanisms and the common industrial equipment for measuring temperature, pressure, and so forth should refer to the appropriate books or articles.[14,23]

Fig. 10.1 shows schematically various factors to be measured and controlled in an aerobic fermentation. The fact that the fermentor must be operated aseptically presents a new problem in design; the transfer of the inoculum to the main fermentor and the intermittent sampling of the broth during the fermentation require special precautions. These will be elaborated in the first section.

An important variable in the fermentation which must be measured and controlled is pH, which will be discussed in the second section. Although the theory of the glass electrode for measuring pH, together with its practical application to biological science, has been established for the past 40 years, its application to the fermentation industry has only recently become possible. The principal reason for this is the difficulty in producing a glass electrode able to withstand repeated sterilizations with steam at 120°C.

For the satisfactory operation of any aerobic fermentation, the amount of dissolved oxygen (D.O.) in the fermentation broth must be measured and controlled, as will be discussed in Section 10.3. If the value of D.O. falls below a certain critical level, the yield and metabolic activity of the organisms will be adversely affected.

Dynamometers can be used for the measurement of power input into fermentors, but they must be mounted in a way that permits aseptic operation of the fermentor. Later in this chapter the use of a strain gauge for measuring the power input into a jar fermentor will be described.

Finally, physical methods will be discussed for the determination of such properties of the fermentation broth as its viscosity, the density of fermentation gases,

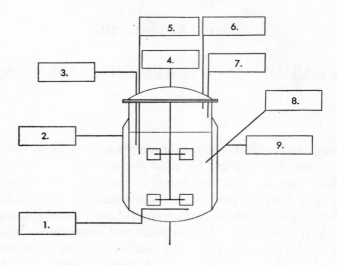

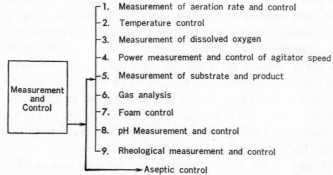

1. Measurement of aeration rate and control
2. Temperature control
3. Measurement of dissolved oxygen
4. Power measurement and control of agitator speed
5. Measurement of substrate and product
6. Gas analysis
7. Foam control
8. pH Measurement and control
9. Rheological measurement and control

→ Aseptic control

FIG. 10.1.   Outline of the measurements and controls needed in a fermentation.

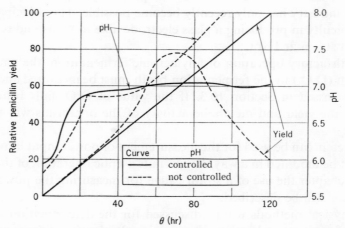

FIG. 10.2.   Relative yield of penicillin with and without pH control.[5]

and the optical measurement of substrate or product.[7,8] Such methods can be readily transferred to automatic systems and appear to have great promise for the fermentation industry.

10.1.　Aseptic Operation

10.1.1.　Pipe lines and valves

The pipe lines transporting sterile air, seed, and other materials required for aseptic use should be sterilized with steam (usually at 120°C for 20 to 30 minutes). It is important that the pipe line be free from steam condensate after steriliza-tion; therefore, the line should be constructed as simply as possible. Except in particular fermentations which are vulnerable to metals, ordinary steel pipes may be employed for the transport of fluids.

It is usually necessary to install valves in the pipe line. If a high order of sterility is needed, the diaphragm type of valve is recommended, since the diaphragm valve has no packing gland and is less liable to contamination, but the design of sterile valves for the fermentation industry deserves more attention from engineers. From considerations of cost, the conventional stop, angle, and globe valves are frequently used in the fermentation industry.

10.1.2.　Aseptic inoculation and sampling

Fig. 10.3 shows the connections required for the aseptic transfer of a spore suspen-sion to a seed tank. The spore-suspension vessel and its piping is first sterilized and the spores introduced into the vessel; the system is connected at both A and B with a pipe line leading to a seed tank. The connections at A and B are first slackened so that steam bleeds from A and B when steam flows through valves E, F, and G, with valves D, H, I, and C closed (see figure). After sterilization with steam at 120°C

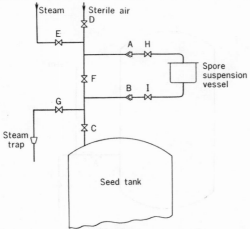

FIG. 10.3.　The aseptic transfer of a spore suspension into a seed tank.[17]

for about 20 minutes, valves E and G are closed and the connections at A and B are tightened. Valve D is then opened and the line is cooled to the desired level under positive pressure with sterile air.

At the correct temperature, valve F is closed, valves H, I, and C are opened, and sterile air is used to blow the spore suspension from the vessel to the seed tank. Valves D, C, H, and I are then closed and the spore suspension vessel is disconnected at A and B.

Fig 10.4 illustrates another technique for aseptic inoculation of a fermentor from a seed tank. Two vessels are connected with a flexible pipe at joints A and B. To sterilize the medium in the fermentor, steam from valves J and G passes through D, E, and F into the fermentor to heat the medium to 120°C for 20 minutes. During this period, valve C is closed, while valves H and I are slightly opened to bleed steam and to remove condensate. With the completion of steam sterilization, valves G, J, H, and I are closed, while valves F, E, and D are left open. The medium

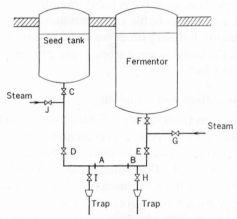

FIG. 10.4. Services to allow aseptic inoculation of a fermentor.[17]

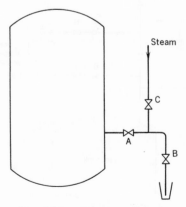

FIG. 10.5. Sampling point.[17]

is cooled to the incubation temperature under positive pressure using sterile air (connections to the sterile air are not shown in Fig. 10.4). Valve C is then opened and the seed culture is transported to the fermentor either by gravity or by the pressure difference between the seed tank and the fermentor. Finally, valves C and F are closed and the inoculation line is resterilized with steam before the flexible pipe is detached from A and B.

It is frequently necessary to sample the broth during fermentation; Fig. 10.5 shows a sampling point which can be steam sterilized. Normally valves A, B, and C are closed and the end of the sampling pipe is immersed, for example, in 40% formaldehyde solution.

When a sample is required, the vessel containing the germicide is removed and steam is blown through C and B long enough to sterilize the section. After that, C and B are partly closed to bleed some steam and condensate through B. Valve A is then opened slightly to let some broth pass to waste and to cool the line. Valve C is closed and broth from the fermentor is collected in a sterile bottle. After sampling, the outlet is resterilized with steam by closing A and then put in the out-of-use arrangement.

10.1.3. Aseptic seals

The aseptic seal discussed briefly below is used to seal the rotating shaft for a conventional type of fermentor.

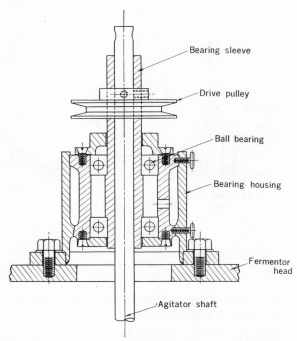

FIG. 10.6.   Bearing assembly for a 30-liter jar fermentor.[9]

While the seal does not present any serious problem in the case of laboratory-scale fermentors, close attention should be paid to the seal of large-scale fermentors.

Fig. 10.6 is an example of a bearing assembly in a 30-liter jar fermentor.[9] The bearing housing through which an agitator shaft penetrates, as shown in the figure, is of conventional design. In the figure, a drawing of the seal is omitted for convenience.

An aseptic seal for a jar fermentor is exemplified in Fig. 10.7. In this example, aseptic conditions are achieved with a rotating seal (Magnolia bearing bronze)[9] and a stationary seal (Oilite bushing insert).[9] The surface of the bronze bearing is provided with a radial slot, into which either silicone or petroleum grease is charged for lubrication. It is usual to lubricate the seals before sterilization with a silicone grease which does not become fluid during sterilization at 120°C for 20 minutes (for instance, Dow Corning 44 grease).[9]

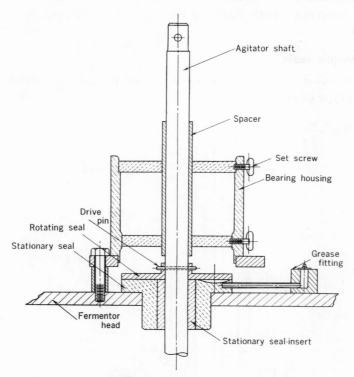

FIG. 10.7. Shaft seal.[9]

Another type of seal is a stuffing box in which asbestos impregnated with lubricating grease is tightly packed in the space between the wall of the stuffing box and the agitator shaft which passes through the box. Fig. 10.8 is a schematic drawing of a stuffing box type of seal, equipped with a lantern ring to allow steam to penetrate to the shaft. This type of seal is used for large fermentors where the penetration of steam into the sealing materials of the gland may be inadequate. In addition, the "mechanical" type of seal is used for large fermentors.

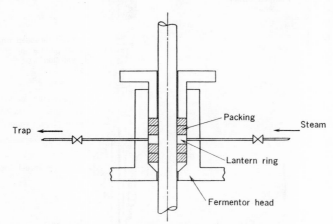

FIG. 10.8.   Steam-sealed gland.[17]

10.2.   CONTROL OF pH

10.2.1.   Sterilizable electrodes

The automatic addition of acid and alkali to fermentations can be achieved by techniques already in use in other chemical industries, but special glass electrodes had to be developed for use in the fermentation industry.

Fig. 10.9 shows a sterilizable pH electrode with which Gualandi *et al.*[12] measured the pH of fermenting broth with a device placed directly into the fermentor. The half cell of the glass electrode was composed of Ag/AgCl saturated with solid KCl. The solid KCl increases the mechanical resistance of the glass electrode to external force by depositing fine particles of KCl on the glass surface during heat sterilization and cooling of the electrode.

The half cell of the reference electrode consisted of the same material as the glass electrode, asbestos or porcelain cylinder being used as the junction material.

To ensure good insulation, both the glass and reference electrodes were mounted in Teflon gaskets and silicone rubber washers (see Fig. 10.9). The internal resistance of the electrode was 300 to 500 megohm. Both electrodes were protected by steel sleeves provided with several holes to allow free passage of the broth, as shown in the figure.

Although the chemical composition of the glass membrane was not given in the publication of Gualandi *et al.*, it is noted that these electrodes were used successfully and continuously without replacing KCl for 200 hours, and during this period, the electrodes were sterilized with steam three times.

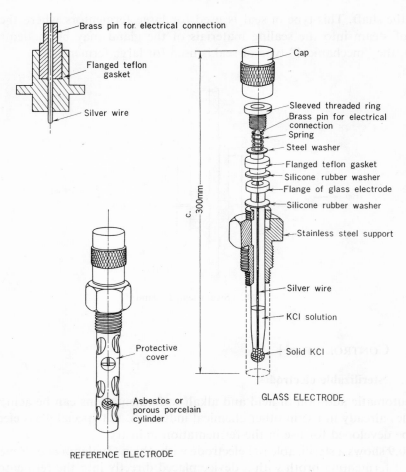

FIG. 10.9.   Sterilizable pH electrode.[12]

In the glass and reference calomel electrodes manufactured by Toa Electronics, Ltd., Tokyo, the glass membrane fused on the electrode surface contains a rare metal such as Li or La to decrease the internal resistance to 30 to 40 megohm.

The dimensions of both the glass and reference electrodes manufactured by Toa Electronics are shown in Figs. 10.10 and 10.12. It is claimed that these electrodes can withstand 20 sterilizations with steam at 120°C for 1 hour.

10.2.2.   Flow sheets of pH measurement and control

Fig. 10.10 is a flow sheet of pH measurement and control in a jar fermentor. The glass and reference electrodes (HG-8001 L and HC 802 L) can be setrilized in the fermentor either by blowing live steam into the jar or by setrilizing the whole unit in an autoclave. The electrodes can withstand 50 to 60 sterilizations with steam at 120°C for 1 hour. When the temperature of the unit reaches the temperature of fermentation, the measurement of pH can begin without making any adjustment to the electrodes. The accuracy of pH measurement and control is claimed to be ± 0.1 for the electrodes made by Toa Electronics.

A flow sheet adopted by Denison *et al.*[5] to measure continuously the pH values of a fermentation is shown in Fig. 10.11. The glass electrode (Beckman No. 8990-90) and the reference electrode (Beckman No. 19700) could withstand steam sterilization at 120°C for 45 minutes more than 30 times. The electrodes in this case

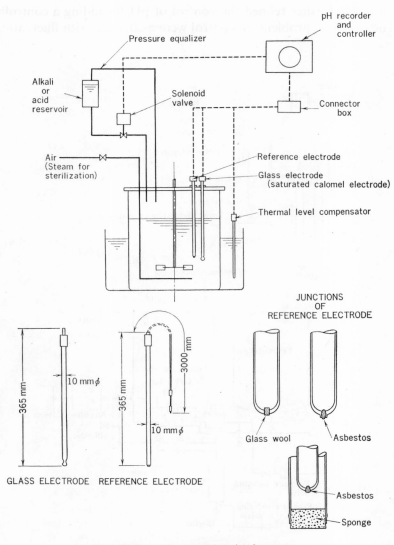

FIG. 10.10.   pH control in a jar fermentor.

were set up outside the fermentor (200 liter) in a flow assembly (Beckman No. 4210) as shown in the figure.

The KCl solution in the reference electrode diffused continuously at a rate of about 2 ml/day into the fermenting broth to preclude an abnormal potential developing between the electrode and the broth. The KCl solution was sterilized with 1% benzyl alcohol, and compressed air from outside the flow assembly was used to force the KCl into the fermentor. An inverted glass test tube packed with glass wool minimized the entrance of fermenting broth into the reference electrode.

In this system, the broth flowing from the fermentor returned with an air lift after passing through the flow assembly in which the electrodes were mounted.

Denison et al.[5] further refined the control of pH by adding a controller to the system. The principal problems in control were associated with fluctuations in the

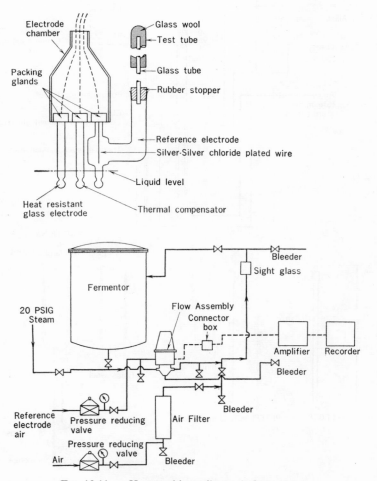

FIG. 10.11. pH control in a pilot-scale fermentor.[5]

air pressure in the flow assembly, the properties of the fermentation broth itself, and foaming of the broth. The best pH control achieved was within ± 0.05.

Another type of pH measurement and control in a large-scale fermentor is illustrated in Fig. 10.12. The glass and saturated calomel reference electrodes (HG 6009 and HC 209 of Toa Electronics Ltd., Tokyo) projected through the wall of the fermentor as shown in the figure. The electrodes could be sterilized more than 50 times at 120°C for 1 hour without malfunction.

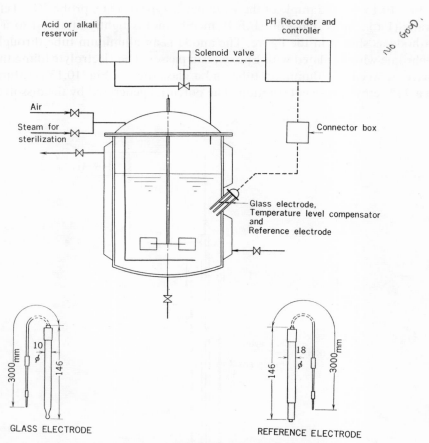

FIG. 10.12.   pH control in a production-scale fermentor.

10.3.   DISSOLVED OXYGEN

10.3.1.   Sensors of dissolved oxygen (D.O.) with a Teflon membrane

The sensors of dissolved oxygen have made remarkable progress during the past few years. Until recently D.O. in the fermentation broth could be measured only by removing samples intermittently and determining the oxygen in solution pola-rographically or chemically; these methods are tedious and liable to contamination, making it difficult to study changes of D.O. concentration during the fermentation. The introduction of Teflon membranes which can be sterilized with steam has improved D.O. sensors considerably, and now D.O. values can be determined continuously during the fermentation. Only a few of the D.O. sensors will be re-viewed here; a detailed review of the sensors now available has been published in the Proceedings of I.A.M. Symposia on Microbiology.[2]

Fig. 10.13 is an example of the voltametric type of D.O. probe. The Teflon mem-brane (1 to 2 mils, Du Pont F.E.P. membrane) is tightly attached to a platinum cathode as shown in the figure. The anode is an aluminum tube through which a nichrome wire insulated with Epoxy resin passes. The electrolyte filling the annular space between the aluminum tube and a glass tube in Fig. 10.13 is saturated KCl in a 95% ethylene glycol solution. The potential generated by the dissolved oxygen

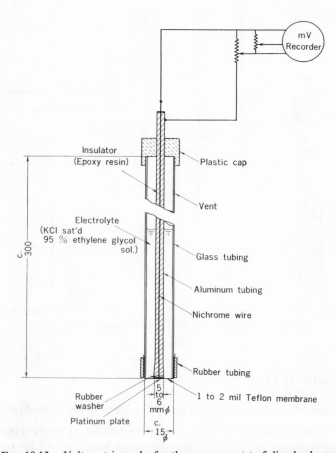

FIG. 10.13.   Voltametric probe for the measurement of dissolved oxygen.[4]

is detected potentiometrically. The electrochemical reactions between the cathode and anode are as follows:

$$\text{Cathode: } 3O_2 + 6H_2O + 12e \longrightarrow 12OH^-$$
$$\text{Anode: } 4Al^{+++} + 12Cl^- \longrightarrow 4AlCl_3 + 12e$$

Although a linear relationship between the D.O. concentration and the potential difference is expected, several problems affecting the sensitivity and durability of this sensor remain to be solved. However, according to Merck, Sharp & Dohme, this type of electrode has performed satisfactorily for periods up to two months with 45 consecutive sterilizations.[4]

A sensor consisting of a long Teflon tube attached to a continuous gas analyzer is shown in Fig. 10.14. The dissolved oxygen in the broth diffuses through the walls of the Teflon tube into nitrogen gas, which is flowing continuously through the tube. The oxygen in the emerging gas is passed to an oxygen analyzer and the concentration is recorded.

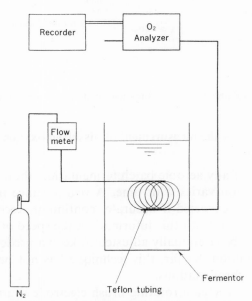

FIG. 10.14.　A probe of Teflon tubing coupled to a gas analyzer for the measurement of dissolved oxygen.[2]

Another type of Teflon sensor was constructed by Humphrey to measure the dissolved oxygen in a 5-liter jar fermentor (see Fig. 10.15).[15] This probe is a combination of the gas-diffusion principle and the voltametric determination of oxygen; the electrodes are Ag and Pb with KOH as electrolyte. According to Humphrey, this kind of sensor can also be used to measure dissolved gases such as carbon dioxide and methane.[15] However, detailed technical information on these points has not yet been published.

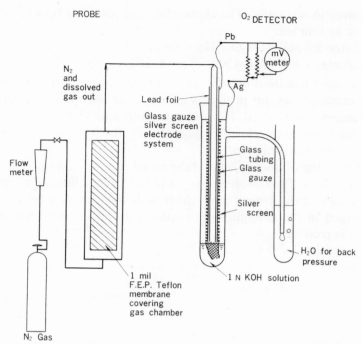

FIG. 10.15. Teflon probe suitable for the measurement of dissolved oxygen in pilot-plant equipment.[15]

10.3.2. Application of the measurement of dissolved oxygen to fermentation control

During the course of any aerobic batch fermentation, the demand for oxygen by the microbial population varies with time. A real advance in the control of the fermentation might be expected if accurate, continuous recordings of dissolved oxygen could be achieved. With this information, the speed of the agitator and the rate of aeration could be continually adjusted to keep a predetermined concentration of oxygen in solution. So far, this technique has not been exploited to any extent in commercial fermentations.

Gualandi *et al.* constructed a rotating-brush electrode to measure continuously the D.O. levels during fermentations.[11] The rotating-brush electrode functions on the same principle as the dropping-mercury electrode for polarographic measurements; the surface of the silver-amalgam electrode is renewed constantly by the action of a rotating brush. Measurements of the D.O. levels with this assembly in penicillin and tetracycline fermentations (1,000-liter-capacity vessel) were made successfully over the entire period of each fermentation.[11] They did not attempt in this case to control the aeration rate or agitator speed in either fermentation. However, since the continuous measurement of D.O. was successful, its control seems feasible.

Fig. 10.16 is a flow sheet of the apparatus with which Shu[19] controlled the rate of oxygen uptake by microbes by varying the agitator speed; the rate of aeration was kept constant. After removing CO_2 and humidity from the effluent gas, a magnetic gas analyzer (Model F-3, Arnold O. Beckman Inc., South Pasadena, Calif.) was employed to measure the oxygen concentration in the exit gas.

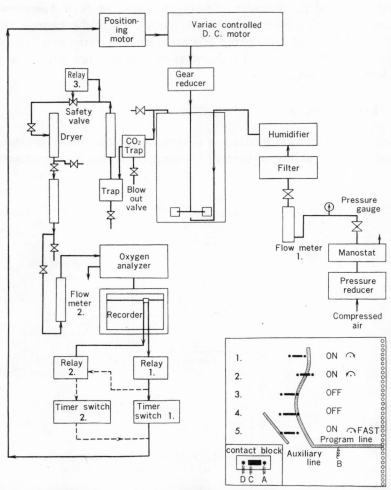

FIG. 10.16.   Flow sheet of apparatus for controlling the rate of oxygen uptake by organisms.[19]

On a recorder chart, a program line was set with a silver paint. A contact box of Plexi-glas into which copper-relay contacts were embedded (A, C, and D as shown in the lower right-hand side of the figure) was used to detect any deviation from the selected oxygen concentration in the effluent gas.

The lower section of the figure illustrates the working principle of this control. If the contact box is off the program line (Position 1), the oxygen concentration is too low; Relay 1 in Fig. 10.16 is actuated so that the rotational speed of the agitator is reduced through the activation of the Positioning Motor. When the contact box is in Position 2, the oxygen concentration is too high in the exit gas; the Positioning Motor is then activated to increase the agitator speed. When contact D is on an auxiliary line, Relay 2 is actuated so that the agitator speed is quickly reduced to correct for the deviation from the programed line.

Shu first measured the characteristic oxygen uptake rates of *Xanthomonas uredovorus* and *Aspergillus niger* in a 13-liter vessel. Then the change of oxygen concentration in the exit gas during fermentation was programed to reproduce the oxygen uptake rates measured in the previous studies. In each case, the accuracy obtained was satisfactory.[19]

10.4. FOAM CONTROL

Foaming of fermentation media is a common problem; many substances have been tested for their ability to control foaming; in addition, a mechanical foam

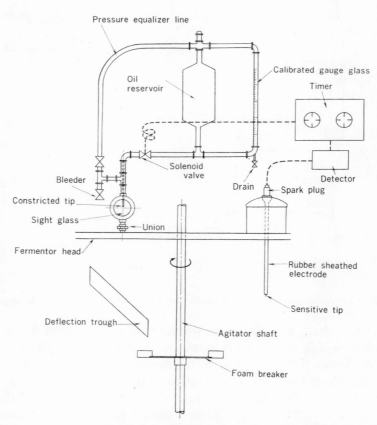

FIG. 10.17. Ancillary equipment to control foaming in fermentation broths.[16]

disintegrator attached to the agitator shaft (see Fig. 10.17) often supplements the action of antifoam agents. However, many problems associated with the destruction of foams remain to be clarified, particularly the physico-chemical properties of foams.

Fig. 10.17 shows an antifoam system; if the foam contacts a rubber sheathed electrode, an electric unit actuates a solenoid valve to allow the passage of a sterile antifoam agent into the fermentor. To secure uniformity of dispersion of the agent on the surface of the broth, a deflection trough is provided as shown in Fig. 10.17. The antifoam agent is thus distributed uniformly over the foaming surface; its action is supplemented by the centrifugal effect of the foam breaker. The amount of antifoam entering the fermentor is usually controlled by a timer in the circuit to the solenoid valve.

Fig. 10.18 is an example of an electronic circuit for activating the solenoid valve.[18] The electrode to detect the foam is connected with the grid of a vacuum tube (either V_2 or V_3 in the figure). Contact of the foam with the insulated electrode renders the grid potential negative compared with the cathode. This will immediately reduce the plate current of the tube to allow the passage of antifoam agent through a solenoid valve as shown in Fig. 10.18. The length of time during which the agent is added is regulated with S_4, an automatic time switch.

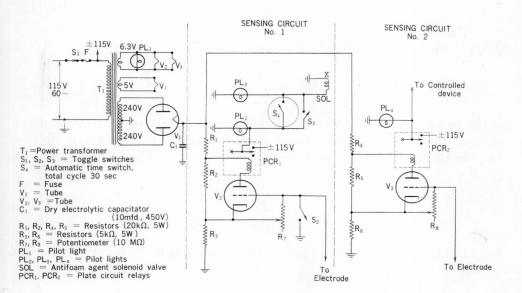

T_1 = Power transformer
S_1, S_2, S_3 = Toggle switches
S_4 = Automatic time switch,
　　　total cycle 30 sec
F = Fuse
V_1 = Tube
V_2, V_3 = Tube
C_1 = Dry electrolytic capacitator
　　　(10mfd, 450V)
R_1, R_2, R_4, R_5 = Resistors (20kΩ, 5W)
R_3, R_6 = Resistors (5kΩ, 5W)
R_7, R_8 = Potentiometer (10 MΩ)
PL_1 = Pilot light
PL_2, PL_3, PL_4 = Pilot lights
SOL = Antifoam agent solenoid valve
PCR_1, PCR_2 = Plate circuit relays

FIG. 10.18.　Example of an electronic circuit for foam control.[18]

10.5.   MEASUREMENTS OF AGITATOR POWER AND CAPACITY COEFFICIENTS OF MASS TRANSFER

10.5.1.   Strain-gauge type of dynamometer

Despite the importance of measuring the net power consumed in an agitated fermentor, it is only in recent years that attempts have been made to install dynamometers in fermentors. As has already been made clear in the chapter on scale-up, the power input per unit volume of liquid may serve as a basis for scale-up. Moreover, a continuous record of the power consumed during a fermentation may assist in control of the fermentation.

It is usual to measure the power consumption with a wattmeter attached to the motor of the agitator in a large-scale fermentor. Although this approximation in measuring the power is permissible in commercial equipment, it can not be adopted in a bench-scale fermentor, primarily because friction in the stuffing box contributes significantly to the loading of the motor.

A strain-gauge dynamometer has advantages for the measurement of the power requirement of an agitator, and a practical example of its application to a jar fermentor will now be described; needless to say, the strain-gauge type of dynamometer can also be installed in fermentors of production size.

Fig. 10.19 depicts the principles of this dynamometer; in Fig. 10.19 (a) the gauge (electric resistance$=R_{g1}$) is connected in series with a resistor (resistance$=R_1$) and a potential V is applied over these resistances. The electric current, i will be:

$$i = \frac{V}{R_{g1}+R_1} \qquad (10.1)$$

The potential e_1 which will appear between the ends of the gauge is:

$$e_1 = \frac{R_{g1}V}{R_{g1}+R_1} \qquad (10.2)$$

If the strain-gauge is subjected to either longitudinal or transverse stress, the resistance R_{g1} changes by $\pm dR_{g1}$. Suppose that the gauge in Fig. 10.19 (a) is subjected to a simple longitudinal stress, σ, resulting in a strain, ε. Then, differentiating Eq. (10.2),

$$de_1 = \frac{R_{g1}R_1V}{(R_{g1}+R_1)^2} \frac{dR_{g1}}{R_{g1}}$$

Introducing K_s, which is defined below, and substituting it into the above equation,

$$K_s = \frac{\frac{dR_{g1}}{R_{g1}}}{\varepsilon}, \qquad de_1 = \frac{R_{g1}R_1V}{(R_{g1}+R_1)^2} K_s\varepsilon \qquad (10.3)$$

The term K_s represents a characteristic of the gauge in responding to external stress imposed on it. Materials with K_s values from 2 to about 100 under normal temperatures and pressures are available.

If the value of R_1 in Fig. 10.19 (a) is equated to that of R_{g1}, Eq. (10.3) will be:

$$de_1 = \frac{V}{4} K_s \varepsilon \qquad (10.4)$$

Next, the gauge is incorporated in an electric bridge as shown in Fig. 10.19 (b). Setting the values of resistances R_1, R_2, and R_3 equal to R_{g1} (the latter value being the electric resistance prior to imposing stress, σ, on the gauge), the potential e_1, described in the figure, is zero.

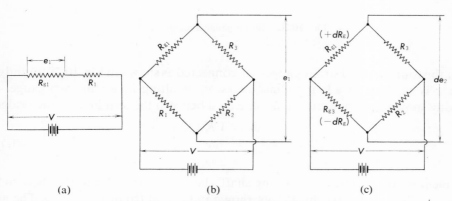

(a)   (b)   (c)

FIG. 10.19.   Principles of a strain-gauge.

If the gauge is subjected to σ, the potential, de_1, which appears between the terminals of the circuit can readily be calculated as follows:

$$de_1 = \frac{V}{4} K_s \varepsilon \qquad (10.5)$$

Furthermore, when the circuit containing resistances R_{g1} and R_{g3} is incorporated, and when the reisistances are $R_{g1} = R_{g3} = R_2 = R_3$, the value of de_2 corresponding to the case of simple longitudinal stress imposed on R_{g1} and R_{g3} will be calculated as shown below. This calculation applies when the strain-gauges are placed at right angles to each other so that the direction of longitudinal stress in each gauge is reversed, resulting in the same magnitude of increase and decrease of electric resistances as shown in Fig. 10.19 (c).

$$de_2 = 2de_1$$

$$= 2 \frac{V}{4} K_s \varepsilon \qquad (10.6)$$

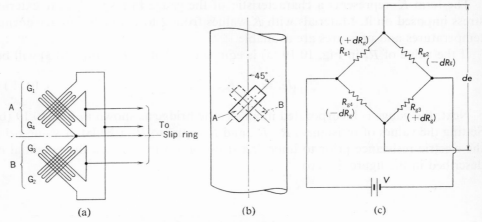

Fig. 10.20.   Strain-gauge dynamometer.[3]

If the four identical strain-gauges are connected as shown in Fig. 10.20 (c) and each gauge is exposed to a longitudinal stress, σ, resulting in $\pm\varepsilon$ in each gauge, it is readily shown that the value of de generated between the terminals of the bridge is:

$$
\begin{aligned}
de &= VK_s\varepsilon \\
&= 4de_1 \\
&= 2de_2
\end{aligned}
\qquad (10.7)
$$

To measure the torque of a rotating shaft, the gauges are fixed to the shaft so that they are tilted to the axis by 45°, as shown in (a) and (b) of Fig. 10.20. The angle of 45° is selected because the shearing strain, ε, becomes maximum, ε_{max}, in this arrangement.[22]

The following equation shows that the magnitude of pure shearing strain, $\gamma/2$, which appears on each gauge, is composed of longitudinal and transverse strains in the rotating shaft, σ/E and $-\sigma/mE$, respectively.[22]

$$
\frac{\gamma}{2} = \frac{\sigma}{E} - \frac{-\sigma}{mE} = \frac{\sigma}{E}\left(1 + \frac{1}{m}\right)
\qquad (10.8)
$$

The value of ε in Eq. (10.7) can be substituted by $\gamma/2$ in Eq. (10.8) for the specific arrangement of strain-gauges on the shaft shown in Fig. 10.20. provided:

E = Young's Modulus, Kg/cm^2

m = reciprocal of Poisson's ratio

Namely,

$$
de = VK_s(\gamma/2)
\qquad (10.9)
$$

Furthermore, in the strain-gauge described in Fig. 10.20 (b), the value of σ can be equated to τ_{max} as shown in the following equation:

$$\frac{\gamma}{2} = \frac{\sigma}{E}\left(1 + \frac{1}{m}\right) = \frac{\tau_{\max}}{E}\left(1 + \frac{1}{m}\right) \tag{10.10}$$

On the other hand,

$$\tau = G\gamma \tag{10.11}$$

$$\tau_{\max} = \frac{16Md_0}{\pi(d_0^4 - d_i^4)} \tag{10.12}^{22}$$

where

$G =$ modulus of rigidity, Kg/cm²
$M =$ torque, Kg cm
$d_0 =$ outer diameter of hollow shaft, cm
$d_i =$ inner diameter of hollow shaft, cm

A hollow shaft was selected because the terminals of the gauges attached to the shaft in the fermentor can be easily connected to the exterior.

From Equations (10.9), (10.11), and (10.12),

$$de = VK_s \frac{8Md_0}{\pi(d_0^4 - d_i^4)G} \tag{10.13}$$

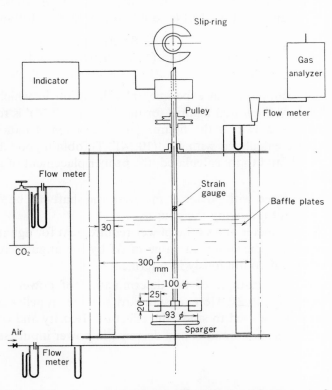

FIG. 10.21.   Fermentor equipped with strain-gauge dynamometer.[3]

Eq. (10.13) shows that the value of de is proportional to M for a given setting of a strain-gauge dynamometer on the surface of a rotating shaft.

Fig. 10.21 is an experimental set-up for measuring the power requirements of a jar fermentor.[3] The gauges are fixed on a shaft ($d_0=1.2$ cm; $d_i=0.92$ cm) as shown in Fig. 10.20. The wires from the bridge are taken out of the fermentor through a hole in the shaft and via a slip ring as shown in Fig. 10.21.

The value of de can be obtained by amplifying the indicator reading, $[R]$ (see Fig. 10.21). Thus,

$$[R] = \kappa de = \kappa V K_s \frac{8Md_0}{\pi(d_0^4-d_i^4)G}$$

$$= \frac{1}{\alpha} \frac{8Md_0}{\pi(d_0^4-d_i^4)G} \tag{10.14}$$

where

κ = factor of conversion which varies depending on the specific indicator used

$1/\alpha = \kappa V K_s$

Since the α value was shown (by the strain-gauges and the indicator used in the example of Fig. 10.21) to be 0.75×10^{-6} ($d_0=1.2$ cm, $d_i=0.92$ cm and G (steel)$=0.8\times10^6$ Kg/cm^2 [22]), Eq. (10.14) could be modified as follows:

$$[R] = \frac{1}{0.75\times10^{-6}} \frac{8\times M\times1.2}{3.14\times(1.2^4-0.92^4)(0.8\times10^6)}$$

$$= 3.76M \tag{10.14'}$$

Fig. 10.22 is an example of an experimental calibration in which the reading $[R]$ of the indicator was plotted against torque M; Eq. (10.14)' is represented by the solid straight line drawn in the figure. The experimental data points agree fairly well with those calculated with Eq. (10.14)'. To obtain good agreement between the data points and those calculated, the proper placement of gauges on the shaft is important.

If the gauges are coated with polyester material, the shaft can be sterilized with steam at 120°C without removing the gauges.

This type of dynamometer allows the power requirement for agitation, which is obtained by multiplying the observed value of M by the angular velocity of the impeller, to be recorded continuously in a fermentation.

Fig. 10.23 is another example of the determination of power input with the apparatus shown in Fig. 10.21. Here, a standard turbine impeller and a strain-gauge dynamometer were used to study the effect of viscosity and consistency on the relation between aeration number and decrease in power input (see Chapter 6) in a gassed system.

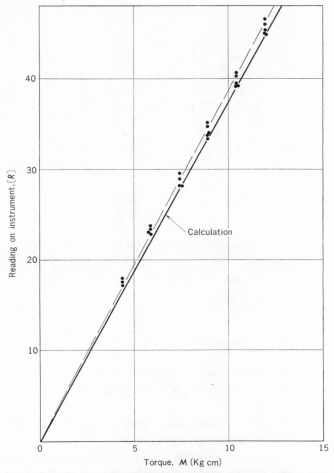

FIG. 10.22. Example of calibration.[3] The indicator reading, $[R]$, is plotted against torque, M, imposed on the dynamometer; linear relationship between $[R]$ and M is calculated with Eq. (10.14)'.

10.5.2. Gas analysis as applied to the measurement of the capacity coefficient of mass transfer[13]

In a fermentation which is being aerated continuously from the bottom (partial pressure of oxygen$=p_1$), it is assumed that over a short period of time, an equilibrium exists between the oxygen being supplied from air bubbles and the oxygen consumed by the organisms. It is also assumed that during this short period, the respiratory activity, the cell population, and the physical properties of the broth remain constant.

Then,

$$\frac{k_L A}{V_0}(C_i^* - C_i) = k_r C_m \qquad (10.15)$$

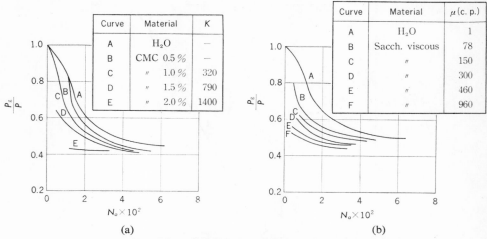

Curve	Material	K
A	H₂O	—
B	CMC 0.5 %	—
C	" 1.0 %	320
D	" 1.5 %	790
E	" 2.0 %	1400

Curve	Material	μ (c. p.)
A	H₂O	1
B	Sacch. viscous	78
C	"	150
D	"	300
E	"	460
F	"	960

(a)   (b)

FIG. 10.23.   Effect of liquid viscosity (or consistency) on P_g/P, [3]
where P_g = power consumption for agitation in gassed system, Kg m/sec; P = power consumption for
agitation without aeration, Kg m/sec; N_a = aeration number (= Q/nD_i^3); Q = air flow rate, m³/sec; D_i =
impeller diameter, m; n = rotation speed of impeller, 1/sec; for the aeration number, see Chapter 6.

where

$\dfrac{k_L A}{V_0}$ = capacity coefficient of mass transfer, 1/hr

k_L = mass (oxygen)-transfer coefficient, m/hr

A = interfacial area between liquid and gas bubbles, m²

V_0 = liquid volume, m³

C_i^* = concentration of dissolved oxygen in liquid in equilibrium with gas
 prior to step-change, kg mole/m³

C_i = concentration of dissolved oxygen in liquid prior to step-change of
 oxygen partial pressure in inlet gas, kg mole/m³

k_r = respiration rate constant, kg mole O₂/g/hr

C_m = microbial concentration in liquid, g/m³

Furthermore, if the value of p_1 is increased step-wise by $p_2 - p_1$ by adding oxygen
to the inlet gas changing neither the total pressure nor the total flow rate, then the
oxygen balance during the unsteady state will be:

$$\frac{k_L A}{V_0}(C^* - C) - k_r C_m = \frac{dC}{d\theta} \qquad (10.16)$$

The addition of oxygen to the inlet gas is assumed to be such that the area of the
gas/liquid interface, A, remains constant. At the same time, it is assumed that
the increase of dissolved oxygen concentration, C above C_i does not affect the
value of $k_r C_m$ which applied to the pre-addition condition.

Although the value of C will increase with time according to Eq. (10.16), it is expected that the values of C and C^* will eventually attain those of C_f and C_f^* res-

pectively and so reach another steady state condition in terms of oxygen supply and consumption. Then,

$$\frac{k_L A}{V_0}(C_f^* - C_f) = k_r C_m \tag{10.17}$$

On the other hand, the over-all oxygen balance corresponding to the rate Equations (10.16) and (10.17) will yield:

$$\frac{V_2}{V_0}\left(\frac{p_2}{P-p_2} - \frac{p}{P-p}\right) - k_r C_m = \frac{dC}{d\theta} \tag{10.18}$$

$$\frac{V_2}{V_0}\left(\frac{p_2}{P-p_2} - \frac{p_f}{P-p_f}\right) = k_r C_m \tag{10.19}$$

where

> P = total pressure, atm
> V_2 = flow rate of inert gas after step-change, kg mole/hr
> p_2 = partial pressure of oxygen at inlet after step-change, atm
> p_f = partial pressure of oxygen at outlet after step-change (final value), atm
> p = partial pressure of oxygen at outlet during unsteady state, atm

Substituting Equations (10.15) and (10.19) into Equations (10.16) and (10.18) respectively will cancel out the term, $k_r C_m$,

$$\frac{k_L A}{V_0}\left\{(C^* - C_i^*) - (C - C_i)\right\} = \frac{dC}{d\theta} \tag{10.20}$$

$$\frac{V_2}{V_0}\left(\frac{p_f}{P-p_f} - \frac{p}{P-p}\right) = \frac{dC}{d\theta} \tag{10.21}$$

Integrating Eq. (10.21) either between $\theta = \theta_i$ and $\theta = \theta$ or between $\theta = \theta_i$ and $\theta = \theta_f$,

$$\int_{\theta=\theta_i}^{\theta=\theta} \frac{V_2}{V_0}\left(\frac{p_f}{P-p_f} - \frac{p}{P-p}\right) d\theta = C - C_i \tag{10.22}$$

$$\int_{\theta=\theta_i}^{\theta=\theta_f} \frac{V_2}{V_0}\left(\frac{p_f}{P-p_f} - \frac{p}{P-p}\right) d\theta = C_f - C_i \tag{10.23}$$

where

> θ_i = time at which p_1 is changed step-wise to p_2
> θ_f = time at which steady state of C is realized $(C = C_f)$

From the value of p measured continuously with a gas analyzer during the unsteady state, and from the integration of Eq. (10.22), the values of $k_L A/V_0$ can be calculated from Equations (10.20), (10.21), and (10.22), provided $C^* = H(p_2 - p)$ $/\ln(p_2/p)$ can be calculated. In other words, the value of Henry's constant, H, should be known for a specific fermentation broth; the value of H can be determined as follows. From Equations (10.15) and (10.17),

$$C_f - C_i = C_f^* - C_i^* \qquad\qquad (10.24)$$

The values of H can be determined either from Eq. (10.25) or from Eq. (10.26).

$$C_f^* - C_i^* = H \left\{ \frac{p_2 - p_f}{\ln (p_2/p_f)} - \frac{p_1 - p_i}{\ln (p_1/p_i)} \right\} \quad (k_r C_m \neq 0) \qquad (10.25)$$

$$C_f^* - C_i^* = H(p_2 - p_1) \qquad\qquad (k_r C_m = 0) \qquad (10.26)$$

From Equations (10.23), (10.24), (10.25), and (10.26), the values of H for any fermentation broth can be determined simply by measuring p continuously in the exit gas from the fermentor during the artificially created unsteady state.

Because of the space existing between the liquid surface and the gas analyzer, the experimental data is recorded in terms of p' vs. θ, and must then be converted to those of p vs. θ. To do this, it is assumed that the gas emerging from the liquid follows the pattern of complete mixing. Then the material balance of oxygen in the space will be expressed by:

$$\underbrace{V'\left(\frac{p}{P}\right) d\theta}_{\text{in}} - \underbrace{V'\left(\frac{p'}{P}\right) d\theta}_{\text{out}} = \underbrace{V_G \frac{P}{RT} \frac{1}{P} dp'}_{\text{accumulation}} \qquad (10.27)$$

where

$V' = $ gas flow rate in dead space, kg mole/hr
$V_G = $ dead space, m³
$R = $ gas constant, m³ atm/°K kg mole
$T = $ absolute temperature, °K

Rearranging Eq. (10.27),

$$\frac{dp'}{d\theta} + \frac{V'}{V_G} \frac{RT}{P} p' = \frac{V'}{V_G} \frac{RT}{P} p \qquad (10.28)$$

Fig. 10.24 is an example of experimental results obtained with sodium carboxymethyl cellulose (CMC) solutions using the gas-analysis method; in this example, no microbes were present, and for ease of experimentation, CO_2 was used in lieu of oxygen. If the liquid film resistance is assumed to be controlling also in the case of CO_2,[10] then the procedures described earlier to measure the capacity coefficient of mass transfer can be directly applied to this case. Moreover, since it can be assumed that the values of liquid film coefficient, k_L, do not make any significant difference between O_2 and CO_2, the capacity coefficient values measured with CO_2-enriched air (see below) can be converted to those of O_2 without any serious error.

With the equipment shown in Fig. 10.21, CO_2 was mixed with air to give a final concentration of 3 to 4% CO_2. Liquid which was in equilibrium with normal air was then exposed to CO_2-enriched air, thus creating an unsteady state. The CO_2 concentration in the exit gas was then measured with a gas analyzer of the Rauter type (Mitaka Kogyoh Co., Ltd., Tokyo).

It is apparent from Fig. 10.24 that the value of K (consistency) of the CMC solution markedly affects the value of $k_L A/V_0$. The value of K was determined with a concentric type of viscometer (Fig. 10.25) and calculated from the following power law.

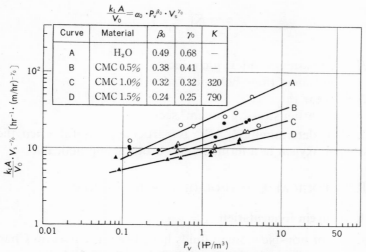

$$\frac{k_L A}{V_0} = \alpha_0 \cdot P_v{}^{\beta_0} \cdot V_s{}^{\gamma_0}$$

Curve	Material	β_0	γ_0	K
A	H_2O	0.49	0.68	—
B	CMC 0.5%	0.38	0.41	—
C	CMC 1.0%	0.32	0.32	320
D	CMC 1.5%	0.24	0.25	790

FIG. 10.24.   Mass-transfer capacity coefficient in solutions of carboxymethyl cellulose of different consistencies.[3]

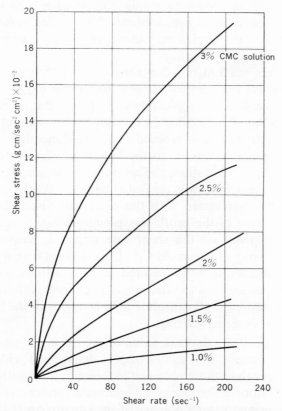

FIG. 10.25.   Flow curves in solution of carboxymethyl cellulose of different concentrations, used for the determination of the consistency index, K.[3]

$$\tau = K\left(\frac{du}{dr}\right)^n \tag{10.29}$$

where

K = consistency index, g/cm $\sec^{2-n}$

n = exponent (flow behavior index)

du/dr = shear rate, $\sec^{-1}$

τ = shearing stress, g cm/cm^2 sec^2

This method of determining $k_L A/V_0$ is particularly useful when the measurement of dissolved oxygen in a fermentation broth is impracticable.

10.6. Rheological Control of Fermentations

10.6.1. Kanamycin fermentation

The properties of non-Newtonian fluids have been discussed in Chapter 7, and it is well known that fermentation broths of either fungi or Actinomycetes exhibit non-Newtonian, either Bingham or pseudoplastic, behavior.

Pencillium chrysogenum grown in media composed principally of corn-steep liquor and lactose usually shows pseudoplastic flow, while *Coniothyrium helleborio* used for the conversion of steroids may show either plastic or pseudoplastic flow at different stages of the fermentation.[5]

As a broth exhibits marked non-Newtonian characteristics, it becomes more difficult to disperse nutrients uniformly and to supply oxygen to the microbial population. Therefore, it may be possible to improve the performance of a fermentation by controlling its viscosity. For example, the medium could be diluted, thus allowing the fermentation to proceed more satisfactorily.

The application of this technique to the kanamycin fermentation is shown in Fig. 10.26. During the fermentation, the amount of oxygen (I_{O_2}) taken up per ml of fermentation broth per hour was measured with the Warburg apparatus, while the value of $\mu_{app.}$ was determined with the rotational viscometer. According to Sato,[20] the flow behavior of the broth was pseudoplastic. Since the value of the apparent viscosity depends on the shear rate imposed, Sato used a rotational viscometer (Type-B, Tokyo Instrument Co., Ltd., Tokyo) with a fixed rotar speed. The viscosity of each sample was measured at 27°C 3 times within 1 minute of sampling, with the rotar speed of the viscometer at 60 rpm. Although this procedure does not necessarily represent the absolute flow behavior of the broth, the relative change in $\mu_{app.}$ can be detected reliably.

It is clear from Fig. 10.26 that the value of $\mu_{app.}$ changes markedly during the course of the fermentation. The values of $\mu_{app.}$ determined with non-Newtonian broths are much larger than those obtained in fermentations with bacteria or yeast.

Sato was able to improve the rate of a kanamycin fermentation by diluting the broth without decreasing the final potency of the kanamycin.[20] The results follow-

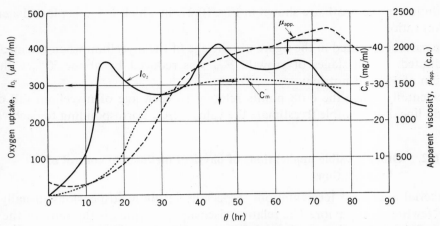

FIG. 10.26.   Changes in respiration, cell mass, and viscosity during a kanamycin fermentation,[20] where $I_{O_2} = \mu lO_2/hr/ml$ used by the mold; C_m = dry weight of mold/ml; $\mu_{app.}$ = apparent viscosity; θ = time.

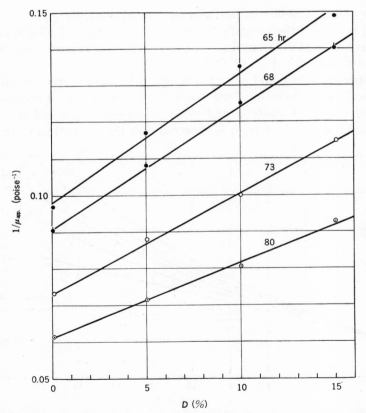

FIG. 10.27.   Effect of the dilution ratio (D) on the apparent viscosity ($\mu_{app.}$) of kanamycin fermentation broths sampled at different stages of growth.[20]

ing dilution of the broth are shown in Fig. 10.27, in which $1/\mu_{app.}$ is plotted against dilution ratio, D.

The parameters used in the figure are the age of the mycelium when the medium was diluted. At all stages of growth, $\mu_{app.}$ was reduced by about 50% with the addition of 15% of nutrient.

Incidentally, since the data points relating to each age of mycelium fall on a straight line, it is possible to estimate the value of $\mu_{app.}$ corresponding to each value of D.

10.6.2.   Other possible applications of physical methods to control of fermentations

Bacterial and yeast fermentations, especially in dilute suspensions, usually exhibit Newtonian behavior. The relative viscosity, μ_R, which is the ratio of the viscosity of the suspension to that of the suspending medium, is expressed by the Einstein formula as follows:

$$\mu_R = 1 + 2.5\phi \qquad (10.30)$$

where

$\phi =$ volume fraction of particles suspended in media

Eq. (10.30) is derived theoretically for a dilute suspension of solid spheres. Other workers have derived different formulae to express theoretically the values of μ_R; these are summarized in Fig. 10.28.

With respect to spheroidal particles, Simha calculated correction factors which are the functions of the ratio of the major to the minor axis of the particle.[1]

It is clear that both bacteria and yeast are not spherical and are not, strictly speaking, solid. Consequently, it is expected that the theoretical formulae shown

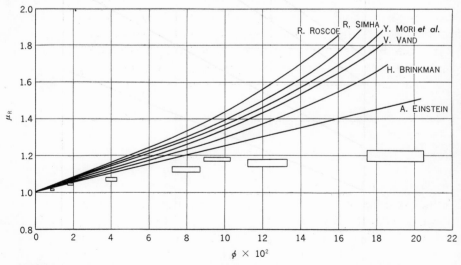

FIG. 10.28.   Relationship of the relative viscosity (μ_R) to the volume fraction of particles in suspension (ϕ), as derived by different workers.[1]

in Fig. 10.28 will not represent correctly the value of μ_R for microbial suspensions.

The rectangular regions described in the figure are the results of experimental determinations of μ_R with the Ostwald viscometer with *Saccharomyces cerevisiae* suspended in buffer solutions.[1] Although problems associated with the measurement of ϕ require further study, it may be that the relation between ϕ and μ_R cannot be shown simply by these theoretical formulae; the reason why the value of μ_R deviates from the theoretical equations deserves further attention.

Provided accurate sensors could be developed, it is evident from Fig. 10.28 that the value of μ_R could be used as a measure of ϕ. In other words, one could trace the variation of ϕ, which indicates the progress of fermentation, without resorting to conventional means of sampling.

In addition to the control of fermentations by rheological methods, optical density measured with the electrophotometer could be used to follow continuously variations in the density of microbial suspensions.[21]

Furthermore, the measurement of hindered settling rates of microbial suspensions either in a gravity or in a centrifugal field might be used to follow continuously the course of fermentations.

**10.7.   EXAMPLE OF THE CALCULATION OF THE MASS-TRANSFER
            CAPACITY COEFFICIENT**

Fig. 10.29 (see p. 278) is an example of the experimental results obtained while determining the value of $k_L A/V_0$ by the continuous gas-analysis method. Here the partial pressure of CO_2 in the inlet gas to a jar fermentor (free of organisms) was changed, and the subsequent change in partial pressure of CO_2 (p') in the outlet gas was detected with a gas analyzer. The data in Fig. 10.29 were obtained with a fermentor having a standard flat blade turbine impeller and an air flow rate of 10 l/min (the volume of the fermentor, $V_0 = 18\,l$; the dead space, $V_G = 0.4\,l$; $V'RT/P = 2\,l$/min where $V' = $ gas flow rate in the dead space; the speed of the impeller $= 200$ rpm). The ordinate in Fig. 10.29 is the partial pressure of CO_2 in the outlet gas, p', after a change in the partial pressure of CO_2 in the inlet gas and the abscissa is time, θ.

It is desired to calculate the value of $k_L A/V_0$, hr^{-1}, from the experimental curve of p' vs. θ given in Fig. 10.29.

Solution

Up to $\theta = 4$ min, the value of $\varDelta\theta$ was taken arbitrarily as 1/3 min, while from $\theta = 4$ min to $\theta = 9$ min, $\varDelta\theta$ was set at 1 min.

Assuming that the liquid film resistance is rate limiting in the transfer of CO_2 from gas to liquid, as in the case of O_2, it is clear that Equations (10.15) to (10.28) can be used.

The procedure of estimating the values of $k_L A/V_0$ is shown in Table 10.1. In this calculation, the arithmetic mean value of $\bar{p}$ was used instead of the logarithmic mean.

It is apparent from Table 10.1 that the value of $k_L A/V_0$ markedly depends on the

TABLE 10.1

EXAMPLE OF CALCULATION SHEET.

PROTOCOL FOR THE CALCULATION OF $k_L A/V_0$ FROM THE DATA OF FIG. 10. 29.

$\Delta\theta$, min		$\frac{1}{3}$	$\frac{1}{3}$	$\frac{1}{3}$	$\frac{1}{3}$	$\frac{1}{3}$	$\frac{1}{3}$
θ, min		0	$\frac{1}{3}$	$\frac{2}{3}$	1.0	$1\frac{1}{3}$	$1\frac{2}{3}$
$p' \times 10^2$, atm		5.90	5.30	4.10	3.10	2.45	2.10
$\Delta p' \times 10^2$, atm		−0.60	−1.20	−1.00	−0.65	−0.35	−0.30
$\Delta p'/\Delta\theta \times 10^2$, atm/min		−1.80	−3.60	−3.00	−1.95	−1.05	−0.90
$\left(p' + \dfrac{\Delta p'}{2}\right) \times 10^2$, atm		5.60	4.70	3.60	2.78	2.28	1.95
Eq. (10.28), $\quad \times 10^2$, atm $p = \left(p' + \dfrac{\Delta p'}{2}\right) + \dfrac{1}{5}\dfrac{\Delta p'}{\Delta\theta}$		5.24	3.98	3.00	2.39	2.07	1.77
$\dfrac{p_f}{P-p_f}=0, \quad \left(\dfrac{p_f}{P-p_f} - \dfrac{p}{P-p}\right) \times 10^2$		−5.53	−4.14	−3.09	−2.45	−2.11	−1.80
Eq. (10.21), $\quad \Delta C/\Delta\theta \times 10^4$, g mole/liter/min		−13.71	−10.27	−7.66	−6.08	−5.23	−4.46
$\Delta C \times 10^4$, g mole/liter		−4.57	−3.42	−2.55	−2.03	−1.74	−1.49
Eq. (10.22), $\quad (C - C_i) \times 10^4$, g mole/liter		−4.57	−7.99	−10.54	−12.57	−14.31	−15.80
$p_1 \times 10^2 = p_i \times 10^2 = 5.90, \quad p_2 = 0,$ atm $\bar{p} = \left\{\dfrac{1}{2}(p_2 + p) - \dfrac{1}{2}(p_1 + p_i)\right\} \times 10^2$, atm		−3.28	−3.91	−4.40	−4.70	−4.86	−5.01
$C_i = C_i^* = 24.36 \times 10^{-4}$, g mole/liter $C_f = C_f^* = 0.$							
Eq. (10.26), $\quad H = \dfrac{C_i^*}{p_1} = \dfrac{24.36 \times 10^{-4}}{5.90 \times 10^{-2}} = 4.13 \times 10^{-2}$, g mole/liter/atm							
$(C^* - C_i^*) = H\bar{p} \times 10^4$, g mole/liter		−13.54	−16.15	−18.17	−19.41	−20.07	−20.69
Eq. (10.20), $\quad \{(C^* - C_i^*) - (C - C_i)\} \times 10^4$, g mole/liter		−8.97	−8.16	−7.63	−6.84	−5.76	−4.89
Eq. (10.20), $\quad \dfrac{k_L A}{V_0}$, 1/min		1.53	1.26	1.00	0.89	0.91	0.91
1/hr						53	55	55

	$\frac{1}{3}$	$\frac{1}{3}$	$\frac{1}{3}$	$\frac{1}{3}$	$\frac{1}{3}$	$\frac{1}{3}$	1.0	1.0	1.0	1.0	1.0
2.0	$2\frac{1}{3}$	$2\frac{2}{3}$	3.0	$3\frac{1}{3}$	$3\frac{2}{3}$	4.0	5.0	6.0	7.0	8.0	9.0
1.80	1.50	1.30	1.10	0.95	0.85	0.75	0.50	0.33	0.18	0.05	0.00
	−0.30	−0.20	−0.20	−0.15	−0.10	−0.10	−0.25	−0.17	−0.15	−0.13	−0.05
	−0.90	−0.60	−0.60	−0.45	−0.30	−0.30	−0.25	−0.17	−0.15	−0.13	−0.05
	1.65	1.40	1.20	1.03	0.90	0.80	0.63	0.42	0.26	0.12	0.03
	1.47	1.28	1.08	0.94	0.84	0.74	0.58	0.39	0.23	0.09	0.02
	−1.49	−1.30	−1.09	−0.95	−0.85	−0.75	−0.58	−0.39	−0.23	−0.09	−0.02
	−3.70	−3.22	−2.70	−2.36	−2.11	−1.86	−1.44	−0.97	−0.57	−0.22	−0.05
	−1.23	−1.07	−0.90	−0.79	−0.70	−0.62	−1.44	−0.97	−0.57	−0.22	−0.05
	−17.03	−18.10	−19.00	−19.79	−20.49	−21.11	−22.55	−23.52	−24.09	−24.31	−24.36
	−5.16	−5.26	−5.36	−5.43	−5.48	−5.53	−5.61	−5.70	−5.78	−5.85	−5.89
	−21.31	−21.72	−22.14	−22.43	−22.63	−22.84	−23.17	−23.54	−23.87	−24.16	−24.33
	−4.28	−3.62	−3.14	−2.64	−2.14	−1.73	—	—	—	—	—
	0.86	0.89	0.86	0.89	0.99	1.08					
	52	53	52	53							
	↓										
	53 (± 2)										

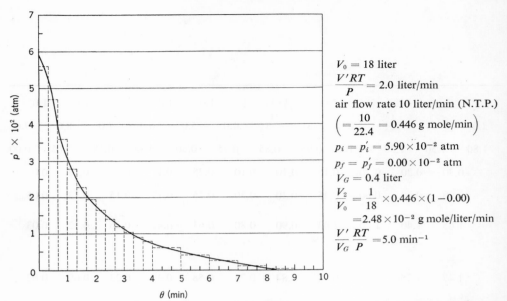

$V_0 = 18$ liter

$\dfrac{V'RT}{P} = 2.0$ liter/min

air flow rate 10 liter/min (N.T.P.)

$\left(= \dfrac{10}{22.4} = 0.446 \text{ g mole/min} \right)$

$p_i = p_i' = 5.90 \times 10^{-2}$ atm

$p_f = p_f' = 0.00 \times 10^{-2}$ atm

$V_G = 0.4$ liter

$\dfrac{V_2}{V_0} = \dfrac{1}{18} \times 0.446 \times (1 - 0.00)$

$\qquad = 2.48 \times 10^{-2}$ g mole/liter/min

$\dfrac{V'}{V_G} \dfrac{RT}{P} = 5.0$ min^{-1}

FIG. 10.29.   Example of gas analysis data; change in the partial pressure of CO_2 (p') in the exit gas from a fermentor following a change in CO_2 partial pressure; time $= \theta$.

time at which $\Delta\theta$ is selected from the curve in Fig. 10.29. Early in the experiment, calculations of $k_L A/V_0$ are not reliable because of the difficulty of achieving the first step-change accurately, and in the final phases the driving force (C^*-C) is very small and subject to a large percentage of error. Therefore, only the values of $k_L A/V_0$ corresponding to the intermediate phases can be adopted. Assuming that the values of $k_L A/V_0$ determined thus are associated with about 10% error, the true value of $k_L A/V_0$ is in the range 51 to 55 hr^{-1}.

NOMENCLATURE

$A =$ interfacial area between liquid and gas bubbles, m^2

$C =$ concentration of dissolved oxygen in liquid during unsteady state, kg mole/m^3, g mole/liter

$C^* =$ concentration of dissolved oxygen in equilibrium with gas during unsteady state $\left(H \dfrac{p_2 - p}{\ln(p_2/p)} \right)$, kg mole/m^3, g mole/liter

$C_i =$ concentration of dissolved oxygen in liquid prior to step-change of oxygen partial pressure in inlet gas, kg mole/m^3, g mole/liter

$C_i^* =$ concentration of dissolved oxygen in liquid in equilibrium with gas prior to step-change $\left(H \dfrac{p_1 - p_i}{\ln(p_1/p_i)} \right)$, kg mole/m^3, g mole/liter

$C_f =$ concentration of dissolved oxygen in liquid (final value) after step-change, kg mole/m^3, g mole/liter

C_f^* = concentration of dissolved oxygen in liquid in equilibrium with gas after step-change

$$\left(H\,\frac{p_2-p_f}{\ln(p_2/p_f)} \right),\ \text{kg mole/m}^3,\ \text{g mole/liter}$$

C_m = microbial concentration in liquid, g/m³, mg/ml

D = dilution ratio

D_i = impeller diameter, m

d_0 = outer diameter of hollow shaft, cm

d_i = inner diameter of hollow shaft, cm

E = Young's Modulus, Kg/cm²

e, e_1, e_2 = electric potentials

G = modulus of rigidity, Kg/cm²

H = Henry's constant, kg mole/m³ atm, g mole/liter atm

i = electric current

I_{O_2} = respiration activity measured with the Warburg method, $\mu l O_2$/hr/ml

K = consistency index, g/cm sec^{2-n}, (g/cm sec^{2-n})×100 in Figs. 10.23 and 10.24

K_s = gauge factor

k_r = respiration rate constant, kg mole O_2/g/hr

k_L = mass-transfer coefficient, m/hr

m = reciprocal of Poisson's ratio

M = torque, Kg cm

N_a = aeration number

n = exponent; rotation speed of impeller, sec^{-1}

p = partial pressure of oxygen at outlet ($\theta=\theta$) during unsteady state, atm

p' = partial pressure of oxygen measured with gas analyzer, atm

p_i = partial pressure of oxygen at outlet ($\theta=\theta_i$) prior to step-change, atm

p_1 = partial pressure of oxygen at inlet prior to step-change, atm

p_2 = partial pressure of oxygen at inlet after step-change, atm

p_f = partial pressure of oxygen at outlet after step-change at $\theta=\theta_f$, atm

P = total pressure, atm; power requirements of agitation without aeration, HP, Kg m/sec

P_g = power requirements of agitation in gassed system, HP, Kg m/sec

P_v = power consumed per unit volume of liquid, HP/m³

Q = air flow rate, m³/sec

R = gas constant, 0.08205 m³ atm/°K kg mole

$[R]$ = indicator reading

R_1, R_2, R_3 = electric resistance of resistor

R_{g1}, R_{g3}, R_{g4} = electric resistance of strain gauge

T = absolute temperature, °K

du/dr = shear rate, sec^{-1}

V = electric potential

V' = gas flow rate in dead space, kg mole/hr, g mole/min

V_2 = flow rate of inert gas after step-change, kg mole/hr, g mole/min

V_0 = liquid volume, m³, liter

V_G = dead space, m³, liter

V_s = superficial gas velocity, m/hr

Greek letters

$\alpha = 1/(\kappa V K_s)$, Eq. (10.14)

α_0 = coefficient, Fig. 10.24

β_0 = exponent, Fig. 10.24

γ_0 = exponent, Fig. 10.24

$\gamma/2$ = pure shearing strain (rotating shaft)

ε = strain

ε_{max} = maximum strain

θ = time

κ = factor, Eq. (10.14)

$\mu_{app.}$ = apparent viscosity, g/cm sec

μ_R = relative viscosity (viscosity of suspension/viscosity of medium)

σ = stress, Kg/cm^2

τ = shearing stress, Kg/cm^2, g cm/cm^2 sec^2

τ_{max} = maximum value of shearing stress, Kg/cm^2

ϕ = volume fraction of microbes

REFERENCES

1. AIBA, S., KITAI, S., and ISHIDA, N. (1962). "Density of yeast cell and viscosity of its suspension." *J. Gen. Appl. Microbiol.* **8**, 103.
2. AIBA, S. (1963). Panel discussions on oxygen transfer problems in the fermentation technology—particularly, on dissolved oxygen measurement procedures and its application to control in the fermentation industry—*Proc. 5th Symposium, Inst. Appl. Microbiol. Univ. of Tokyo*, 66.
3. AIBA, S., OKAMOTO, R., and SATOH, K. (1965). "Two sorts of measurements with a jar type of fermentor—power requirements of agitations and capacity coefficient of mass transfer in bubble aeration." *J. Ferm. Tech. (Japan).* **43**, 137.
4. DAY, J. (1962). "Ferm. Tech.; dissolved oxygen electrode." Interoffice memorandum, Merck.
5. DENISON, F.W. JR., WEST, I.C., PETERSON, M.H., and SYLVESTER, J.C. (1958). "Large-scale fermentations—A practical system for pH control." *Ind. Eng. Chem.* **50**, 1260.
6. DEINDOERFER, F.H., and WEST, J.M. (1960). "Rheological properties of fermentation broths." *Advances in Applied Microbiology* **2**, 265. (Ed.). UMBREIT, W.W. Academic, N.Y.
7. FULD, G.J. (1960). "Control applications in fermentation processes." *ibid.* **2**, 351.
8. FULD, G.J., and DUNN, C.G. (1957). "New process control applications in fermentation." *Ind. Eng. Chem.* **49**, 1215.
9. FRIEDLAND, W.C., PETERSON, M.H. and SYLVESTER, J.C. (1956). "Fermentor design for small scale submerged fermentation." *ibid.* **48**, 2180.
10. GIBBS, R.K., and HIMMELBLAU, D.M. (1963). "Effect of concentration on the gas-liquid mass transfer coefficient." *Ind. Eng. Chem. Fundamentals* **2**, 55.
11. GUALANDI, G., MORISI, G., UGOLINI, G., and CHAIN, E.B. (1959). "Continuous measure of dissolved oxygen in fermentations in the presence of microorganisms." *Sci. Repts. Istituto Superiore di Sanita* **2**, 4.
12. GUALANDI, G., CALDAROLA, E., and CHAIN, E.B. (1959). "Automatic continuous measure and control of pH by means of steam sterilizable glass electrode." *ibid.* **2**, 50.
13. HANHART, J., KRAMERS, H., and WESTERTERP, K.R. (1963). "The residence time distribution of the gas in an agitated gas-liquid contactor." *Chem. Eng. Sci.* **18**, 503.
14. HOLZBOCK, W.G. (1962). *Instruments for measurement and control* 2nd Ed. Reinhold, N.Y.
15. HUMPHREY, A.E. (1963). "Some observations of continuous fermentation." *Proc. 5th Symposium, Inst. Appl. Microbiol. Univ. of Tokyo*, 215.
16. NELSON, H.A., MAXON, W.D., and ELFERDINK, T.H. (1956). "Equipment for detailed fermentation studies." *Ind. Eng. Chem.* **48**, 2183.
17. PARKER, A. (1958). "Sterilization of equipment, air and media." *Biochemical Engineering* p.97, ((Ed.). STEEL, R.) Heywood, London.
18. PFEIFER, V.F., and HEGER, E.N. (1957). "Electronic foam controller for fermentors." *Appl. Microbiol.* **5**, 44.

19. SHU, P. (1956). "Control of oxygen uptake in deep tank fermentations." *Ind. Eng. Chem.* **48**, 2204.
20. SATO, K. (1961). "Rheological studies on some fermentation broths (I and IV). Rheological analysis of Kanamycin and Streptomycin fermentation broths. Effect of dilution rate on rheological properties of fermentation broth." *J. Ferm. Tech. (Japan)* **39**, 347, 517.
21. SHICHIJI, S. (1961). "Process automatic control of fermentation—feedback element for process automatic control of fermentation." *Repts. Ferm. Research Inst. Japan,* **19**, 11.
22. TIMOSHENKO, S., and MACCULLOUGH, G.H. (1949). *Elements of strength of materials* 3rd Ed. D. van Nostrand, Princeton, N.J.
23. ZOSS, L.M. (Ed.). (1959). *Frequency response for process control* McGraw-Hill, N.Y.

CHAPTER 11

MECHANICAL SEPARATION AND DISINTEGRATION OF CELLS FOR PRODUCT RECOVERY

It is easily seen from Fig. 11.1 that mechanical separations such as filtration, precipitation, and centrifugation, and operations involving mass and heat transfer, such as drying, crystallizing, adsorption, extraction, and solvent recovery, are widely used for the recovery of antibiotics. Before beginning the recovery proper, the pH of the fermentation broth (see Table 11.1) is usually adjusted to facilitate the recovery process (see Treatment tank in Fig. 11.1 and Section 11.3). Naturally, where cell material is the principal product, as in the case of yeast, mechanical separation of the cells is the prime consideration.

In heat and mass transfer operations, the broth is generally freed of microbial cells, so the recovery of product from the cell-free broth follows the usual procedures of chemical engineering. The principles underlying the design and operation of equipment for adsorption (ion-exchange), crystallization, drying, and solvent recovery can be obtained from the appropriate books on chemical engineering.[6, 18]

This chapter begins with descriptions of the recovery of fermentation products by mechanical separation. The principles of mechanical separation, especially those relating to the hindered settling of particles, will be mentioned first, followed by a brief review of the principles of mechanical filtration of materials suspended in liquid. Although information about cell densities is indispensable for the design and operation of all types of separators, there are relatively few data upon which calculations for design can be based. As an example of the usefulness of such data, the rationale for the design of equipment to separate yeast cells and mycelium from fermentation broths will be outlined.

In the last section, the mechanical disintegration of cells will be discussed, as this is important for the extraction of intracellular materials such as nucleic acids and enzymes. Many methods are available for the extraction of enzymes for research purposes on a laboratory scale, but very few of these techniques have been scaled-up. These processes have, however, great potential interest for the fermentation industry.

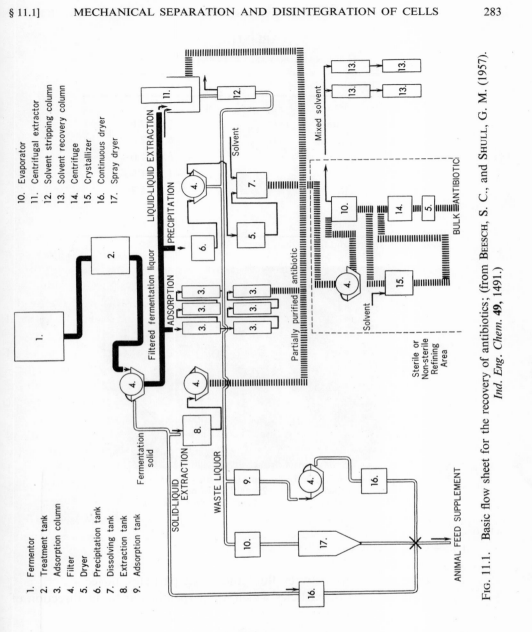

1. Fermentor
2. Treatment tank
3. Adsorption column
4. Filter
5. Dryer
6. Precipitation tank
7. Dissolving tank
8. Extraction tank
9. Adsorption tank

10. Evaporator
11. Centrifugal extractor
12. Solvent stripping column
13. Solvent recovery column
14. Centrifuge
15. Crystallizer
16. Continuous dryer
17. Spray dryer

Fig. 11.1. Basic flow sheet for the recovery of antibiotics; (from BEESCH, S. C., and SHULL, G. M. (1957). *Ind. Eng. Chem.* **49**, 1491.)

11.1.   Principles of Mechanical Separation

11.1.1.   Hindered settling in gravitational and centrifugal fields

According to Newton's law, the resistance, R, of single particles placed in a flowing fluid of infinite extent is expressed by:

$$R = (1/2g_c) C_D \rho_m U_0^2 A \qquad (11.1)$$

TABLE 11.1

pH RANGES FOR VARIOUS FERMENTATIONS.*

Process	pH range
Baker's yeast	~4.5~
2,3-Butanediol	~7.0 – 7.6~
Dextransucrase	~6.5 – 7.0~
Gluconic acid	~6.0 – 7.0~
Itaconic acid	~1.8 – 1.9~
Lactic acid	~5.4 – 5.7~
Penicillin	~7.0~
Torula yeast	~5.0~

* Approximate and final values in each fermentation.

FIG. 11.2.   De Laval centrifuges for yeast cream.
Each capacity = 25,000 l/hr of broth.
(*Courtesy   Oriental Yeast Co., Ltd., Tokyo.*)

where

C_D = drag coefficient

ρ_m = fluid density, kg/m³

U_0 = relative velocity between fluid and single particles, m/sec

A = sectional area of particles which are perpendicular to the direction of fluid motion, m²

g_c = conversion factor, kg/Kg m sec²

The relation between drag coefficient, C_D, and the Reynolds number, N_{Re}, of particles ($=D_p U_0 \rho_m / \mu'$) for spherical, disk-like, and cylindrical particles is shown in Fig. 11.5.[18] In a range of $N_{Re} < 0.3$ for spherical particles,

$$C_D = 24/N_{Re} \qquad (11.2)$$

Eq. (11.2) has been derived theoretically from

$$Rg_c = 3\pi\mu' D_p U_0 \qquad (11.2)'$$

FIG. 11.3.   Solvent recovery plant. Capacity = Acetone, 300 kg/hr; Methanol, 200 kg/hr.
(*Courtesy   Kaken Chem. Co., Ltd., Fujieda.*)

FIG. 11.4.   Semi-automatic filter press for the removal of cells. Example of constant pressure filtration: area = 33 m²; pressure = 6 Kg/cm² gauge; rate ≑ 1 ton/hr of an actinomycete's broth.
(*Courtesy   Shionogi Co., Ltd., Amagasaki.*)

Eq. (11.2) or (11.2)' is Stokes' law of resistance, when μ' and D_p are fluid viscosity and particle diameter respectively.

For microbial suspensions which are diluted so that the effect of neighboring particles on the motion of single particles can be neglected, Stokes' law of resistance may generally be applied. For ease of description, microbial particles will first be assumed spherical; the effect of deviation from the spherical shape will be discussed later.

Since particles like microbes attain an equilibrium state in which the resistance exerted on the microbes becomes almost immediately equal to the driving force of motion, the settling velocity, U_0, of single particles also represents the terminal velocity in the following discussions.

In a gravitational field, therefore, from Eq. (11.2)',

$$3\pi\mu'D_pU_0 = \frac{\pi}{6}D_p^3(\rho_y-\rho_m)g$$

$$U_0 = \frac{gD_p^2(\rho_y-\rho_m)}{18\mu'} \tag{11.3}$$

where

ρ_y = density of microbial particles, kg/m³

g = acceleration due to gravity, m/sec²

In the centrifugal field, likewise,

$$U_{c0} = \frac{gZD_p^2(\rho_y-\rho_m)}{18\mu'} = ZU_0 \tag{11.4}$$

where

U_{c0} = velocity of single particles in a centrifugal field, m/sec

Z = centrifugal effect $(=r\omega^2/g)$

r = radial distance from center of rotation, m

ω = angular velocity of rotation, radian/sec

As the cell concentration is increased, the interfering effect of adjacent particles on the motion of single particles cannot be ignored. The value of U_0 is decreased to U in these cases, and the settling of a swarm of such particles is called "hindered settling." The separation of a suspension of microbial cells in either a gravitational or a centrifugal field belongs to this general category of hindered settling.

The resistance, R', exerted on spherical particles which move with velocity, U, in hindered settling will be shown as follows:

$$R' = 3\pi\mu'D_pU(1+\beta_0D_p/L) \tag{11.5}$$

provided:

L = distance between neighboring particles

β_0 = coefficient

According to Smoluchowski,[23] the value of β_0 was calculated to be 1.16 for a rectangular arrangement of particles.

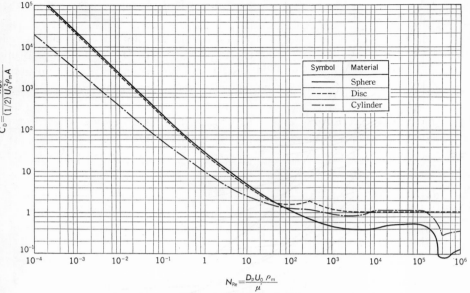

FIG. 11.5.   Drag coefficient vs. Reynolds number.[18]

It is evident from Eq. (11.5) that in a dilute suspension in which the value of D_p/L becomes approximately zero, the value of R' approaches that of R in Eq. (11.2)'.

The following equation will hold true for various shapes of particles in cubic arrangements if appropriate substitutions for the value of D_p are made in cases where particles are not spherical:[2]

$$D_p/L = \beta c^{1/3} \qquad\qquad (11.6)$$

where

β = geometrical factor
c = volume fraction of particles

Although Eq. (11.5) should strictly apply only to a dilute suspension of particles, the assumption that β_0 is a function of c will be made, as shown in the following equation:

$$\beta_0 = \beta_0' + f(c) \qquad\qquad (11.7)$$

where

$\beta_0 = \beta_0'$ when c approaches zero

From Equations (11.5), (11.6), and (11.7),

$$R' = 3\pi\mu' D_p U[1 + \{\beta_0' + f(c)\}\beta c^{1/3}]$$
$$= 3\pi\mu' D_p U(1 + \alpha c^{1/3})$$

provided:

$$\alpha = \beta\{\beta_0' + f(c)\} \qquad\qquad (11.8)$$

Since $R = R'$ in the case of settling,

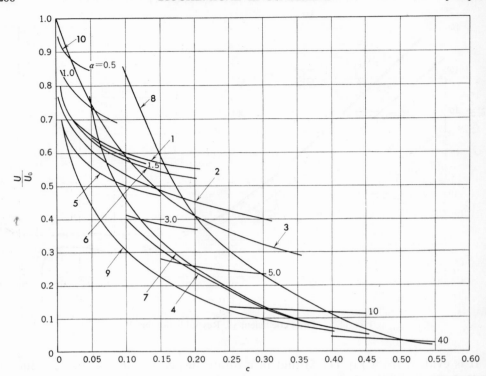

No.	Equation $\dfrac{U}{U_0} =$	Author (Year of Publication)	Particle	Reference
1	$1/(1 + 1.44c^{1/3})$	Smoluchowski, M.S. (1912)	Sphere (dilute range, cubic arrange.)	23
2	$1/\{1 + c(-1 + 3.04c^{1/3} + 1.74c^{-2/3})\}$	Burgers, J.M. (1941)	Sphere	5
3	$1/(1 + 6.875c)$	Burgers, J.M. (1942)	Sphere (random distri.)	19
4	$1 + \dfrac{3}{4}c\{1 - \sqrt{(8/c) - 3}\}$	Brinkman, H.C. (1947)	Sphere	5
5	$1/(1 + 2.1c^{1/3})$	Uchida, S. (1949)	Sphere (dilute range)	27
6	$1/(1 + 1.6c^{1/3})$	McNown, J.S. et al. (1952)	Sphere (dilute range)	11
7	$1\Big/\dfrac{8}{9}\displaystyle\int_0^1 \left\{\dfrac{(a/R)^2 - 1}{1 + \frac{1}{3}(a/R)^4 - \frac{4}{3}(a/R)^2 - \frac{4}{3}\ln(R/a)}\right\}\dfrac{dh}{b}$	Richardson, J.F. et al. (1954)	Sphere (hexagonal arrange. 1)	19
8	"	" "	" . 2)	19
9	$(3 - \dfrac{9}{2}c^{1/3} + \dfrac{9}{2}c^{2/3} - 3c^2)/(3 + 2c^{5/3})$	Happel, J. (1958)	Sphere	11
10	$1/(1 + \alpha c^{1/3})$		Spherical and angular	

FIG. 11.6. Effect of change in the volume fraction of particles, c, on their velocity of hindered settling U/U_0 as calculated by different formulae.

$$\frac{U}{U_0} = \frac{1}{1+\alpha c^{1/3}}$$

(11.9)

Arbitrarily taking various values of α, the relation between U/U_0 and c derived from Eq. (11.9) is shown graphically in Fig. 11.6. In the figure, theoretical equations which have been published previously on hindered-settling rates are also included. It appears that a theoretical equation to represent the values of U/U_0 over a wide range of c has seldom been presented; this point will be discussed later.

From a practical point of view, it is convenient to use Eq. (11.9) instead of the-oretical equations if the value of α can be correlated with c for each case. To ascer-tain the value of α as a function of c, the experimental data of many workers were rearranged to allow comparison of U/U_0 with c. In rearranging these data, the values of U_0 published in the original studies of angular or flocculated particles were also adopted. From the group of curves derived with Eq. (11.9), some of which are exemplified in Fig. 11.6 (parameter $= \alpha$), the values of α which best fitted the experimental results were determined.[2]

Needless to say, the experimental data employed in the determination of α are concerned with the so-called "free" rates of hindered settling or fluidization. Furthermore, the values of U or U_c were determined from the following relation-ship:

$$U = \frac{u}{1-c} \quad \text{or} \quad U_c = \frac{u_c}{1-c}$$

(11.10)

provided:

   $u =$ rate of subsidence of the interface in hindered settling under gravity or the superficial velocity of the fluid based on the cross-sectional area of the vessel in fluidization

   $u_c =$ rate of subsidence of the interface in hindered settling in a centrifugal field

The values of α so determined are plotted against c in Fig. 11.7.

Although the data points are scattered considerably, Curves A and B may be drawn through the points as shown in the figure. Curve A represents the behavior of angular and flocculated particles, while Curve B refers to spherical particles. Since the value of α represents the degree of interference of neighboring particles on the motion of the particles in suspension, it is seen from Fig. 11.7 that the in-terference effect of irregularly shaped particles becomes conspicuous only in concentrated suspensions.

On the other hand, the effect of particle shape on the value of α is of less signi-ficance in dilute suspension. Empirical equations relating α and c can then be derived from Fig. 11.7 as follows:[3]

For Curve A (irregular particle),

$$\alpha = 1+305 c^{2.84}$$

(11.11)

provided: $0.5 > c > 0.15$

For Curve B (spherical particle),

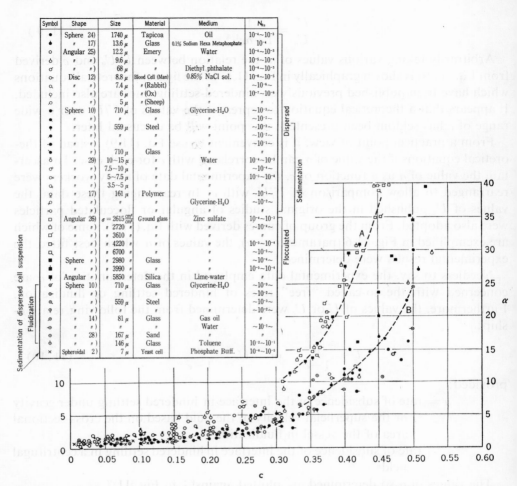

FIG. 11.7. Interference to the sedimentation of suspensions of different shaped particles, as measured by different values of α, with change in the volume fraction, c, of the particles.[2] Numerical figures in the 2nd column of the sheet attached indicate Reference No. at the end of this chapter.

$$\alpha = 1 + 229\,c^{3.43} \tag{11.12}$$

provided: $0.5 > c > 0.2$

For dilute suspensions,

$$\alpha = 1 \sim 2 \tag{11.13}$$

provided: $c < 0.15$

Subsequently, with reference to Fig. 11.7 or to Equations (11.11) to (11.13), it may be possible to test the applicability of the theoretical equations for the estimation of U/U_0 described in Fig. 11.6. For instance, Curve No. 2 in Fig. 11.6 can only be used for small values of c, while Curve No. 8 should preferably be used for large values of c.

It is apparent that Fig. 11.7 or Equations (11.11) to (11.13) can be used to estimate the value of U in both gravitational and centrifugal fields.

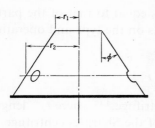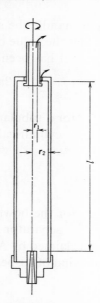

FIG. 11.8.   Schematic diagram of two types of centrifuges.

Here some reference will be made to centrifuges. The right diagram of Fig.11.8 is a schematic drawing of a tubular type of centrifuge (Sharples), while the left one represents the separator bowl of another type of centrifuge (De Laval).

The settling of single particles in centrifuges will be considered; it will become apparent from the discussions which follow that particles in centrifuges exhibit hindered settling. The distance of travel, x, of single particles in a centrifugal field is given by the following equation (see Eq. (11.4)):

$$x = U_{co}\theta$$
$$= \frac{r\omega^2 D_p^2(\rho_y - \rho_m)}{18\mu'} \frac{V}{Q} \qquad (11.14)$$

where
V = volume of liquid in the centrifuge, m³
Q = rate of liquid flow through the centrifuge, m³/sec

Substituting $x = S_e/2$ and $r = r_e$ in Eq. (11.14),

$$Q = 2\left\{\frac{D_p^2(\rho_y - \rho_m)}{18\mu'}\right\} \frac{r_e\omega^2 V}{S_e}$$
$$= 2\left\{\frac{gD_p^2(\rho_y - \rho_m)}{18\mu'}\right\} \frac{r_e\omega^2 V}{gS_e}$$
$$= 2U_0\Sigma \qquad (11.15)$$

provided:
S_e = effective distance of settling, m
r_e = effective radius of rotation in centrifuge, m
$\Sigma = r_e\omega^2 V/gS_e$, m² [4]

The value of Σ corresponds to the surface area of the gravity settling basin,

whose capacity to handle the suspension is equal to that of the particular centrifuge. It is clear that the value of Σ depends on the type and operating conditions
of the centrifuge.   It has been shown that

$$\Sigma = \frac{2\pi l \omega^2}{g} \left(\frac{3}{4}r_2^2 + \frac{1}{4}r_1^2 \right)$$
(11.16)

for a tubular type of centrifuge,[4,13] where $l =$ length of
cylindrical separator of the Sharples centrifuge

and

$$\Sigma = \frac{2\pi n' \omega^2 (r_2^3 - r_1^3)}{3g \tan \phi}$$
(11.17)

for the bowl type of centrifuge, where $n' =$ number of
separator bowls (see Fig. 11.8).[4,13]

It has also been claimed by Ambler[4] that the following equation holds true when
treating the same kind of suspension in centrifuges that differ from each other only
in size:

$$Q_1 = Q_2 \frac{\Sigma_1}{\Sigma_2} = \cdots \cdots$$
(11.18)

provided: subscripts 1 and 2 refer to large and small centrifuges.

Although Eq. (11.18) is an approximation, it is useful for estimating the value of
Q_1 in scale-up.

11.1.2.   Filtration

Fig. 11.9 shows diagrammatically a cell suspension passing through a filter
medium. The filter medium is usually cloth woven either of synthetic fibers or

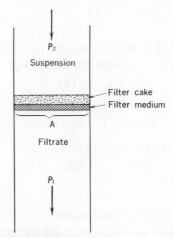

FIG. 11.9.   Schematic diagram of a filter, where
$P_2 - P_1 =$ the pressure drop across the filter, and
$A =$ area of the filter.

other materials. It is not essential for the effective pore size of the filtering medium to be smaller than the cells being removed, as the "bridging phenomenon" which occurs during filtration builds a filter cake. This constitutes a new medium for filtration through which a clear filtrate is obtained. It is the usual practice to pre-coat the filter medium with filter aids such as diatomaceous earth to assist filtration.

The driving force of filtration is $\Delta P = P_2 - P_1$ (see Fig. 11.9). During operation, the resistance to filtration will increase as the layer of filter cake increases. Consequently, the rate of filtration in terms of the volume of filtrate obtained per unit time per unit sectional area of filter medium will decline if the value of ΔP remains constant. This type of "constant pressure filtration" is usual in the fermentation industry.

In certain fermentation plants, for example, in *sake* (Japanese wine) or soy-sauce production, the filter cake is further consolidated after normal filtration by placing it under a hydraulic press. This operation, which is peculiar to the fermentation industry, will be discussed in some detail in Section 11.3.

Referring to Fig. 11.9, the rate of filtration per unit area of filter (total area = A m²) will now be considered. The flow of liquid through the network of the filter cake and through the filter medium is considered to be "viscosity controlled," so the rate equation may be formulated as follows:

$$\frac{dv}{d\theta} = \frac{\Delta P g_c}{(r_m + r_c)\mu'} \qquad (11.19)$$

where

$v =$ volume of filtrate per unit area of filter, m³/m²
$\theta =$ time of filtration, sec
$\Delta P =$ driving force of filtration, pressure drop through the filter medium and the filter cake, Kg/m²
$g_c =$ conversion factor, kg m/Kg sec²
$r_m =$ resistance coefficient of the medium, 1/m
$r_c =$ resistance coefficient of the cake, 1/m
$\mu' =$ viscosity of the filtrate, kg/m sec

Although the value of r_m is a characteristic of the filter medium and is independent of filtration period, the value of r_c will increase during filtration. Generally, after a certain period of operation, the value of r_c far exceeds that of r_m.

Denoting A m² as the cross-sectional area of the filter and W kg as the total amount of solid contained in the original suspension to be filtered, then,

$$r_c = \alpha_R W/A \qquad (11.20)$$

provided:

$\alpha_R =$ proportionality constant
(= specific resistance of cake), m/kg

The value of α_R may depend on the pressure imposed ("compressible") or may be independent of pressure exerted on the cake ("incompressible"). The filter cakes encountered in the fermentation industry are primarily composed of cells and other

organic material, and generally show "compressible" characteristics; these properties will be described in Section 11.3.

At this point, it is convenient to indicate the quantitative relationships existing
between the original suspension, the filtrate, and the filter cake as follows, using
unit mass (kg) of the original suspension as a base:

Denoting,

$$w = \text{mass of dry cake, kg/kg}$$
$$mw = \text{mass of wet cake, kg/kg}$$
$$(1-mw) = \text{mass of filtrate, kg/kg}$$

Then, the liquid contained within the wet cake will be:

$$(m-1)w, \text{ kg/kg}$$

Since the density of the liquid contained in the wet cake is the same as that in the
filtrate,

(volume of wet cake) = (volume of dry cake) + (volume of liquid contained
in wet cake)

$$\frac{mw}{\rho_y} = \frac{w}{\rho_d} + \frac{(m-1)w}{\rho_m}$$

$$\frac{m}{\rho_y} = \frac{1}{\rho_d} + \frac{(m-1)}{\rho_m} \tag{11.21}$$

where

ρ_y = density of the wet cake, kg/m³
ρ_d = density of the dry cake, kg/m³
ρ_m = density of the filtrate, kg/m³

A definite and constant value of m is associated with the process up to the ter-
mination of normal filtration; naturally, the value of m principally depends on
the operating conditions and on the physical properties of the solids (cells)
suspended in the original liquid. During the further consolidation of the
filter cake, which was mentioned as applying in certain fermentation industries,
the value of m decreases as the operation proceeds.

V m³ is designated as the total volume of filtrate corresponding to the total
mass of solid, W kg, obtained from the original suspension with a filter whose
cross-sectional area is A m². From the relationship between w, mw, and $(1-mw)$,
a term $V/(1-mw)/\rho_m = \rho_m V/(1-mw)$ represents the mass (kg) of the original
suspension filtered, resulting in the separation of V m³ and W kg.

Then,

$$W = w \frac{\rho_m V}{1-mw} \tag{11.22}$$

From Equations (11.20) and (11.22),

$$r_c = \alpha_R \frac{w\rho_m}{1-mw} \frac{V}{A} = \alpha_R \frac{w\rho_m v}{1-mw} \tag{11.23}$$

Substituting Eq. (11.23) into Eq. (11.19) and integrating from $\theta=0$ to $\theta=\theta$ ($v=0$ to $v=v$) with $\varDelta P = $ const.,

$$v^2+2vv_0 = k\theta \tag{11.24}$$

where

$$v_0 = r_m \frac{1-mw}{\alpha_R w \rho_m}, \quad \text{m} \tag{11.25}$$

$$k = \frac{2(1-mw)g_c}{\alpha_R w \rho_m \mu'} \varDelta P, \quad \text{m}^2/\text{sec} \tag{11.26}$$

Multiplying both sides of Eq. (11.24) with A^2 and considering that $vA = V$,

$$V^2+2VV_0 = K\theta \tag{11.27}$$

provided:

$$V_0 = v_0 A, \quad \text{m}^3 \tag{11.28}$$

$$K = kA^2, \quad \text{m}^6/\text{sec} \tag{11.29}$$

Eq. (11.24) or (11.27) indicates that the relation between v (or V) and θ is parabolic; this relationship was derived by Ruth *et al.* and so is known as Ruth's Equation[21] for constant pressure filtration. Equations (11.24) to (11.29) are still in frequent use for design and in the analysis of industrial filtrations.

In a rotating-drum filter, the drum is covered with a filter cloth and rotated at a constant speed (n rps). Since the period of time during which filtration is carried out is ϕ_0/n sec per revolution of the drum (see Fig. 11.10), Equations (11.24) and (11.27) will be modified respectively as follows:

$$\left(\frac{v_u}{n}\right)^2+2\left(\frac{v_u}{n}\right)v_0 = k\left(\frac{\phi_0}{n}\right) \tag{11.30}$$

$$\left(\frac{V_u}{n}\right)^2+2\left(\frac{V_u}{n}\right)V_0 = K\left(\frac{\phi_0}{n}\right) \tag{11.31}$$

provided:

$v_u = $ filtrate per unit time per unit area of filter surface, m³/m² sec
$V_u = $ filtrate per unit time, m³/sec

In Equations (11.30) and (11.31), (v_u/n) or (V_u/n) represents the respective value for one revolution of the filter drum. Equations (11.25), (11.26), (11.28), and (11.29) are applicable to the drum type of filter, provided that $A = 2\pi R_0 L$ and $L = $ axial length of drum.

The driving force of filtration in the continuous filter is obtained by reducing the pressure inside the drum. After the filter cake formed on the surface of the drum is washed, as shown in Fig. 11.10, the cake is pealed off with a "doctor's blade." The Oliver type of drum filter and batch filter presses are commonly used in the fermentation industry.

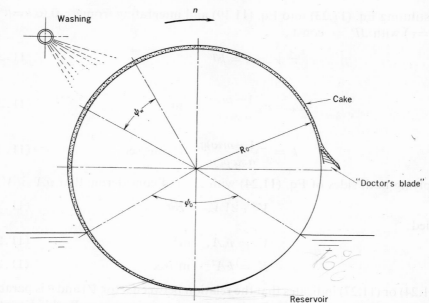

FIG. 11.10. A continuous rotating-drum filter where cells are removed from a reservoir, washed, partially dehydrated, and the cake removed on a "doctor's blade" (Oliver filter).

11.2. Densities and Sizes of Cells Suspended in Liquids

Densities of cells, ρ_y, can be determined from the following equation if the values of ρ_c, ρ_m and c are known:

$$\rho_y = \frac{\rho_c - (1-c)\rho_m}{c} \qquad (11.32)$$

where

ρ_y = density of the cell, g/cm³
ρ_c = density of the suspension, g/cm³
ρ_m = density of the medium, g/cm³
c = volume fraction of the cells in suspension

Although the values of ρ_c and ρ_m can be determined accurately for each case with picnometers, the exact determination of c is more difficult. No standard procedure has yet been established to determine the values of c for cell suspensions, and so methods differ from case to case. Cell material is liable to deform under pressure, especially in the case of mycelia, and it is evident that the value of c for fungi cannot be determined by measuring the volume fraction of the sediment obtained after centrifuging, although this method would be satisfactory for bacteria.

By the same token, it is not permissible to estimate the value of c from the dry weight of suspended particles, since many particles, especially those of multicellular organisms or activated sludge, have a certain amount of liquid associated with them and the whole behaves as an aggregate within the suspension. Cell numbers and cell size can be determined microscopically and the value of c calculated, but this is difficult to apply in practice.

An alternative procedure for measuring the value of c and eventually determining the cell density ρ_y in suspensions of yeast, bacteria, and fungi and in activated sludge will be described. The method may be criticized as being purely empirical, but its empirical nature does not necessarily invalidate the practical usefulness of the data obtained.

11.2.1. Yeast

The determination of the particle volume fraction, c, of a baker's yeast *Saccharomyces cerevisiae* will be outlined.[3] A part of the cell suspension was transferred to a graduated tubiform glass vessel, 10 cm³. The vessel was then centrifuged at about 700 times gravity for 10 minutes; the ratio of the sediment volume to that of the original suspension gave the value of c. After measuring the values of ρ_c and ρ_m with a picnometer, the values of ρ_y could be determined.

TABLE 11.2

CALCULATION OF THE DENSITY, ρ_y, AND THE EQUIVALENT SIZE, d_e, OF YEAST.[3]

Run No.	c	u (mm/hr)	U (cm/sec)	d_e (microns) $\alpha=0$	$\alpha=1$	$\alpha=2$	$\bar{d}_e$ (microns) calculated $\alpha=0$	$\alpha=1$	$\alpha=2$	Obs. microscopically
3.14.1.	0.0080	3.53	0.99×10^{-4}	4.8	5.2	5.7				
3.14.2.	0.0240	3.07	0.88	4.5	5.1	5.7				
3.14.3.	0.0400	2.97	0.86	4.5	5.2	5.8				
3.15.1.	0.0195	2.70	0.76	4.2	4.7	5.2				
3.15.2.	0.0390	2.67	0.77	4.2	4.9	5.5				
3.15.3.	0.0585	2.57	0.76	4.2	4.9	5.6				
3.15.4.	0.0780	2.63	0.79	4.3	5.1	5.8	4.4 ± 0.1	5.0 ± 0.1	5.5 ± 0.2	5.5 ± 0.5
3.16.1.	0.0164	3.03	0.86	4.5	5.0	5.5				
3.16.2.	0.0246	2.90	0.83	4.4	5.0	5.5				
3.16.3.	0.0410	2.87	0.83	4.4	5.1	5.7				
3.16.4.	0.0574	2.67	0.79	4.3	5.0	5.7				
3.19.1.	0.0052	3.00	0.84	4.4	4.8	5.1				
3.19.2.	0.0104	2.93	0.82	4.3	4.8	5.2				
3.19.3.	0.0156	2.80	0.79	4.3	4.8	5.2				
3.19.4.	0.0195	2.80	0.79	4.3	4.8	5.3				

$$\rho_y = 1.09 \text{ g/cm}^3 \ (\pm 0.008)$$
$$\rho_m = 1.00 \text{ g/cm}^3 \ (\pm 0.004)$$
$$\mu' = 11.3 \times 10^{-3} \text{ g/cm sec} \ (\pm 0.2 \times 10^{-3})$$

Experimental data of ρ_y are shown as a footnote to Table 11.2. Unless otherwise noted, the $\pm$ figures accompanying ρ_y, ρ_m, μ' (measured with the Ostwald viscometer) and the equivalent diameter, d_e, in this section are the deviations from mean values with 5% level of significance.[3]

The yeast cells used for this determination were cultured at 30°C for about 48 hours in shaken flasks. The culture medium was composed of meat extract (0.3%), yeast extract (0.3%), peptone (0.5%), and glucose (1%) (pH = 5.0).

After cultivation, the cells were separated and washed repeatedly with a 0.05 M KH_2PO_4 (pH = 5.0) buffer and re-suspended in the same solution for the determination of c at room temperature (11~17°C) and for the experiments on settling rates which will be discussed later.

According to the data of Haddad *et al.*[9] relating to a haploid yeast culture, No. 13778, suspended in a 1% dextrose solution at 30°C,

$$\rho_y = 1.087 \pm 0.026 \text{ g/cm}^3$$

They determined the above value of ρ_y by taking slow-motion pictures of individual cells flowing freely through the solution under gravity and by applying Stokes' law to the measured settling rate, U_0 (*cf*. Eq. (11.3)).

By resorting to another tedious method of counting the cell numbers,[1] it was determined that

$$\rho_y = 1.0725 \pm 0.0012 \text{ g/cm}^3$$

Since the values of ρ_y shown in Table 11.2 are not significantly different from the two values mentioned above, the new procedure for determining values of c for yeast suspensions seems reliable.

In other experiments, suspensions of yeast were transferred to glass vessels ($15\phi \times 200$ mm) where the initial height of the suspension was 130 mm. The rate of subsidence of the interface under gravity was measured; the experimental results in Fig. 11.11 show the distance, m_i, which the suspension interface fell in a given time, θ. Assuming a straight line relationship between m_i and θ for each value of c and computing the line by the method of least squares, the rate of subsidence of the interface, u, could be determined. Then, from Equations (11.10), (11.9), and (11.3) the values of D_p (or d_e) could readily be calculated from Eq. (11.33), provided

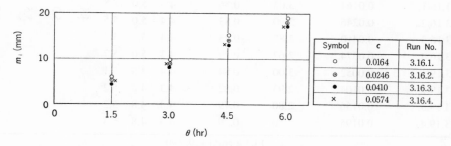

Symbol	c	Run No.
o	0.0164	3.16.1.
⊙	0.0246	3.16.2.
•	0.0410	3.16.3.
×	0.0574	3.16.4.

FIG. 11.11.   Subsidence of the interface of a yeast suspension under gravity, where m_i=distance traveled by the interface, θ=time, hr, and c=particle volume fraction.[3]

the values of α which are necessary to relate the values of U with those of U_0 are given (cf. Fig. 11.7).

$$D_p = d_e = \sqrt{\frac{18U_0\mu'}{g(\rho_y - \rho_m)}} \qquad (11.33)$$

The equivalent diameter, d_e, was introduced into Eq. (11.33) to compensate for the shape of the yeast cell, which is actually spheroidal, the major axis of each cell being the axis of revolution.[1] The concept of d_e, which is another expression of Stokes' diameter, is especially useful when considering microbial cells with more complicated shapes; these will be referred to later in this section.

With reference to Fig. 11.7 or to Eq. (11.13), the values of d_e calculated from the experimental data of u (and U) are summarized in Table 11.2. The values of ρ_y, ρ_m and μ' were measured separately and used in the calculation of d_e with Eq. (11.33). In addition, the table includes the values of d_e determined directly by averaging the measurements of individual cells, assuming all cells, even those with buds, to be spherical. The case of $\alpha = 0$ (to which Stokes' law was applied) was included for reference in Table 11.2. It is apparent from the table that the calculated value of d_e obtained when $\alpha = 2$ agreed best with the observed value of $\bar{d}_e$.

11.2.2.   Bacteria

To illustrate the settling of bacterial suspensions, *Serratia marcescens* was chosen by Aiba *et al.*[3] To determine the value of c of the suspension, a portion of it was transferred to a graduated, transparent cylindrical vessel (acrylic resin; $9\phi \times 98 \times 5$ mm in internal diameter, height, and wall thickness respectively) and allowed to settle in a centrifugal field about 10^4 times gravity for 15 minutes. An inclined interface formed during the treatment in the centrifuge; this was converted to a horizontal interface by subjecting the tube to a second centrifugation at about 1,700 times gravity for 5 minutes in a suspended type of centrifuge; and the volume of sediment was then measured. With the predetermined values of ρ_c and ρ_m, the values of ρ_y for the bacteria could be calculated from Eq. (11.32).

The experimental data of ρ_y thus determined are shown as a footnote to Table 11.3. The cells had been cultured in shaken flasks at 30°C for 48 hours using a medium composed of meat extract (1 %), peptone (1 %), glucose (2 %), and NaCl (0.2 %) (pH = 7.0). After cultivation, the cells were harvested and washed repeatedly with Michaelis buffer solution and re-suspended in the same solution (pH = 7.0).

To determine the values of d_e, the cell suspension was transferred to another cylindrical vessel of glass (size = $12\phi \times 105$ mm; initial height of suspension = 80 mm). Each suspension was centrifuged for a definite period of time (10 to 30 minutes) in a suspended type of centrifuge. At intervals, the centrifuging was temporarily stopped to measure the distance the interface had traveled and the effective magnitude of the centrifugal force operating during each period.[3] Some of the

TABLE 11.3

CALCULATION OF THE DENSITY, ρ_y, AND THE EQUIVALENT SIZE, d_e, OF BACTERIA.[3]

Run No.	c	u_c (cm/sec)	U_c (cm/sec)	d_e (microns) without correct.	d_e (microns) Temp. correct.	$\bar{d_e}$ (microns) calculated without correct.	$\bar{d_e}$ (microns) calculated Temp. correct.	Obs. micro-scopic-ally
8.1.1.	0.31	8.97×10^{-4}	13.00×10^{-4}	1.72	1.55			
8.1.2.	0.35	5.55	8.54	1.63	1.47			
8.1.3.	0.43	4.32	7.58	2.09	1.88			
8.2.1.	0.37	3.78	6.00	1.47	1.32			
8.2.2.	0.45	3.51	6.38	2.06	1.86			
8.3.1.	0.36	4.43	6.92	1.52	1.37	1.7 ± 0.2	1.5 ± 0.1	1.0 ± 0.2
8.3.2.	0.40	3.86	6.43	1.72	1.55			
8.3.3.	0.44	2.26	4.04	1.58	1.42			
8.8.1.	0.28	9.14	12.69	1.51	1.36			
8.8.2.	0.31	6.99	10.13	1.51	1.36			
8.9.1.	0.24	10.37	13.64	1.36	1.23			
8.9.2.	0.31	7.45	10.80	1.57	1.41			
8.9.3.	0.36	6.76	10.56	1.88	1.69			

$$\rho_y = 1.03 \text{ g/cm}^3 \ (\pm 0.008)$$
$$\rho_m = 1.00 \text{ g/cm}^3 \ (\pm 0.001)$$
$$\mu' = 8.3 \times 10^{-3} \text{ g/cm sec} \ (\pm 0.3 \times 10^{-3})$$
$$Z = 1000 \ (\pm 20)$$

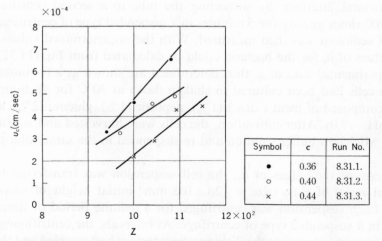

Symbol	c	Run No.
●	0.36	8.31.1.
○	0.40	8.31.2.
×	0.44	8.31.3.

FIG. 11.12. The rate of settling, u_c, of bacterial suspensions having different values of volume fraction, c, in centrifugal fields having different values of centrifugal effect, Z. [3]

experimental data are shown in Fig. 11.12, where the rate of subsidence of the interface, u_c, is plotted against the centrifugal effect, Z. For each value of c, straight correlations between u_c and Z were assumed and the line calculated by the method of least squares. For convenience, the values of u_c at $Z = 10^3$ will be employed to assess the values of d_e from Eq. (11.34) (shown below). The values of α expressed by Eq. (11.12), and those of ρ_y, ρ_m and μ' from Table 11.2 and Equations (11.9) and (11.10), were used in this assessment.

$$d_e = \sqrt{\frac{18U_0\mu'}{Zg(\rho_y-\rho_m)}} \qquad (cf. \text{ Eq. }(11.4)) \qquad (11.34)$$

The values of d_e determined in this way are shown in Table 11.3. The column for temperature correction in the table is concerned with a correction of μ' in Eq. (11.34) multiplied by a factor of 0.812. This was necessary because the temperature of the liquid rose about 10°C above room temperature (at which the values of ρ_y, ρ_m and μ' were determined) owing to the repeated suspension and centrifugation required to measure the values of u_c as described above.

However, the data of $\bar{d}_e$ determined with the settling experiments are apparently about 50% larger than the size measured microscopically. This disagreement is of significance and is worthy of further discussion.

Assuming a cubic arrangement of bacterial particles in the suspension,

$$\frac{\pi}{6}\bar{d}_e^3 n_0 = c$$

provided:

$n_0 =$ number of bacterial cells per unit volume of liquid

Then, the distance, L, between cells in the suspension will be:

$$L \sim n_0^{-1/3} \doteqdot \frac{\bar{d}_e}{(2c)^{1/3}} \qquad (11.35)$$

Substituting the c values of Table 11.3 into Eq. (11.35),

$$L \sim \frac{\bar{d}_e}{(2\times0.45\sim2\times0.24)^{1/3}} \doteqdot (1\sim1.3)\bar{d}_e$$

The above calculation implies that the cells in the concentrated suspensions settled as aggregates rather than as discrete particles. The values of $\bar{d}_e$ determined by the settling experiment may thus enable one to judge to what extent a cell suspension is flocculated.

In the preceding example of determining the value of $\bar{d}_e$ for a yeast suspension by settling experiments, the values were in good agreement with those observed microscopically, as shown in Table 11.2.

Substituting c values of the table into Eq. (11.35),

$$L \sim \frac{\bar{d}_e}{(2\times0.078\sim2\times0.0052)^{1/3}} \doteqdot (2\sim5)\bar{d}_e$$

Therefore, in the case of yeast, the cells appear not to have flocculated appreciably, since the values of $\bar{d}_e$ determined indirectly in the settling experiment agreed well with those of $\bar{d}_e$ observed directly with a microscope (see Table 11.2).

11.2.3. Fungi

Streptomyces griseus was studied as an example of an actinomycete.[3] Although this species does not belong to the normal category of fungi, the complicated network of hyphae in a broth culture of *Streptomyces griseus* represents a typical mutlicellular system.

The cells used for this study were cultured at 27°C for 48 hours in shaken flasks. The medium for the cultivation and the buffer solution for washing and resuspending the mycelium were the same as those used in preparing bacterial suspensions.

Suspensions with various concentrations of cells were transferred to graduated glass cylinders (size $= 60\phi \times 400$ mm; initial height of the suspension $= 150$ mm) and allowed to settle under gravity at room temperature (23 to 25°C).

Some of the results obtained from the settling experiments are shown in Fig. 11.13, in which the distance of travel, m_i, of the interface is plotted against time, θ. It is clear from the figure that the relation between m_i and θ was linear only for the short period of settling after the start of the experiment. This suggests that the free rate of hindered settling of the suspension terminates after a short period of operation. The values of u adopted in this series of experiments were determined from the slopes of the respective linear relationships between m_i and θ.

It is also apparent from Fig. 11.13 that the volume of sediment in each experiment approached asymptotically a definite value. The value of c was determined with the volume of sediment which had settled 72 hours after the start of the settling experiment. This procedure of determining the value of c may seem arbitrary; further discussion of this point will appear later.

The values of ρ_y, determined from Eq. (11.32) by substituting the values of ρ_m, ρ_c (measured with picnometers), and c (determined above), are shown as a footnote to Table 11.4. The difference between ρ_y and ρ_m is exceedingly small. This may be

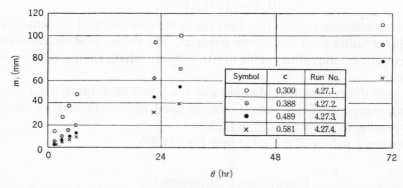

FIG. 11.13.   Distance traveled by the interface, m_i, of suspensions of *Streptomyces griseus* having different values of volume fraction, c, plotted against time, θ. [3]

due to the cells settling and incorporating a considerable amount of still liquid within the cell network.

The procedure for determining the values of d_e with Equations (11.10), (11.11) (α for irregular particles), (11.9) (relation between U and U_0), and (11.33) (definition of d_e) is the same as was described for the previous tables. The values of d_e so determined are shown in Table 11.4, together with the size observed directly with a microscope.

Although samples taken from the suspension for microscopic observation might have deformed appreciably, it was ascertained that the network of hyphae in the original suspension showed discrete aggregations. The value of $\bar{d}_e$ was, then, determined by measuring the maximum and minimum dimensions of more than 20 aggregates.

At first sight, the use of the $\bar{d}_e$ concept may seem unacceptable, but it is interesting to find that the values of $\bar{d}_e$ determined from the settling experiment are of the same order of magnitude as those measured directly. It is also significant that the experimental values of $\bar{d}_e$ seemingly depend on the values of c as shown in Table 11.4; the larger values of c tend to increase the value of $\bar{d}_e$. These facts support the inference that the multicellular suspension of *Streptomyces griseus* forms discrete aggregates containing a considerable amount of liquid.

TABLE 11.4

CALCULATION OF THE DENSITY, ρ_y, AND THE EQUIVALENT SIZE, d_e, OF *Streptomyces griseus*.[3]

Run No.	c	u (mm/hr)	U (cm/sec)	d_e (microns)	$\bar{d}_e$ (microns)
4.27.1.	0.300	7.53	2.99×10^{-4}	211	
4.27.2.	0.388	3.33	1.52	213	
4.27.3.	0.489	2.23	1.21	268	
4.27.4.	0.581	1.67	1.10	332	
5.30.1.	0.215	6.93	2.46	131	
5.30.2.	0.298	4.90	1.94	169	143 ± 21 Observed microscopically
5.30.3.	0.388	3.13	1.42	206	
5.30.4.	0.532	2.33	1.39	326	
6. 4.1.	0.209	9.67	3.40	150	
6. 4.2.	0.281	5.37	2.07	162	
6. 4.3.	0.353	4.47	1.92	210	
6. 4.4.	0.395	3.03	1.39	210	
6. 4.5.	0.672	0.90	0.76	346	

$$\rho_y = 1.003 \text{ g/cm}^3 \ (\pm 0.0003)$$
$$\rho_m = 1.002 \text{ g/cm}^3 \ (\pm 0.0004)$$
$$\mu' = 9.7 \times 10^{-3} \text{ g/cm sec} \ (\pm 0.2 \times 10^{-3})$$

11.2.4. Activated sludge

Activated sludge containing miscellaneous species of microbes has been used extensively for the biological treatment of sewage and industrial wastes. In the so-called activated-sludge process of waste treatment, aeration and separation of the sludge are the two principal operations involved. The separation of the sludge from the mixed liquor is generally conducted by sedimentation under gravity. The density and size of the sludge floccules are, therefore, worthy of attention for proper management of the process.

In the following experiments, activated sludge was obtained from the Mikawashima Sewage Treatment Plant, Tokyo. The sludge suspension (mixed liquor) was transferred to a cylindrical vessel (graduated, size $= 60\phi \times 400$ mm; initial height of the suspension $= 350$ mm) and allowed to settle under gravity for a definite period of time at 10 to 12°C. [3]

Some of the experimental results obtained are shown in Fig. 11.14. For a rather short time after the start of each experiment, the relation between m_i and θ was linear, as shown by Fig. 11.14, but later settling of the interface virtually stopped, as was the case with *Streptomyces griseus*. The volume of the sediment from the activated sludge observed 24 hours after the start of each experiment was arbitrarily chosen to define the value of c. To avoid disintegration of the sludge during the 24-hour period, the experiments were conducted at 10 to 12°C. To recapitulate, the volume of sediment in the cylinder beyond which the suspension could not apparently be reduced with the lapse of time was used to define the value of c.

The values of ρ_y determined with Eq. (11.32) after measuring c, ρ_c, and ρ_m (the latter two items with picnometers) are shown as a footnote to Table 11.5.

The value of U_0 was estimated from U using the relation between α and c for irregular and flocculated particles (Eq. (11.11)), and the values of $\bar{d}_e$ were calculated as explained previously and set out in the columns of Table 11.5.

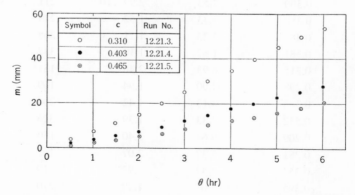

Symbol	c	Run No.
o	0.310	12.21.3.
●	0.403	12.21.4.
⊙	0.465	12.21.5.

FIG. 11.14.   Distance traveled by the interface, m_i, of activated sludge having different values of volume fraction, c, plotted against time, θ. [3] For ease of experimentation the mixed liquor from the sewage treatment plant was concentrated to the extent of about 5,200 – 15,500 ppm in terms of suspended solid (s.s.). The usual value of s.s. is far below the above level and the rate of sedimentation is much faster than that exemplified in this figure.

TABLE 11.5

CALCULATION OF THE DENSITY, ρ_y, AND EQUIVALENT SIZE, d_e, OF ACTIVATED SLUDGE.[3]

Run No.	c	u (mm/hr)	U (cm/sec)	d_e (microns)
12.11.1.	0.194	49.92	17.21×10^{-4}	99
12.11.2.	0.253	11.94	4.44	66
12.11.3.	0.292	9.40	3.69	71
12.18.1.	0.155	32.11	10.56	66
12.18.2.	0.184	22.05	7.51	63
12.18.3.	0.246	11.50	4.23	62
12.18.4.	0.308	8.24	3.31	72
12.18.5.	0.370	4.84	2.13	74
12.18.6.	0.432	6.02	2.94	109
12.21.1.	0.217	20.22	7.18	71
12.21.2.	0.279	10.61	4.09	71
12.21.3.	0.310	9.34	3.75	78
12.21.4.	0.403	4.82	2.24	86
12.21.5.	0.465	3.71	1.93	99

$$\rho_y = 1.013 \text{ g/cm}^3 \ (\pm 0.0004)$$
$$\rho_m = 1.000 \text{ g/cm}^3 \ (\pm 0.0004)$$
$$\mu' = 12.5 \times 10^{-3} \text{ g/cm sec} \ (\pm 0.1 \times 10^{-3})$$

As was seen with the actinomycete, Table 11.5 shows that activated sludge appears to form aggregates of definite size. At first sight, the use of $\bar{d}_e$ may be unacceptable for activated sludge since these calculated values cannot be checked microscopically, but from the behavior of *Streptomyces griseus* it is inferred that the values of $\bar{d}_e$ in Table 11.5 are reliable.

However, the value of ρ_y for activated sludge was considerably higher than that for *Streptomyces griseus*. Various sorts of inorganic materials are usually associated with the sludge in addition to the cells, and this may account for the difference between the values of ρ_y of the two systems.

11.3. MECHANICAL SEPARATION IN THE FERMENTATION INDUSTRY

11.3.1. Yeast

In the production of yeast, the fermented broth is first separated with a continuous centrifuge (usually a DeLaval type) (*cf.* Fig. 11.2); the yeast cream is then commonly dehydrated on a filter press before being packaged. It is clear that as dehydration with a filter press cannot be conducted continuously and requires considerable man power, this process could become a limiting factor in production.

Recently a rotary-drum yeast dehydrator was developed by Svenska Jastfabriks Aktiebolaget Co., Sweden (Fig. 11.15). With certain strains of yeast, dehydration of the yeast cream is comparable with, or even better than, the conventional type of filter press. In addition, the rotary-drum filter has a large capacity (1 to 1.2 tons per hour) and it can be operated continuously for a long period; this permits automation of the plant. Several yeast production plants have adopted this type of dehydrator, discarding the filter press entirely.

FIG. 11.15.   Continuous yeast dehydrator. Capacity=1 ton/hr as pressed yeast; Drum diameter=2 m.
(*Courtesy   Oriental Yeast Co., Ltd., Tokyo.*)

In this type of filter, a drum surface is covered with a cloth, usually pre-coated with filter aids such as starch granules, and rotated at a constant speed (about 6 rpm). To assist in dehydration of the yeast cells, 3% NaCl is added to the yeast cream before it reaches the filter drum. During passage through the reservoir of yeast cream, the filter cake is gradually formed; the cake is washed to remove sodium chloride, dehydrated by withdrawing water into the partial vacuum inside the drum, and finally peeled off continuously with a blade. The whole operation occurs within one revolution of the drum.

According to Okazawa,[16] however, dehydration with this equipment remains to be further studied as far as the production of yeast in Japan is concerned. Although the capacity and the degree of dehydration were satisfactory for short periods of operation, several problems associated with the cell size of yeast and with uncertainties concerning the formation of starch (filter aid) layer on the drum surface remain to be solved.

11.3.2.   Actinomycetes

It is well known that broth cultures of actinomycetes, for instance *Streptomyces griseus*, exhibit tremendous resistance to filtration. Many attempts have been made to overcome the difficulty of separating the mycelium from broth on an industrial scale. In the recovery of streptomycin, the resistance of the mycelium to filtration has been reduced by heating the fermentation broth.[22] The coagulation of mycelial protein with heat to accelerate filtration may have wide application in the fermentation industry.

The filter used to obtain the data in Fig. 11.16 had an area of 110 cm² and was equipped with a cotton cloth; the filter aid was Radiolite (Showa Chemicals Ltd., Tokyo) a diatomaceous earth, and pressure was applied constantly at 2 Kg/cm² gauge. The sample of broth used in these experiments was taken from a

a)

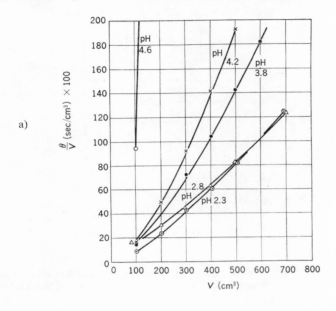

b)

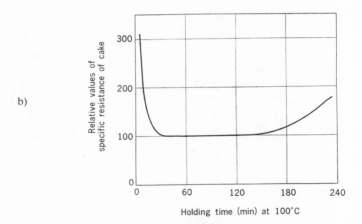

FIG. 11.16.   a)   Effect of pH on the rate of filtration of *Streptomyces griseus* (filter aid 2%, 30 minutes required to raise the temperature of the broth to 90°C).   b)   Effect of holding time at elevated temperature (100°C) on the specific resistance of *Streptomyces griseus* broth to filtration.[22]

large batch fermentor (60 m³) which had been operated for 3 to 4 days. The original culture medium consisted of glucose and soybean powder, supplemented by inorganic salts and dried yeast.

In Fig. 11.16 a) θ/V is plotted against V, parameters being pH values. It can be seen that the data points for each pH did not lie on a straight line starting from the origin, indicating that the mycelial cake was compressible. However, assuming that the relation between θ/V and V is nearly linear, it is apparent that the specific

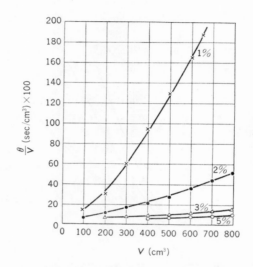

FIG. 11.17.   Effect of filter aid on the specific resistance to filtration of *Streptomyces griseus* broth[22] (pH = 3.7 to 3.8; 30 minutes required to raise the temperature of broth to 90°C).

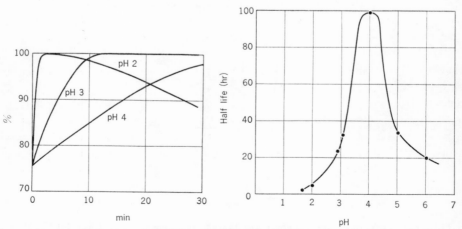

FIG. 11.18.   Left: the elution rate of streptomycin from the mycelium at 80°C; Right: the effect of pH on the decomposition rate of streptomycin at 80°C. [22]

resistance to filtration of the mycelium is markedly affected by the pH. In addition, the specific resistance is affected by the amount of filter aid added (Fig. 11.17), since the slope of each line is proportional to α_R (cf. Equations (11.24) to (11.29)).

Although the data points of Figs. 11.16 a) and 11.17 were obtained at 90°C and the time required to raise the broth temperature was 30 minutes, it is evident from Fig. 11.16 b) that the period of time during which the broth is exposed to elevated temperatures is also of prime importance. The coagulation of mycelial protein has apparently been achieved after 30 to 40 minutes at 100°C, but a longer exposure of the broth to heat has adversely affected the filtration rate, presumably due to disintegration of coagulated protein.

It was found that the rate of decomposition of streptomycin at 80°C followed the mono-molecular reaction pattern. By varying the pH values, the half-life (=0.693/reaction rate constant) was determined as shown in the right part of Fig. 11.18. It is apparent that the fraction of streptomycin decomposed at 80°C at pH 3.7 to 4.3 in 30 minutes will be negligible. On the other hand, the elution of streptomycin from the mycelium at pH=4.0 shows that the antibiotic will be almost completely extracted into the broth after 30 minutes (left part of Fig. 11.18); the streptomycin would be stable for this period. It is apparent from the figure that about 75% of the antibiotic had been extracted from the broth prior to the extraction of the mycelium.

To summarize, the industrial filtration of *Streptomyces griseus* for the recovery of streptomycin was successful with the pH at 3.7 to 4.3 and the temperature at 80° to 90°C, using 30 to 60 minutes to raise the broth to the desired temperature and 2 to 3% filter aid. These data were obtained from Figs. 11.16 to 11.18.

11.3.3. Specific mashes

In the production of *sake* (Japanese wine), soy-sauce, vinegar, and so forth by fermentation, it is traditional to consolidate fermentation mashes with hydraulic presses to secure a cake whose liquid content is reduced to an extreme extent. It is questionable whether such extreme consolidations of fermentation mashes are really necessary.

However, in order to allow these processes to be converted to continuous operation, it would be possible to use a normal filtration to clarify the broth and then to subject the filter cake from the first filtration to a second hydraulic consolidation. The theoretical aspects of hydraulic consolidation will be discussed below.

For convenience, it will be assumed that the term, v, which was defined earlier as volume of filtrate, represents the volume of liquid expressed in the process of consolidation. From Equations (11.19) and (11.20),

$$\frac{dv}{d\theta} = \frac{\Delta P g_c}{(r_m+r_c)\mu'} = \frac{\Delta P g_c}{(r_m+\alpha_R \frac{W}{A})\mu'} = \frac{\Delta P g_c}{(r_m+\alpha_R w')\mu'} \qquad (11.36)$$

provided:

$$w' = W/A$$

The value of r_m can usually be neglected, if Eq. (11.36) is applied to the consolidation rate equation. Namely,

$$\frac{dv}{d\theta} = \frac{\Delta P g_c}{\alpha_R w' \mu'} \tag{11.37}$$

According to Nagai et al.,[15] it was assumed that the rate of expression of liquid in the consolidation process would be well represented by:

$$\frac{dv}{d\theta} = \frac{\Delta P g_c m}{\alpha_c w' \mu'} \tag{11.38}$$

where

α_c = specific resistance of cake, m/kg

The idea involved in Eq. (11.38) is that the values of m and α_c are not constant in the process of consolidation; this is contrary to the constant value of m assumed in an ordinary filtration. Therefore,

$$m = \frac{\text{initial wet mass} - \text{mass of liquid squeezed out}}{\text{dry solid mass}} \tag{11.39}$$

$$= m_0 - (v \rho_m / w') \qquad \text{based on unit area of press}$$

Substituting Eq. (11.39) into Eq. (11.38) and integrating, assuming that the value of α_c remains unchanged ($\bar{\alpha}_c$) in each short interval during $\theta = 0$ to $\theta = \theta$ with ΔP = constant,

$$\ln\left(1 + \frac{v}{m_0} a'\right) = a' K' \theta \tag{11.40}$$

provided:

$$a' = -\frac{\rho_m}{w'}$$

$$K' = \frac{\Delta P g_c}{\bar{\alpha}_c \mu' w'} \tag{11.41}$$

Nagai et al.[15] determined accordingly the values of $\bar{\alpha}_c$ from Equations (11.40) and (11.41) for soy-sauce mashes. The consolidometer they employed had an area (28.4 cm²) which was covered both with a filter cloth and a filter paper. The values of ΔP they used extended from 2.8 to 32 Kg/cm² and the temperature of the mash was 21°C.

The experimental result is shown in Fig. 11.19 plotting $\bar{\alpha}_c$ against θ. It is apparent that the specific resistance of the cake sharply increased with time for each pressure applied and that the value of $\bar{\alpha}_c$ leveled off after 30 minutes of consolidation.

Furthermore, in a range of θ corresponding to the leveling-off of $\bar{\alpha}_c$ values, it can be shown approximately from Fig. 11.19 that

$$\bar{\alpha}_c \propto \Delta P$$

The above fact implies that the value of v when $\bar{a}_c \propto \varDelta P$ is a function of θ only and is independent of $\varDelta P$. This condition also indicates that the cake is in equilibrium with the pressure applied.

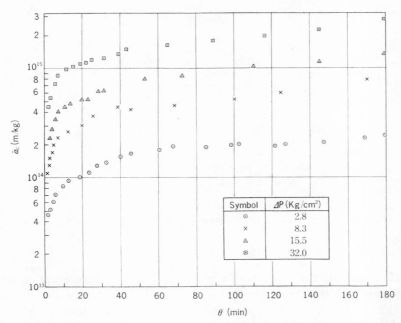

FIG. 11.19.   Effect of length of exposure, θ, at different pressures, $\varDelta P$, on the specific resistance, $\bar{a}_c$, of filter cakes from soy-sauce fermentations.[15]

11.4.   MECHANICAL DISINTEGRATION OF CELLS

Mechanical disintegration of cells has a potentially wide application in the fermentation industry, for instance for extracting enzymes and nuclear material or for preparing cell walls without resorting to chemical agents, but only a few papers have been published up to the present time on this subject. One type of apparatus to disrupt cells is based on the change in structure of a frozen suspension of cells following an increase in pressure. Another apparatus uses high-speed abrasion between cells and glass beads. Although both of these methods are available only on the laboratory scale, each is considered worthy of a short review.

11.4.1.   Press

In this apparatus, the frozen suspension of cells, precooled at $-60°C$ for 30 minutes, is forced by hydraulic pressure between a piston and a disk provided with several holes 1.5 to 2.5 mm in diameter (see Fig. 11.20). As the hydraulic pressure is increased, the material between the piston and the disk finally flows down through the holes. The pressure required for the operation is 1 to 2.5 tons/cm².

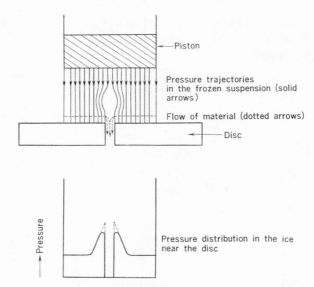

FIG. 11.20.   Pressure trajectories in a press to disintegrate cells.[7]

Fig. 11.21 illustrates the changes of state of ice structure depending on temperature and pressure. A shift from Phase I to Phase III in the figure (for instance, at −22°C and 2115 Kg/cm²) is accompanied by a decrease in volume of 0.185 cm³/g. However, in a shift from Phase III to V, the variation of ice volume is only 0.0546 cm³/g.   If the large variation of volume following the transformation of crystal structure is used effectively, the cells suspended in ice will readily be destroyed.

Edebo[8] studied the destruction of cells with the press using *Escherichia coli B, Proteus mirabilis, Staphylococcus aureus* 209, and 8 other strains of bacteria and yeast.

Experimental results with *B. megaterium* are shown in Fig. 11.22, the abscissa of which represents the number of passages through a hole (2.5 mm in diameter) bored through a disc, and the ordinate is the reading on a nephelometer. The cells $(8.2 \times 10^9/\text{ml})$ treated with the press (capacity = 2 ml) at −60°C were disintegrated readily as measured by reduction of turbidity and microscopic observations as shown in Fig. 11.22.

11.4.2.   Sonomec

Fig. 11.23 shows the construction of a wave-pulse generator called Sonomec, which was employed by Rogers *et al.*[20] to disintegrate bacteria and yeast. The pot in the figure was 2 to 5 cm and 9 to 25 cm in internal diameter and height respectively. Vibrations are effected by a cam mechanism driven by a 2 ℍP motor. Cell suspensions from 20 ml to 150 ml can be placed with ballotini glass beads in the pot.

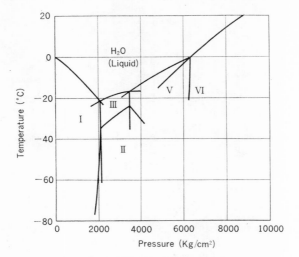

FIG. 11.21.   Change of ice structure.[8]

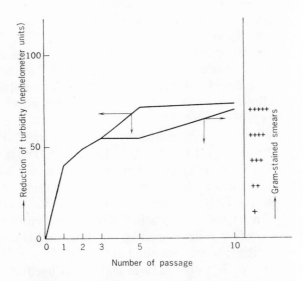

FIG. 11.22.   Disintegration of *B. megaterium*[7].

The cells are disintegrated within a couple of minutes by abrasion between the glass beads; the amplitude and frequency of vibration can be adjusted as seen in Fig. 11.23.

In an experiment to determine the way in which acoustic energy is transferred to the liquid in the pot, an ice-water mixture was poured to a depth of 7.75 cm into a pot which had been pre-cooled with ice. The temperature rise °C in the liquid

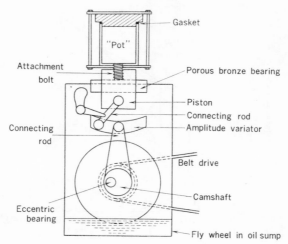

FIG. 11.23.   Construction of the Sonomec.[20]

was measured after a 2-minute vibration. The pot used was 5.2 cm in internal diameter and the frequency of vibration was varied from about 30 c/sec to 175 c/sec with a constant amplitude of 2 mm.

Fig. 11.24 shows the temperature rise due to vibration; it is apparent that an optimum frequency exists around 150 c/sec. Rogers et al.[20] studied various other factors, for instance, the liquid volume in each pot, the amplitude of vibration, and the amount of ballotini beads added, all of which may affect the effectiveness of cell destruction by the Sonomec.

Enzyme activities of fractions prepared by Rogers et al.[20] with the Sonomec from a suspension of baker's yeast are shown in Table 11.6. The table also includes data from studies with the press type of disintegrator. The pot used in this study was 5.2 cm in internal diameter, the frequency and amplitude of vibration were 117 c/sec and 0.3 cm respectively; 150 ml of yeast suspension containing 2.5×10^9 cells/ml were mixed with 50 g of No. 12 ballotini beads and vibrated for 5 minutes. The press used in this study was developed by Hughes[20] and is similar in principle to that previously described; it was operated at $-23°C$.

The material prepared by both procedures was centrifuged at 2°C in a field of 10,000 times gravity for 1 minute for spinning out intact cells (Sonomec—47% intact cells; Press—12.2% intact cells). The resulting cell-free preparations (S_1) were fractionated into (R_2) and supernatant (S_2) in a centrifugal field of 12,000 times gravity for 6 minutes. The supernatant (S_2) was further fractionated into residue (R_3) and supernatant (S_3) by centrifuging at 50,000 times gravity for 10 minutes. The residues R_2 and R_3 were suspended in phosphate buffer and the enzyme activities assayed as are shown in Table 11.6.

Although both methods of disintegration of the yeast cells gave extracts with similar activities, it can be seen from the table that the press preparations contained

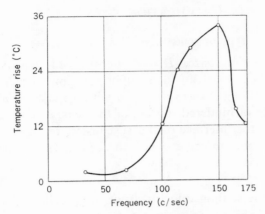

FIG. 11.24.   Effect of frequency of vibration on the temperature in a Sonomec disintegrator.[20]

TABLE 11.6

ENZYME ACTIVITIES OF FRACTIONS PREPARED BY DISINTEGRATION OF BAKER'S YEAST.[20]

Method	Fraction	Fumarase (μ moles fumaric acid /mgN/min)	Lactic dehydrogenase (μ moles dye reduced /mgN/min)	Succinic dehydrogenase (μ moles dye reduced /mgN/min)	Alcohol dehydrogenase (μ moles DPNH formed /mgN/min)
Sonomec	S_1	790	27.7	2.0	3.4
//	S_2	340	36.0	6.3	3.5
//	S_3	304	36.0	1.9	4.9
//	R_2	193	12.0	3.8	0.5
//	R_3	2110	4.8	8.2	1.9
Press	S_1	297	18.75	1.2	3.5
//	S_2	416	19.5	4.3	2.8
//	S_3	403	24.0	2.1	2.6
//	R_2	0	35.0	22.0	0.2
//	R_3	258	41.0	41.0	1.3

more lactic and succinic dehydrogenase activity than the Sonomec preparations, while the situation was reversed in the case of fumarase activity. Alcohol dehydrogenase activity seemed to be similar, irrespective of the method of disintegration.

Rogers et al.[20] made successful preparations of cell walls of *Lactobacillus casei*, *Corynebacterium xerosis*, and *Staphylococcus albus* with the Sonomec.

11.5. EXAMPLES OF CALCULATION

11.5.1. Suspension type of centrifuge

A bacterial suspension (size, $D_p=1$ micron; cell density, $\rho_y=1.03$ g/cm³; volume fraction of cell, $c=0.30$) in a buffer solution (density, $\rho_m=1.00$ g/cm³; viscosity, $\mu'=1.01\times10^{-2}$ g/cm sec) is treated with a suspended type of centrifuge. Assuming a free rate of hindered settling of the cells, it is desired to estimate the time, θ, required for the interface of the suspension to travel from $r_1=9$ cm to $r_2=10$ cm from the rotation center when the centrifuge is operated at a revolutional speed, $N=5,000$ rpm.

Solution

From Eq. (11.3) the settling velocity, U_0 of single cells under gravity,

$$U_0 = \frac{gD_p^2(\rho_y-\rho_m)}{18\mu'} = \frac{(981)(1\times10^{-4})^2(1.03-1.00)}{(18)(1.01\times10^{-2})}$$

$$= 1.62\times10^{-6}\,\text{cm/sec}$$

From Equations (11.9) and (11.12) the hindered-settling rate, U, of single cells under gravity,

$$U = \frac{U_0}{1+\alpha c^{1/3}} = \frac{U_0}{1+(1+229c^{3.43})c^{1/3}}$$

$$= \frac{1.62\times10^{-6}}{1+\{1+229(0.30)^{3.43}\}(0.30)^{1/3}}$$

$$= 3.90\times10^{-7}\,\text{cm/sec}$$

From Eq. (11.10) the rate of subsidence, u, of the suspension interface under gravity will be:

$$u = (1-c)U = (1-0.30)(3.90\times10^{-7}) = 2.73\times10^{-7}\,\text{cm/sec}$$

The rate of subsidence, u_c, of the suspension interface in a centrifugal field will be:

$$u_c = \frac{dr}{d\theta} = u\,\frac{r\omega^2}{g}$$

Integrating the above equation from r_1 to r_2 and substituting the values appropriate to this problem, the time, θ, is calculated as follows:

$$\theta = \frac{g}{u\omega^2}\ln\frac{r_2}{r_1}$$

$$= \frac{981}{(2.73\times10^{-7})(\frac{2\pi\times5000}{60})^2}(2.303)\log\left(\frac{10}{9}\right)$$

$$= 1,366\,\text{sec}$$

$$= 22.8\,\text{min}$$

11.5.2. Sharples centrifuge

The bacterial suspension of the previous problem is treated using a laboratory type of Sharples centrifuge ($r_1=0.5$ cm, $r_2=2.5$ cm, $l=30$ cm, $N=24{,}000$ rpm) at a rate of 270 cm³/min. The result of this operation was satisfactory. It is required to estimate the capacity of the same type of centrifuge ($r_1=1.5$ cm, $r_2=7.5$ cm, $l=90$ cm, $N=15{,}000$ rpm) in separating the cell suspension on an industrial scale.

Solution

From Eq. (11.16) for the laboratory centrifuge,

$$\Sigma_2 = \frac{2\pi l \omega^2}{g}\left(\frac{3}{4}r_2^2 + \frac{1}{4}r_1^2\right)$$

$$= \frac{2\pi\times 30}{981}\left(\frac{2\pi\times 24{,}000}{60}\right)^2\left\{\frac{3}{4}(2.5)^2 + \frac{1}{4}(0.5)^2\right\}$$

$$= 5.77\times 10^6 \text{ cm}^2$$

For the large centrifuge,

$$\Sigma_1 = \frac{2\pi\times 90}{981}\left(\frac{2\pi\times 15{,}000}{60}\right)^2\left\{\frac{3}{4}(7.5)^2 + \frac{1}{4}(1.5)^2\right\}$$

$$= 6.09\times 10^7 \text{ cm}^2$$

From Eq. (11.18),

$$Q_1 = Q_2\,\frac{\Sigma_1}{\Sigma_2}$$

$$= 270\left(\frac{6.09\times 10^7}{5.77\times 10^6}\right)$$

$$= 2.85 \text{ liter/min}$$

NOMENCLATURE

A = cross-sectional area which is perpendicular to direction of motion or filter area, m²
a = factor, see Reference 19 or Fig. 11.6; as for b, also see Reference 19
$a' = -\rho_m/w'$, Eq. (11.40)
C_D = drag coefficient
c = cell volume fraction or volume fraction of particles
D_p = particle diameter, m
d_e = equivalent diameter, m, microns
g = acceleration due to gravity, m/sec², cm/sec²
g_c = conversion factor, kg m/Kg sec², g cm/Gr sec²
$k = \dfrac{2(1-mw)g_c}{\alpha_R w \rho_m \mu'}\,\Delta P$, m²/sec
$K = kA^2$, m⁶/sec
$K' = \dfrac{\Delta P g_c}{\overline{\alpha}_c \mu' w'}$
L = distance between particles or length of drum type of filter, m
l = length of cylindrical separator in Sharples type of centrifuge, m; Fig. 11.8

m = mass ratio of wet to dry cake, kg/kg

m_0 = initial value of m, kg/kg; Eq. (11.39)

m_i = distance of travel of interface, cm, mm

N = rotation speed of centrifuge, rpm

N_{Re} = Reynolds number ($= D_p \rho_m U_0 / \mu'$)

n = rotation speed of drum, rps

n' = number of separator bowls

n_0 = number of cells per unit volume of liquid

P = pressure, Kg/cm²

ΔP = pressure drop, Kg/cm², Kg/m²

Q = rate of liquid flow through continuous centrifuge, m³/sec

R = resistance, Kg

R' = resistance, Kg (hindered settling)

R_0 = radius of rotary drum type of filter, m; Fig. 11.10

r = radial distance from rotation center, cm, m

r_1 = radial distance between inner liquid surface and center of rotation in Sharples type of centrifuge, m; radius of separator bowl, m; Fig. 11.8.

r_2 = radius of outer cylinder in Sharples type of centrifuge, m; radius of circular center line of separator port, m; Fig. 11.8

r_c = resistance coefficient of cake, 1/m

r_e = effective radius of rotation in centrifuge, m

r_m = resistance coefficient of filter medium, 1/m

S_e = effective distance of settling, m

U = settling velocity of a swarm of particles under gravity, m/sec, mm/hr

U_0 = settling velocity of single particles under gravity, m/sec

U_c = settling velocity of a swarm of particles in centrifugal field, m/sec, mm/hr

U_{c0} = settling velocity of single particles in centrifugal field, m/sec, m/hr

u = rate of subsidence of interface in suspension under gravity, cm/sec, mm/hr

u_c = rate of subsidence of interface in suspension in centrifugal field, cm/sec, mm/hr

$V_0 = v_0 A$, m³

V = volume of filtrate or volume of liquid in centrifuge, m³

$v_0 = r_m \dfrac{1 - mw}{\alpha_R w \rho_m}$, m

v = volume of filtrate per unit area of filter, m³/m²

V_u = filtrate volume obtained per unit time, m³/sec

v_u = filtrate volume obtained per unit time and per unit area of filter surface, m³/m² sec

W = total solid content in original suspension, kg

w = mass of dry cake per unit mass of original suspension, kg/kg

$w' = W/A$, kg/m²

x = distance of travel, m

Z = centrifugal effect (ratio of centrifugal acceleration to gravitational acceleration)

Superscript:

      —: average

Greek letters

$\alpha = \beta \{\beta_0' + f(c)\}$

α_c = specific resistance of cake, Eq. (11.38), m/kg

$\bar{\alpha}_c$ = mean value of α_c, m/kg

α_R = specific resistance of cake, Eq. (11.20), m/kg

β, β_0' = geometrical factor, Eq. (11.6) and empirical constant, Eq. (11.7)

β_0 = coefficient, Eq. (11.5)
θ = time, hr, sec, min
μ' = medium viscosity or filtrate viscosity, kg/m sec, g/cm sec
ρ_y = cell density or density of wet cake, g/cm³, kg/m³
ρ_c = density of suspension, g/cm³
ρ_m = medium density or filtrate density, g/cm³, kg/m³
ρ_d = density of dry cake, kg/m³
σ = specific surface area of irregular particles, cm²/cm³
Σ = $r_e\omega^2 V/g\,S_e$, m²
ϕ = one half the apex angle of separator bowl, Fig. 11.8
ϕ_0 = radian of drum surface immersed in suspension reservoir, Fig. 11.10
ϕ_w = radian of drum surface which is subjected to washing, Fig. 11.10
ω = angular velocity of rotation, radian/sec

REFERENCES

1. AIBA, S., KITAI, S., and ISHIDA, N. (1962). "Shape and size of yeast cell. Density of yeast cell and viscosity of its suspension." *J. Gen. Appl. Microbiol.* **8**, 99,103.
2. AIBA, S., KITAI, S., and ISHIDA, N. (1962). "Experimental studies on sedimentation of yeast cells." *ibid.* **8**, 109.
3. AIBA, S., KITAI, S., and HEIMA, N. (1964). "Determination of equivalent size of microbial cells from their velocities in hindered settling." *ibid.* **10**, 243.
4. AMBLER, C.M. (1959). "The theory of scaling up laboratory data for the sedimentation type centrifuge." *J. Biochem. Microbiol. Tech. & Eng.* **1**, 185.
5. BRINKMAN, H.C. (1947). "A calculation of the viscous force exerted by a flowing fluid on a dense swarm of particles." *Appl. Sci. Research* **A1**, 27.
6. BROWN, G.G. (1950). *Unit Operations* Wiley, N.Y.
7. EDEBO, L. (1960). "A new press for the disruption of microorganisms and other cells." *J. Biochem. Microbiol. Tech. & Eng.* **2**, 453.
8. EDEBO, L., and HEDÉN, C.-G. (1960). "Disruption of frozen bacteria as a consequence of changes in the crystal structure of ice." *ibid.* **2**, 113.
9. HADDAD, S.A., and LINDEGREN, C.C. (1953). "A method for determining the weight of an individual yeast cell." *Appl. Microbiol.* **1**, 153.
10. HANRATTY, T.J., and BANDUKWALA, A. (1957). "Fluidization and sedimentation of spherical particles." *A.I.Ch.E. Journal* **3**, 293.
11. HAPPEL, J. (1958). "Viscous flow in multiparticle systems: slow motion of fluids relative to beds of spherical particles." *ibid.* **4**, 197.
12. KERMACK, W.O., M'KENDRICK, A.G., and PONDER, E. (1929). "The stability of suspension. Part 3. The velocity of sedimentation and of cataphoresis of suspensions in a viscous fluid." *Proc. Roy. Soc. Edinburgh.* **49**, 170.
13. KUWAI, G., and INOUE, I. (1950). "Theoretical considerations about the separating characteristics of the DeLaval-type centrifuge." *Chem. Eng. (Japan)* **14**, 90.
14. MERTES, T.S., and RHODES, H.B. (1955). "Liquid-particle behavior. Part 1 and Part 2." *Chem. Eng. Progress* **51**, 429, 517.
15. NAGAI, S., IGARASHI, M., TAGUCHI, H., and TERAMOTO, S. (1963). "Studies on the filtration and compression of fermentation mashes. Part 3. New approach for the analysis of average filtration resistance." *J. Ferm. Tech.* **41**, 413.
16. OKAZAWA, K. (1963). "Some problems of baker's yeast industry." *Food Tech. (Japan)* **6**, 73.
17. OLIVER, D.R. (1961). "The sedimentation of suspensions of closely-sized spherical particles." *Chem. Eng. Sci.* **15**, 230.

18. PERRY, J.H. (1963). *Chemical Engineers' Handbook* 4th Ed. McGraw-Hill, N.Y.
19. RICHARDSON, J.F., and ZAKI, W.N. (1954). "The sedimentation of a suspension of uniform spheres under conditions of viscous flow." *Chem. Eng. Sci.* **3,** 65.
20. ROGERS, A., and HUGHES, D.E. (1960). "The disintegration of microorganisms by shaking with glass beads." *J. Biochem. Microbiol. Tech. & Eng.* **2,** 49.
21. RUTH, B.F., MONTILLON, G.H., and MONTONNA, R.E. (1933). "Studies in filtration I. Critical analysis of filtration theory. II. Fundamental axiom of constant-pressure filtration." *Ind. Eng. Chem.* **25,** 76, 153.
22. SHIRATO, S., and ESUMI, S. (1963). "Filtration of the cultured broth of *Streptomyces griseus.*" *J. Ferm. Tech.* **41,** 87.
23. SMOLUCHOWSKI, M.S. (1912). "On the practical applicability of Stokes' law of resistance, and the modification of it required in certain cases." *Proc. 5th International Congress of Mathematics.* Cambridge, **2,** 192.
24. STEINOUR, H.H. (1944). "Rate of sedimentation. Part 1. Nonflocculated suspensions of uniform spheres." *Ind. Eng. Chem.* **36,** 618.
25. STEINOUR, H.H. (1944). "Rate of sedimentation. Part 2. Suspensions of uniform-size angular particles." *ibid.* **36,** 840.
26. STEINOUR, H.H. (1944). "Rate of sedimentation. Part 3. Concentrated flocculated suspensions of powders." *ibid.* **36,** 901.
27. UCHIDA, S. (1954). "Slow viscous flow through a mass of particles." *ibid.* **46,** 1194.
28. VERSCHOOR, H. (1944). "Experimental data on the viscous force exerted by a flowing fluid on a dense swarm of particles." *Appl. Sci. Research* **A2,** 155.
29. WILSON, B.W. (1953). "The sedimentation of dense suspensions of microscopic spheres." *Australian J. Appl. Sci.* **4,** 274.

AUTHOR INDEX

Numbers in italics indicate the page on which the reference numbers in parentheses here are listed without mentioning authors' names in the text. Example: *240*(2).

SUBJECT INDEX

of cells from fermentations, 56.
of growth, 110.
of product based on cell mass, 110.
of product based on limiting substrate,
110.
Yield$_{ATP}$, 55.
Yield$_{Substrate}$, 55.
Yield value of stress,

for Bingham plastic, 178, 180.
Young's Modulus, 264.

Z

Zygomycetes,
cell walls of, 22, 30.
Zygote, 29, 33.